P9-CMF-267

MODERN PRACTICAL
ARITHMETIC

BY

INA M. HAYES
CHARLES S. GIBSON
GEORGE R. BODLEY
BRUCE M. WATSON

UPPER GRADES

D. C. HEATH AND COMPANY

BOSTON   NEW YORK   CHICAGO
ATLANTA   SAN FRANCISCO   DALLAS
LONDON

INTRODUCTION

THE *Modern Practical Arithmetics* have been prepared to meet the requirements of the newer syllabi, which, as they appear from time to time, place a new emphasis upon some particular phase of arithmetic study and teaching. Great care has been taken to provide proper presentation of all the fundamental processes and abundant exercises for thorough drill.

Frequent drills, mental tests, and lessons in review are presented according to a cumulative plan which is a distinctive feature of this series of arithmetics.

The relation of factor and product has been developed with extreme care and is so presented that it becomes a vital part of the child's mathematical sense.

Along with a realization of the preëminent usefulness of arithmetic in the everyday affairs of life, the authors have had constantly in mind also the fact that arithmetic is the path by which the student enters the greater field of general mathematics. It is essential to the student's further progress that facts and processes as presented in his arithmetic course shall conform to those he is to meet in his later study.

The problem study should not be confined to material contained in the book. It is essential that real problems be brought in from the immediate community upon which pupils may try their skill.

As a rule, projects are suggested rather than given in detail because, to be of greatest value, they must have their origin in a local situation, — a store, a factory, a home, or a farm in the immediate community. The project should afford interesting practice in the processes already learned rather than serve as the main reliance in teaching new matter.

It is possible for all normal children to learn the fundamental facts of arithmetic. Some will learn them much more quickly than others. Some will be able to solve more difficult problems than others. The *Modern Practical Arithmetics* furnish material adapted to these various grades of ability. It is as grievous an error to permit the stronger pupils to pass along by meeting merely the minimum requirement, as to expect the weaker ones to perform tasks beyond their ability.

The child benefits most and takes greatest delight in solving problems from the world about him, which he or his teacher has brought to the class room to replace or supplement those of the textbook.

Over one hundred years ago, Thomas Dilworth in England and Nathan Daboll in America each called his arithmetic "The Schoolmaster's Assistant," — a significant title. It is the desire of the authors that these books shall be helpful assistants to the teachers of our time.

To the many teachers whose advice, suggestion, and contributions of material have aided in the preparation of this series the thanks of the authors are gratefully tendered.

SUGGESTIONS TO TEACHERS

First — Teach   Third — Test
Second — Drill   Fourth — Review

This plan, so prominent in the earlier books of the series, is definitely continued in this book. Ample exercises for following it persistently are provided. As in the preceding books, standardized tests are included that the teacher may compare the progress of the class with others of the same grade in different sections of the country.

The factor-product plan is brought to bear upon the problems of percentage to the end that these processes will be much simplified and the pupil advanced materially toward the abstractions of algebra. The teacher will do well to call attention to cases of factors and product in which one of the factors is either greater or less than unity.

The underlying principle that interest is the product of three factors is presented first and the special methods follow. This plan has ample justification in all good pedagogy.

The treatment of the applications of percentage are all modern, practical and carefully graded. The work in intuitive geometry and preliminary algebra may be used with the assurance that the class will have no unusual difficulty in mastering it.

STANDARDIZED TESTS

CERTAIN standardized tests in arithmetic have been inserted in appropriate places. These tests can be used in two ways. In the first place, they set a number of definite goals to be attained by pupils. The examples of a given test define a definite ability, *i.e.*, the ability to do examples of this particular type. The standard for the test defines the degree of ability which pupils should attain by the time they complete the year's work in which the test is included. It is probably not wise to drill the pupils on such examples, except occasionally, after they have reached the standard.

The standardized tests also furnish a means of measuring the abilities of pupils. The tests have been inserted in the text at the places where their use is most important, but they may profitably be used at other times. In using the tests, the pupils should not be permitted to write the answers in the book. In doing all of the examples except the ones in division and common fractions, a sheet of plain paper should be placed with the edge just below the first row of examples. When doing the tests on common fractions, the sheet of paper is to be placed at the right hand side of the row. In division it will be necessary to copy the examples. In doing the other tests, the pupils should be instructed not to copy the examples, but all of the work and the answers should be done on the sheet of paper. When the first row has been completed, the pupils may turn the paper so that a fresh edge is placed under the next row of examples. If necessary, the paper may be folded so that a fresh edge may be formed.

In giving a test the pupils should be told exactly what to do but not coached on the examples or problems. They should be trained in responding promptly to the signals commonly used in giving standardized tests. When a test is given in the book, the teacher should make certain that each pupil has turned to the right page and is equipped with a blank sheet of paper. Direct the pupils to mark the place by putting the sheet of paper in the book and then to close it. Then say: "Attention! Ready, go!" At the end of the time to be allowed say: "Stop!"

All of the standardized tests are taken from the following well-known tests: Monroe's General Survey Scale in Arithmetic, Monroe's Diagnostic Tests in Arithmetic, and Monroe's Standardized Reasoning Tests. It is worth while, when possible, to obtain and use the regular printed form of these tests. Copies may be purchased from the Public School Publishing Company, Bloomington, Illinois.

DIRECTIONS FOR SCORING STANDARD-IZED TEST — ARITHMETIC PROBLEMS

GENERAL DIRECTIONS

1. In order that a solution may be counted as correct in principle the correct operation must be performed upon the correct numbers. For example, if a problem requires division, the right number must be used as a divisor.

2. A solution is counted as correct in principle when the operation performed is based upon the true relations of the numbers used.

3. The fact that a pupil does not use the shortest method is not to be counted against him. Our thinking is psychological. It is only necessary that each operation in the solution be based upon the true relations of the quantities.

4. Errors in denominate numbers (such as the number of months in a year, number of pounds in a ton, number of square feet in a square yard, etc.) do not affect the correctness of the principle.

5. No credit is given for a problem partially correct in principle. In a two-step problem, no credit is given unless the pupil at least has definitely indicated the last operation.

6. Answers are counted as correct only when the answer is numerically correct. If it contains a fraction, it must be reduced to its lowest terms. Answers need not be labeled; that is, if the answer is square feet, it is not necessary that it be labeled as such.

7. If a solution is incorrect in principle, the answer is also marked incorrect.

8. If a pupil solves a problem correctly and then continues with additional operations which are not called for, his solution becomes incorrect in both principle and answer.

DIRECTIONS FOR SCORING TEST PAPERS

1. Mark each problem for "correct principle" (P) and for "correct answer" (C).

2. These values for the test on pages 216–217 are as follows:

1. P = 2   C = 1
2. P = 2   C = 2
3. P = 2   C = 2
4. P = 3   C = 2
5. P = 1   C = 1
6. P = 1   C = 2
7. P = 3   C = 2
8. P = 2   C = 2

9. P = 1   C = 2
10. P = 2   C = 1
11. P = 3   C = 3
12. P = 3   C = 3
13. P = 2   C = 3
14. P = 1   C = 1
15. P = 2   C = 2

3. These values for the test on pages 218–219 are as follows:

1. P = 2   C = 2
2. P = 2   C = 2
3. P = 2   C = 2
4. P = 2   C = 2
5. P = 3   C = 1
6. P = 1   C = 2
7. P = 3   C = 1
8. P = 2   C = 1

9. P = 3   C = 2
10. P = 1   C = 2
11. P = 1   C = 2
12. P = 2   C = 3
13. P = 3   C = 2
14. P = 1   C = 1
15. P = 2   C = 2

4. For the test on pages 363–364 the values are as follows:

1. P = 2   C = 1
2. P = 2   C = 1
3. P = 2   C = 1
4. P = 3   C = 2
5. P = 2   C = 1
6. P = 2   C = 3
7. P = 2   C = 2
8. P = 2   C = 1

9. P = 2   C = 1
10. P = 2   C = 2
11. P = 3   C = 1
12. P = 1   C = 1
13. P = 2   C = 1
14. P = 2   C = 1
15. P = 3   C = 1

5. Find the sum of the "P" values of the problems correct in principle. This sum is the pupil's score for correct principle.

6. Similarly find the sum of the " C " values of those problems having correct answers. This sum is the pupil's score for correct answer.

7. Below are given detailed directions for scoring the test papers. Study them carefully before beginning to score papers.

CORRECT SOLUTIONS AND ANSWERS

The solutions below are not intended to cover all possible forms. Observe also that for the sake of brevity they are indicated by signs of operation. No importance is to be attached to this form of expression. The essential point is that the operation be performed. In multiplication, if the multiplier and multiplicand are reversed, accept as correct in principle. If the decimal point is wrongly placed, the principle may be correct although the answer must be wrong. The pupils are expected to do all of their work on the test papers.

Answers for test on pages 216–217 :

1. $\frac{3}{4}$ yd. $+ \frac{1}{8}$ yd. $= \frac{7}{8}$ yd.

2. 10 yd. $- 4\frac{3}{8}$ yd. $= 5\frac{5}{8}$ yd.

3. $63 \times 31.5 = 1984.5$ gal.

4. $6 \div \frac{3}{8} = 6 \times \frac{8}{3} = 16$, no. of days.

5. $\$1.90 \div 20 = \$.095$; $\$.095 \times 10 = \$.95$, or $\$1.90 \div 2 = \$.95$.

6. Addition of all items. *Ans.* 6.575.

7. $196 \div \frac{3}{5} = 196 \times \frac{5}{3} = 326\frac{2}{3}$, no. of loaves.

8. $= 33$; $33 \times \$12.85 = \$154.20$; $2\frac{3}{4} \times \$154.20 = \$424.05$, or $12 \times 2\frac{3}{4} = \$424.05$.

9. $\$6.50 + \$12.25$ ⸱⸱ ⸱⸱ + $\$12.00 = \$35.95$. All items must be added in order to be counted c⸱ ⸱⸱ct in principle.

10. $12 \times 1\frac{3}{4}$ cents $= 21$ cents. ⸱⸱⸱ ⸱⸱⸱ if these quantities are expressed in decimal form.

11. $\$12.50 + \$6.75 + \$.42 + \$17.30 + \$9.50 + \$42.75 + \$174.30 = \$263.52$; $\$263.52 - \$75.82 = \$187.70$.

12. $12 \times 2\frac{7}{8}$ yd. $= 34\frac{1}{2}$ yd.; $34\frac{1}{2} \times \$.12\frac{1}{2} = \$4.31\frac{1}{4}$, or $\$4\frac{5}{16}$, or $2\frac{7}{8} \times \$.12\frac{1}{2} = \$.35\frac{15}{16}$; $12 \times \$.35\frac{15}{16} = \$4.31\frac{1}{4}$. It is not necessary that the $\frac{1}{4}$ be written in the answer.

13. $7850 \div 2000 = 3\frac{37}{40}$; $3\frac{37}{40} \times \$3.90 = \$15.31$.

14. $35.75 − $28.50 = $7.25.

15. 500 bu. ÷ 40 = $12\frac{1}{2}$ bu.

Answers for test on pages 218–219:

1. 24.9 mi. + 10.6 mi. + 102.6 mi. + 81.3 mi. = 219.4 mi.

2. 5 gal. − $1\frac{3}{4}$ gal. = $3\frac{1}{4}$ gal.

3. 26 × 8.75 = 227.5, no. of bushels.

4. $28 ÷ 1.75 = 16, no. of days.

5. $4.00 ÷ 8 = $0.50; $6\frac{1}{2}$ × .50 = $3.25. If solved correctly by proportion, count as correct.

6. $27\frac{1}{3}$ lb. + $30\frac{3}{4}$ lb. + $24\frac{1}{4}$ lb. + $32\frac{1}{2}$ lb. + $34\frac{1}{4}$ lb. = $149\frac{1}{12}$ lb.

7. 15 ÷ $\frac{3}{4}$ = 20, no. of lengths.

8. $.12$\frac{1}{2}$ × 8 = $1.00; $1.00 × 6 = $6.00; or 6 × 8 hrs. = 48 hrs.; $.12$\frac{1}{2}$ × 48 = $6.00.

9. $1.00 ÷ $4\frac{1}{2}$ = 0.22\frac{2}{3}$; or 100¢ ÷ $4\frac{1}{2}$¢ = $22\frac{2}{9}$¢.

10. 32 × $9\frac{3}{4}$ = 312, no. of yards.

11. $28.75 + $9.20 + $4.80 + $10.98 = $53.73; $60.00 − $53.73 = $6.27.

12. $1.95 − $1.37 = $.58; $.58 × 36 = $20.88; or $1.95 × 36 = $70.20; $1.37 × 36 = $49.32; $70.20 − $49.32 = $20.88.

13. 207 ÷ 18 = 11.5; 4 × 11.5 = 46, no. of barrels, or 18 ÷ 4 = 4.5; 207 ÷ 4.5 = 46, no. of barrels. If solved by proportion, accept as correct.

14. $7.25 − $5.67 = $1.58.

15. $46 ÷ $9\frac{1}{5}$ = $5.

Answers for test on pages 363–364.

1. $56 × .12$\frac{1}{2}$ = $7, or $56 × $\frac{1}{8}$ = $7.

2. 192.50 ÷ 1750 = .11, or 11%

3. $2.25 × .20 = $.45; $2.25 + $.45 = $2.70, or 20% of $2.25 = $0.45; or $\frac{1}{5}$ of $2.25 = $0.45.

4. 1.00 + .05 = 1.05; $180 ÷ 1.05 = 171\frac{3}{7}$, or $171.43, 105% = $180; 1% = 1\frac{5}{7}$; 100% = 171\frac{3}{7}$, or $171.43.

5. $18.75 ÷ $1250 = .015, or 1.5%.

6. 3125 × .438 = 1368.75, no. of tons of iron.

7. $12,480 ÷ 1000 = $12.48; $13.50 × 12.48 = $168.48. It is necessary that $12,480 be divided by 1000, but this may be done simply by pointing off.

8. .33⅓ × 12 = 4; 12 − 4 = 8, or 1.00 − .33⅓ = .66⅔; .66⅔ × 12 = 8. The problem may also be solved using .33⅓ expressed as ⅓. However, no credit is given unless either 4 or the per cent is subtracted.

9. $640 × .05 = $32. $32 × 4 = $128. Any correct method of finding the interest is to be accepted.

10. $75,000 × .07½ = $5625.

11. 1.00 − .40 = .60; $0.90 ÷ .60 = $1.50, price of the pocket book, also 60% = $0.90; 1% = $0.01½; 100% = $1.50.

12. 356.4 ÷ 9 = 39.6, average rate of train.

13. $1.50 × .10 = $0.15; $1.50 + $.15 = $1.65, selling price; or 1.00 + .10 = 1.10; $1.50 × 1.10 = $1.65, selling price.

14. $167.40 × .33⅓ = $55.80, or $167.40 × ⅓ = $55.80.

15. $3 ÷ .16⅔ = $18, or $3 ÷ ⅙ = $18, or 16⅔% = $3; 1% = $0.18; 100% = $18.

TABLE OF CONTENTS

SEVENTH GRADE — FIRST HALF

SEVENTH GRADE — SECOND HALF

EIGHTH GRADE — FIRST HALF

EIGHTH GRADE — SECOND HALF

MODERN PRACTICAL ARITHMETIC

SEVENTH GRADE — FIRST HALF

A **number** is that which tells how many.

Arithmetic is the study of numbers and their applications.

Notation is a method of writing numbers. **Numeration** is a method of reading numbers.

Uniting two or more numbers into one number is **Addition**. The numbers added are the **addends** and the result is the **sum**. Finding how much greater one number is than another is **Subtraction**. The number subtracted from is the **minuend** and the number subtracted is the **subtrahend**. The result is the **difference**. Subtraction is the reverse of addition.

Finding a number which is a certain number of times another number is **Multiplication**. The numbers multiplied are the **factors**. The factor multiplied is the **multiplicand** and the factor multiplied by is the **multiplier**. The result is the **product**. Finding how many times one number is contained in another is **Division**. The number divided is the **dividend** and the number divided by the **divisor**. The result is the **quotient**. Division is the reverse of multiplication.

These four operations, addition, subtraction, multiplication, and division, are called the **fundamental operations**.

1

Addition

Add by columns, and by lines. Test by adding in the reverse order. Can you add six columns correctly in 3 minutes?

	a.	b.	c.	d.	e.	f.
1.	346	209	169	646	364	766
2.	579	724	742	524	123	981
3.	234	392	936	892	457	312
4.	782	257	544	744	890	464
5.	356	796	395	937	123	385
6.	366	213	387	910	487	135
7.	644	756	793	489	446	132
8.	872	599	554	768	295	915
9.	389	934	692	314	782	715
10.	741	318	947	909	397	799
11.	872	282	428	439	365	793
12.	693	537	784	728	488	336
13.	524	249	396	321	249	969

	g.	h.	i.	j.	k.	l.
14.	781	384	948	463	314	668
15.	496	945	238	944	817	686
16.	604	762	649	381	469	264
17.	748	759	368	785	678	735
18.	697	874	685	456	912	846
19.	704	267	597	789	341	278
20.	443	937	123	321	234	973
21.	349	487	197	468	527	686
22.	827	296	342	375	381	279
23.	396	186	469	626	917	444
24.	207	744	784	497	488	956
25.	398	596	387	342	522	137
26.	527	737	943	563	696	586

Add:

	a	b	c	d	e	f
1.	$14\frac{1}{4}$	$23\frac{1}{4}$	$17\frac{1}{4}$	$5\frac{1}{2}$	$8\frac{3}{4}$	$6\frac{1}{2}$
	$6\frac{1}{2}$	$4\frac{3}{4}$	8	$4\frac{3}{4}$	$3\frac{3}{4}$	$4\frac{1}{2}$
2.	$37\frac{1}{3}$	$6\frac{2}{3}$	$35\frac{1}{2}$	$27\frac{2}{3}$	$14\frac{1}{4}$	$9\frac{1}{3}$
	$9\frac{1}{3}$	$4\frac{1}{3}$	$6\frac{1}{3}$	$8\frac{2}{3}$	$5\frac{1}{3}$	$6\frac{3}{4}$
3.	$24\frac{2}{3}$	$33\frac{1}{5}$	$84\frac{2}{5}$	$62\frac{4}{5}$	$6\frac{1}{5}$	$5\frac{2}{3}$
	$8\frac{3}{4}$	$8\frac{1}{2}$	$7\frac{1}{4}$	$9\frac{1}{2}$	$4\frac{1}{3}$	$1\frac{3}{5}$
4.	$9\frac{3}{5}$	$85\frac{1}{7}$	$63\frac{5}{7}$	$8\frac{3}{8}$	$17\frac{1}{5}$	$21\frac{1}{4}$
	$7\frac{3}{4}$	$7\frac{1}{2}$	$6\frac{1}{3}$	$4\frac{1}{4}$	$6\frac{3}{10}$	$5\frac{5}{8}$
5.	$36\frac{3}{4}$	$45\frac{1}{12}$	$8\frac{1}{4}$	$54\frac{7}{12}$	$11\frac{1}{15}$	$4\frac{11}{15}$
	$9\frac{1}{8}$	$7\frac{2}{3}$	$3\frac{5}{12}$	$9\frac{3}{4}$	$8\frac{2}{3}$	$1\frac{1}{5}$

Add without copying:

6.	7.	8.	9.	10.
$ 2.35	$83.97	$ 18.79	$ 69.00	$ 2.06
.49	.65	4.65	72.35	13.54
8.07	4.82	82.04	670.48	216.17
90.63	.39	9.00	8359.20	13.41
5.84	9.10	501.83	2517.03	26.14
53.69	87.65	7.62	932.45	315.19
708.10	19.74	9.30	8534.06	524.70
524.79	1.93	18.49	92.08	28.15
13.79	83.70	43.86	801.64	405.20
954.68	2.46	97.53	17.32	91.40
30.07	.98	68.12	84.63	56.29
888.94	48.39	835.27	91.02	81.15

In examples 1–4, *add and test, timing yourself.* *Practice until you can get all sums correct in four minutes.*

1.	2.	3.	4.
$ 34.25	9.764	$ 48.39	186.424
69.87	5.20	446.19	4.2468
801.06	49.0742	72.934	.9374
12.14	.894	693.126	102.0738
198.28	2.763	28.987	84.176
79.63	.058	6.104	9.334
918.47	.9278	92.193	19.2376
29.13	4.615	8.56	5.28
40.88	.8923	.79	80.342
60.82	.705	42.138	9.76
41.98	400.0006	8.973	3.582

5. Add four dollars and ninety-one cents, sixty-three dollars seventy-five cents and eight mills, twenty-seven dollars forty-two cents and two mills, three hundred seventy-eight dollars twenty-nine cents and seven mills, nine hundred forty-two dollars, six dollars and seventy-eight cents.

6. Find the sum of eighty-one and eighty-one thousandths, sixty-three and twenty-nine hundredths, two hundred fourteen and one hundred fifty-eight ten-thousandths, five hundred sixteen thousandths, twenty-nine and forty-four ten-thousandths, six hundred eighty-four ten-thousandths, ninety-six ten-thousandths.

GOVERNMENT FIGURES

1. In national, state, county, and city governments, very large numbers must be dealt with. The numbers below indicate the amounts appropriated in one year and requested for the next year for county expenses in one county. How much more was asked for the second year than was appropriated the first year? Read all the numbers aloud.

County Offices	Appropriated	Requested
Controller	$ 114,070.00	$ 128,780.00
Treasurer	9,313,523.75	11,938,978.78
Receiver of Taxes . .	306,810.00	312,780.00
Register of Wills . . .	98,395.00	105,780.00
Recorder of Deeds . .	284,460.00	295,420.00
Revision of Taxes . .	291,930.00	298,830.00
City Solicitor	181,790.00	198,630.00
County Commissioners	2,333,216.00	2,970,124.00
Quarter Sessions . . .	121,500.00	164,300.00
Coroner	70,970.00	84,800.00
District Attorney . .	103,800.00	117,600.00
Sheriff	197,970.00	223,340.00
County Prisons . . .	290,098.00	348,548.00

2. Subscriptions to the second Liberty Loan of 1917 in the twelve Federal Reserve districts were as given here. Find the total. Read all of the amounts and the total.

	Subscriptions
Boston	$ 476,950,050
New York . .	1,550,453,450
Philadelphia . .	380,350,250
Cleveland . . .	486,106,800
Richmond . . .	201,212,500
Atlanta . . .	90,695,750
Chicago . . .	585,853,350
St. Louis . . .	184,280,750
Minneapolis . .	140,932,650
Kansas City . .	150,125,750
Dallas	77,899,850
San Francisco .	292,671,150

3. How much more was subscribed in the New York district than in the last six districts combined? Why could more bonds be sold in the New York district than in other districts?

Subtraction

Subtract:

1. 83964
   42823

2. 93764
   83664

3. 57068
   37059

4. 80005
   30000

5. 29070
   19937

6. 527
   389.19

7. 64.42
   42.93

8. 365
   46.12

9. 98.10
   23.56

10. 384.79
    93.62

11. 3.067
    1.97

12. 7.1916
    3.1412

13. 14.9
    7.84

14. 38.17
    15.386

15. 41.8
    3.47

16. $36\frac{1}{2}$
    $29\frac{1}{4}$

17. $139\frac{2}{3}$
    $48\frac{1}{2}$

18. $18\frac{3}{8}$
    $9\frac{1}{4}$

19. $24\frac{3}{7}$
    $13\frac{1}{14}$

20. $49\frac{4}{5}$
    $38\frac{2}{3}$

21. 19
    $8\frac{1}{2}$

22. 35
    $6\frac{2}{3}$

23. 64
    $7\frac{3}{5}$

24. 16
    $4\frac{4}{7}$

25. 21
    $20\frac{7}{8}$

26. $14\frac{1}{3}$
    $11\frac{2}{3}$

27. $17\frac{1}{8}$
    $9\frac{1}{2}$

28. $29\frac{3}{8}$
    $8\frac{7}{8}$

29. $41\frac{5}{6}$
    $19\frac{11}{12}$

30. $14\frac{3}{7}$
    $9\frac{2}{3}$

31. $10\frac{1}{2}$
    $7\frac{3}{4}$

32. $6\frac{1}{5}$
    $2\frac{1}{3}$

33. $13\frac{7}{8}$
    5

34. 21
    $20\frac{3}{11}$

35. $43\frac{7}{12}$
    $39\frac{5}{6}$

36. $12\frac{3}{5}$
    $7\frac{8}{10}$

37. $9\frac{4}{15}$
    $6\frac{2}{3}$

38. 24
    $19\frac{7}{11}$

39. $13\frac{3}{8}$
    $9\frac{3}{4}$

40. $28\frac{5}{13}$
    $9\frac{7}{26}$

Add :

1.	49,875	2.	795,875	3.	69,875	4.	946;857
	98,647		879,486		90,150		975,976
	85,967		987,579		85,737		869,799
	76,895		698,947		76,324		697,867
	64,784		775,799		50,497		769,986
	59,899		897,964		82,539		488,695
	64,978		968,496		96,578		946,859

Subtract :

5.	90,837	6.	837,415	7.	80,005	8.	378,974
	49,948		496,736		34,697		168,985

Add :

9.	64.85	10.	1,898.35	11.	529.768	12.	270.55
	1,703.347		3.96		7.42		1.087
	8.06		729.24		1,322.707		3,468.27
	89.44		6,147.33		89.59		57.08
	4,976.003		63.82		7.76		1,326.476
	7.8		127.907		4,872.003		10.87
	1,465.45		9.321		24.34		9.009

Subtract :

13.	98.007	14.	187.32	15.	327.455	16.	32.64
	56.38		98.54		159.76		29.77

17.	1,497.35	18.	183.63	19.	3,761.87	20.	456.37
	69.51		87.84		93.99		67.58

21.	930.5	22.	9.736	23.	836.50	24.	947.89
	896.8		4.997		749.68		874.69

Add :

	A	B	C	D	E	F
1.	$9\frac{1}{6}$ $5\frac{2}{3}$	$7\frac{1}{2}$ $3\frac{1}{4}$	$8\frac{1}{2}$ $2\frac{1}{6}$	$4\frac{7}{10}$ $2\frac{3}{4}$	$5\frac{5}{8}$ $4\frac{4}{5}$	$5\frac{1}{2}$ $2\frac{7}{8}$
2.	$4\frac{1}{4}$ $1\frac{3}{8}$	$7\frac{5}{8}$ $3\frac{2}{3}$	$4\frac{1}{2}$ $1\frac{1}{3}$	$7\frac{2}{9}$ $1\frac{3}{4}$	$6\frac{1}{6}$ $5\frac{3}{4}$	$6\frac{1}{8}$ $2\frac{1}{4}$
3.	$5\frac{1}{6}$ $2\frac{1}{3}$	$6\frac{2}{5}$ $3\frac{5}{8}$	$5\frac{1}{3}$ $3\frac{2}{3}$	$6\frac{2}{5}$ $3\frac{1}{2}$	$5\frac{1}{5}$ $3\frac{1}{4}$	$5\frac{7}{16}$ $3\frac{1}{2}$
4.	$9\frac{5}{12}$ $6\frac{1}{2}$	$7\frac{1}{3}$ $3\frac{7}{10}$	$4\frac{1}{5}$ $3\frac{2}{3}$	$7\frac{1}{2}$ $4\frac{3}{4}$	$4\frac{2}{3}$ $1\frac{6}{7}$	$5\frac{9}{16}$ $\frac{3}{4}$
5.	$4\frac{1}{2}$ $3\frac{5}{8}$	$6\frac{2}{3}$ $3\frac{7}{8}$	$7\frac{2}{3}$ $3\frac{5}{6}$	$5\frac{1}{8}$ $3\frac{1}{3}$	$6\frac{1}{2}$ $2\frac{1}{7}$	$7\frac{1}{3}$ $4\frac{7}{9}$
6.	$6\frac{1}{2}$ $4\frac{4}{5}$	$5\frac{2}{3}$ $1\frac{8}{9}$	$7\frac{1}{10}$ $3\frac{2}{3}$	$9\frac{2}{9}$ $4\frac{1}{3}$	$7\frac{3}{8}$ $2\frac{1}{2}$	$5\frac{1}{12}$ $3\frac{1}{3}$
7.	$7\frac{1}{4}$ $2\frac{2}{3}$	$5\frac{1}{3}$ $2\frac{3}{8}$	$7\frac{4}{9}$ $3\frac{2}{3}$	$8\frac{1}{10}$ $6\frac{1}{4}$	$8\frac{2}{3}$ $5\frac{3}{4}$	$7\frac{1}{3}$ $4\frac{1}{2}$
8.	$6\frac{1}{4}$ $1\frac{1}{2}$	$6\frac{3}{7}$ $3\frac{1}{2}$	$6\frac{5}{6}$ $2\frac{1}{2}$	$5\frac{1}{4}$ $2\frac{5}{8}$	$5\frac{1}{2}$ $2\frac{5}{6}$	$6\frac{2}{3}$ $2\frac{5}{8}$

9–16. Subtract the lower number from the upper in each example. Prove each answer.

17. From a car containing $32\frac{1}{4}$ tons of lime $17\frac{7}{8}$ are sold. How many tons remain?

18. From a field containing $12\frac{3}{8}$ acres 15 camp sites are sold. If each site contains $\frac{1}{8}$ of an acre, how many acres remain unsold?

Multiply. Prove each answer :

1. 830 by 13
2. 615 by 19
3. 365 by 24
4. 709 by 27
5. 803 by 30
6. 628 by 14
7. 385 by 17

8. 88 by 88
9. 69 by 41
10. 37 by 19
11. 409 by 28
12. 760 by 15
13. 990 by 19
14. 850 by 17

15. 716 by 17
16. 305 by 13
17. 419 by 27
18. 864 by 38
19. 491 by 17
20. 589 by 26
21. 703 by 99

Find the products. Prove each answer :

22. 350×168
23. 431×217
24. 206×315
25. 225×602

26. 1526×369
27. 3691×436
28. 2062×408
29. 3126×312

30. 4680×213
31. 8426×7028
32. 2691×2807
33. 4152×8056

Multiply :

34. 380 by $\frac{1}{2}$
35. 681 by $\frac{1}{3}$
36. 585 by $\frac{1}{5}$
37. 840 by $\frac{2}{7}$
38. 945 by $\frac{2}{3}$
39. 190 by $\frac{3}{10}$
40. 750 by $\frac{2}{5}$

41. 738 by $\frac{5}{6}$
42. $6\frac{1}{2}$ by 10
43. 12 by $3\frac{1}{3}$
44. $11\frac{1}{4}$ by 8
45. 14 by $5\frac{2}{7}$
46. $13\frac{1}{5}$ by 15
47. 8 by $7\frac{3}{4}$

48. 882 by $\frac{4}{3}$
49. 245 by $\frac{5}{7}$
50. 96 by $\frac{5}{4}$
51. $\frac{7}{11}$ by 44
52. $1\frac{3}{5}$ by 85
53. 64 by $7\frac{5}{8}$
54. 39 by $2\frac{1}{13}$

Multiply. Estimate each answer before multiplying :

55. 891 by 1.3
56. 43.7 by 6.9
57. 1.05 by .6
58. 964 by .06

59. .862 by 30
60. 4.65 by .07
61. 800 by .19
62. 24.9 by .38

63. .006 by .18
64. 3.64 by 1.7
65. 69.3 by .04
66. 8.93 by 1.9

Special Helps in Multiplication

(1) *To multiply an integer by* 10, *or a power of* 10, *annex as many zeros to the integer as there are zeros in the multiplier.*

(2) *To multiply a number by* 25 *multiply it by* 100 *and take $\frac{1}{4}$ of the product.*

44 × 25 = ?
44 × 100 = 4400. $\frac{1}{4}$ of 4400 = 1100 *Ans.*
Why do we take $\frac{1}{4}$ of the product?

(3) *To multiply a number by* 125 *multiply it by* 1000 *and take $\frac{1}{8}$ of the product.*

800 × 125 = ?
800 × 1000 = 800,000. $\frac{1}{8}$ of 800,000 = 100,000 *Ans.*
Why do we take $\frac{1}{8}$ of the product?

(4) *To multiply by* 12$\frac{1}{2}$ *multiply by* 100 *and take $\frac{1}{8}$ of the product.*

160 × 12.5 = ?
160 × 100 = 16,000. $\frac{1}{8}$ of 16,000 = 2000 *Ans.*

(5) *To multiply a number by* .33$\frac{1}{3}$, *take $\frac{1}{3}$ of it. Why?*

(6) *To multiply a number by* .25, *take $\frac{1}{4}$ of it. Why?*

(7) *To multiply a number by* .14$\frac{2}{7}$, *take $\frac{1}{7}$ of it. Why?*

(8) *To multiply a number by* .16$\frac{2}{3}$, *take $\frac{1}{6}$ of it. Why?*

Find the products and give the rule that applies to each:

1. 497 × 1000	10. 645 × .25	19. 3.24 × 25
2. 96 × 25	11. 24.84 × .25	20. 3792 × 125
3. 364 × 25	12. 24.84 × 25	21. 48.20 × .25
4. 720 × 125	13. 36.30 × .12$\frac{1}{2}$	22. 32.08 × .12$\frac{1}{2}$
5. 256 × 125	14. 36.30 × 125	23. 3208 × .12$\frac{1}{2}$
6. 216 × 12$\frac{1}{2}$	15. 35.07 × 14$\frac{2}{7}$	24. 221 × .14$\frac{2}{7}$
7. 7.20 × .12$\frac{1}{2}$	16. 21.06 × 14$\frac{2}{7}$	25. 9.62 × .33$\frac{1}{3}$
8. 3.66 × 33$\frac{1}{3}$	17. 3573 × 16$\frac{2}{3}$	26. 453 × 33$\frac{1}{3}$
9. 34.74 × .33$\frac{1}{3}$	18. 24360 × 16$\frac{2}{3}$	27. 54.6 × .16$\frac{2}{3}$

Articles Sold by the Hundred, by the Thousand, and by the Ton

C stands for hundred, cwt. for hundredweight, and M for thousand.

1. Find the cost of 236 cucumbers at 75¢ per C.

2.36
.75
————
1180
1652
————
1.7700

$236 \div 100 = 2.36$

$2.36 \times .75 = 1.77$

The cucumbers cost $1.77.

In final results, a fraction of a cent equal to or greater than ½ cent is counted as a cent. A fraction less than ½ ¢ is dropped.

2. Find the cost of 1236 fruit baskets at 54¢ per C.

3. What is the cost of 3146 cantaloupes at $8.16 per C?

4. When oranges are quoted at $4.38 per C what is the cost of 2315 oranges?

5. When the cost of shipping freight is 35¢ per cwt. what is the cost of shipping 4864 lb.?

6. What is the cost of 464 lb. bacon at $37½ per cwt.?

7. Find the cost of 7563 laths at 58¢ per C.

8. What is the cost of 2370 feet of pine siding at $68 per M?

2.370
68
————
18960
14220
————
161.160

$2370 \div 1000 = 2.370$

$2.370 \times 68 = 161.16$

The cost is $161.16.

9. What is the cost of 25,250 feet of oak flooring at $115 per M?

10. When envelopes are sold at $4.16 per M, what is the cost of 12,368 envelopes?

11. At $48 per M what will 2-inch planking cost for a sidewalk 5 ft. wide and 64 ft. long?

12. 4260 feet of flooring are required for a floor. What is the cost at $65 per M?

13. What is the cost of 12,250 sheets of bond paper at $2.94 per M?

14. What will 25,280 bricks cost at $18 per M?

15. What will 354 ft. of selected quartered oak cost at $140 per M?

16. What is the cost of 12,564 lb. of hay at $21 per ton?

17. What is the cost of 34,580 lb. of mixed feed at $38 per ton?

18. A coal dealer delivered 4 loads of grate coal, weighing respectively, 4125 lb., 3915 lb., 3560 lb., and 4220 lb. What was the cost of it at $8.10 per ton?

19. Mr. French used 3150 lb. of fertilizer on his corn field. What was the cost at $45 per ton?

20. What is the cost of 560 lb. of chestnut coal at $8.50 per ton?

21. What is the cost of shipping by freight 39,800 lb. furniture at $3.50 per cwt.?

22. What is the cost of 3154 lb. of sugar at $8.25 per cwt.?

23. What is the cost of 6420 lb. corn meal at $48 per ton?

24. What is the cost of 13,500 butter trays at 60¢ per thousand?

25. A feed merchant bought 28,350 lb. of mixed feed at $42 per ton and retailed it at $2.60 per cwt. What was his entire profit?

26. What is the cost of 1562 lb. of maple sugar at $22 per cwt.?

27. Find the cost of 11,300 bricks at $35 per thousand.

Division

Divide:

1. 8877 by 77
2. $\frac{1}{2}$ by $\frac{1}{8}$
3. 8.42 by .02
4. 2064 by 96
5. $\frac{1}{8}$ by $\frac{1}{2}$
6. 3.69 by .3
7. 2369 by 69
8. $2\frac{3}{8}$ by $\frac{1}{2}$
9. 595 by .005
10. 4141 by 82
11. $\frac{1}{2}$ by $\frac{1}{16}$
12. 78.6 by .6
13. 9999 by 81
14. $3\frac{5}{8}$ by $1\frac{3}{4}$
15. 985.61 by 48
16. 918 by 9
17. $6\frac{3}{8}$ by $3\frac{3}{4}$
18. \$4385.60 by 130
19. 8280 by 90
20. $7\frac{1}{2}$ by $3\frac{3}{4}$
21. \$25490.30 by 95
22. 26344 by 74
23. $\frac{1}{3}$ by $\frac{1}{2}$
24. 39.69 by .09
25. 59502 by 94
26. $5\frac{5}{6}$ by $1\frac{1}{2}$
27. 7992 by .81
28. 42918 by 622
29. $6\frac{2}{3}$ by $2\frac{5}{6}$
30. 6250 by 6.25
31. 81048 by 264
32. $17\frac{5}{8}$ by $5\frac{7}{8}$
33. 1664 by .875
34. 96600 by 345
35. $2\frac{2}{5}$ by 16
36. 14860 by 2000
37. 76736 by 218
38. 8 by $9\frac{1}{3}$
39. 314.16 by 3.1416
40. 108375 by 125
41. $12\frac{2}{3}$ by $3\frac{1}{6}$
42. 86.5 by 1.73
43. 120000 by 250
44. $4\frac{4}{5}$ by $1\frac{1}{15}$
45. 106.15 by 9.65
46. 37835 by 47
47. $5\frac{5}{7}$ by $3\frac{3}{14}$
48. 317.34 by 17.63
49. 23712 by 416
50. $6\frac{3}{7}$ by $\frac{9}{14}$
51. 7795.2 by 89.6
52. 65520 by 84
53. $8\frac{4}{5}$ by $1\frac{1}{10}$
54. 663.48 by 9.7
55. 40488 by 64
56. $12\frac{3}{5}$ by $\frac{9}{20}$
57. 69.969 by 8.43
58. 403850 by 82
59. $15\frac{3}{4}$ by $\frac{7}{8}$
60. 843.696 by 6.72

Short Methods
Special Helps in Division

(1) *To divide by* 10, 100, 1000, *etc., move the decimal point to the left, as many places as there are zeros in the divisor.*

$216 \div 10 = 21.6$ $3724 \div 100 = 37.24$ $15,983 \div 1000 = 15.983.$

(2) *To divide a number by* 5, *multiply by* 2 *and divide by* 10.

$324 \div 5 = 648 \div 10.$ $648 \div 10 = 64.8.$

(3) *To divide a number by* 25, *multiply it by* 4 *and divide the product by* 100.

$3604 \div 25 = 14,416 \div 100.$ $14,416 \div 100 = 144.16.$

(4) *To divide a number by* 125, *multiply it by* 8, *and divide the product by* 1000.

$3106 \div 125 = 24,848 \div 1000.$ $24,848 \div 1000 = 24.848.$

(5) *To divide a number by* $33\frac{1}{3}$, *multiply it by* 3 *and divide the product by* 100.

$425 \div 33\frac{1}{3} = 1275 \div 100.$ $1275 \div 100 = 12.75.$

(6) *To divide a number by* $12\frac{1}{2}$, *multiply it by* 8 *and divide the product by* 100.

$463 \div 12\frac{1}{2} = 3704 \div 100.$ $3704 \div 100 = 37.04.$

(7) *To divide a number by* .25, *divide it by* $\frac{1}{4}$.

$216 \div .25 = 216 \div \frac{1}{4}.$ $216 \times \frac{4}{1} = 864.$

(8) *To divide a number by* $.33\frac{1}{3}$, *divide it by* $\frac{1}{3}$.

$341 \div .33\frac{1}{3} = 314 \div \frac{1}{3}.$ $341 \times \frac{3}{1} = 1023.$

(9) *To divide a number by* $.12\frac{1}{2}$, *divide it by* $\frac{1}{8}$.

$216 \div .12\frac{1}{2} = 216 \div \frac{1}{8}.$ $216 \times \frac{8}{1} = 1728.$

(10) *To divide a number by* $.66\frac{2}{3}$, *divide it by* $\frac{2}{3}$.

$200 \div .66\frac{2}{3} = 200 \div \frac{2}{3}.$ $200 \times \frac{3}{2} = 300.$

(11) *To divide a number by* .75, *divide it by* $\frac{3}{4}$.

$300 \div .75 = 300 \div \frac{3}{4}.$ $300 \times \frac{4}{3} = 400.$

Divide by 5:

1. 3482 2. 2936 3. 439.3 4. 1.004 5. 10.056

Divide by 25:

6. 263 7. 418 8. 6.78 9. 3.001 10. 2508

Divide by 125:

11. 314 12. 100.6 13. 37.506 14. 1.0063 15. 286

Divide by $33\frac{1}{3}$:

16. 428 17. 2.63 18. 15.62 19. 14.003 20. 265

Divide by $12\frac{1}{2}$:

21. 168 22. 3.42 23. 30.51 24. 1.163 25. 1056

Divide by .25:

26. 261 27. 216 28. 144 29. 716 30. 436

Divide by $.33\frac{1}{3}$:

31. 222 32. 106 33. 1004 34. 567 35. 126

Divide by $.12\frac{1}{2}$:

36. 72 37. 56 38. 144 39. 208 40. 720

Divide by $.66\frac{2}{3}$:

41. 204 42. 206 43. 912 44. 724 45. 927

Divide by .75:

46. 403 47. 603 48. 720 49. 1608 50. 1000

Divide:

51. $36,502 by 10

52. $254.36 by 5

53. $359.28 by 5

54. $5275 by 1000

55. 362.4 by 25

56. 34.96 by 125

57. 453 by 125

58. 2016 by $12\frac{1}{2}$

59. 38.61 by 25

60. 648 by $.33\frac{1}{3}$

61. 16.42 by 25

62. 3020 by $.66\frac{2}{3}$

63. 3120 by .75

64. 4160 by 125

65. 6072 by $.33\frac{1}{3}$

66. 4120 by $.66\frac{2}{3}$

Multiply. Reduce the answers to simplest form :

1. $\frac{1}{2} \times \frac{1}{3} = ?$ 7. $\frac{3}{4} \times \frac{2}{3} = ?$ 13. $\frac{3}{8} \times \frac{5}{6} = ?$

2. $\frac{2}{3} \times \frac{5}{6} = ?$ 8. $\frac{5}{6} \times \frac{7}{8} = ?$ 14. $\frac{4}{15} \times \frac{5}{8} = ?$

3. $\frac{7}{8} \times \frac{2}{3} = ?$ 9. $\frac{3}{8} \times \frac{1}{4} = ?$ 15. $\frac{5}{12} \times \frac{3}{5} = ?$

4. $\frac{4}{9} \times \frac{2}{5} = ?$ 10. $\frac{7}{12} \times \frac{4}{7} = ?$ 16. $\frac{1}{6} \times \frac{1}{3} = ?$

5. $\frac{4}{5} \times \frac{7}{9} = ?$ 11. $\frac{1}{7} \times \frac{1}{4} = ?$ 17. $\frac{5}{7} \times \frac{4}{5} = ?$

6. $\frac{1}{5} \times \frac{1}{6} = ?$ 12. $\frac{7}{12} \times \frac{2}{3} = ?$ 18. $\frac{7}{8} \times \frac{4}{9} = ?$

Divide. Reduce the answers to simplest form :

19. $\frac{2}{3} \div \frac{1}{3} = ?$ 25. $\frac{1}{5} \div \frac{1}{6} = ?$ 31. $\frac{2}{5} \div \frac{3}{7} = ?$

20. $\frac{1}{2} \div \frac{1}{3} = ?$ 26. $\frac{3}{8} \div \frac{1}{4} = ?$ 32. $\frac{3}{5} \div \frac{3}{4} = ?$

21. $\frac{4}{7} \div \frac{2}{3} = ?$ 27. $\frac{3}{7} \div \frac{4}{5} = ?$ 33. $\frac{3}{8} \div \frac{3}{4} = ?$

22. $\frac{5}{6} \div \frac{5}{8} = ?$ 28. $\frac{8}{9} \div \frac{2}{3} = ?$ 34. $\frac{5}{7} \div \frac{1}{7} = ?$

23. $\frac{7}{8} \div \frac{3}{4} = ?$ 29. $\frac{5}{6} \div \frac{1}{6} = ?$ 35. $\frac{2}{5} \div \frac{4}{7} = ?$

24. $\frac{3}{4} \div \frac{1}{4} = ?$ 30. $\frac{1}{5} \div \frac{1}{2} = ?$ 36. $\frac{5}{7} \div \frac{2}{3} = ?$

Divide. Reduce the answers to simplest form :

37. $15 \div 1\frac{1}{4} = ?$ 43. $21\frac{3}{4} \div 9\frac{2}{3} = ?$ 49. $11\frac{3}{8} \div 5\frac{1}{4} = ?$

38. $20 \div 1\frac{2}{3} = ?$ 44. $10\frac{1}{8} \div 2\frac{1}{4} = ?$ 50. $21\frac{1}{4} \div 4\frac{6}{7} = ?$

39. $18 \div 1\frac{2}{7} = ?$ 45. $33 \div 5\frac{1}{2} = ?$ 51. $14\frac{2}{5} \div 2\frac{4}{7} = ?$

40. $21 \div 3\frac{1}{2} = ?$ 46. $6\frac{2}{3} \div 7\frac{1}{7} = ?$ 52. $22\frac{2}{5} \div 1\frac{5}{9} = ?$

41. $16\frac{4}{5} \div 3\frac{1}{9} = ?$ 47. $8\frac{1}{3} \div 1\frac{3}{7} = ?$ 53. $16\frac{1}{3} \div 3\frac{1}{2} = ?$

42. $17\frac{1}{2} \div 13\frac{1}{3} = ?$ 48. $9\frac{3}{10} \div 4\frac{3}{7} = ?$ 54. $7\frac{2}{9} \div 1\frac{5}{8} = ?$

55. How many packages each containing $\frac{3}{4}$ of a pound can be made from 60 pounds of sweet pea seed?

56. Seven eighths of a pound of bacon is packed in a can. How many cans may be filled from 70 pounds of bacon?

57. Multiply $\frac{9}{13}$ by $\frac{2}{3}$ and divide the product by $\frac{1}{2}$.

Fraction and Decimal

Finding a fractional or decimal part of a number.

> What is $\frac{7}{20}$ of 600?
>
> STATEMENT: $\frac{7}{20}$ of 600 = ?
>
> SOLUTION: $\frac{7}{\cancel{20}}$ of $\cancel{600}^{\,30}$ = 210

In the above example two factors are given to find the product.

First estimate the answer, then find:

1. $\frac{3}{4}$ of \$280
2. .5 of \$9000
3. $\frac{3}{7}$ of \$3500
4. .6 of 2000 lb.
5. $\frac{4}{11}$ of 88 bbl.
6. .12½ of 2400 tons
7. $\frac{5}{8}$ of 168
8. .01 of 1300 ft.
9. $\frac{7}{12}$ of 4800 yd.
10. .37½ of 4000 bu.
11. $\frac{5}{9}$ of 378 men
12. .04 of \$1340
13. $\frac{7}{13}$ of \$3900
14. .66⅔ of 990 quarts
15. $\frac{4}{5}$ of 60000 lb.
16. .47 of \$11000
17. $\frac{1}{15}$ of \$45000
18. .05 of \$370
19. $\frac{7}{8}$ of 80000 bricks
20. .33⅓ of 990 ft.
21. $\frac{15}{17}$ of 3400 tile
22. .035 of \$8964
23. $\frac{2}{3}$ of 2274 ft.
24. 1.06 of \$1800
25. $\frac{6}{11}$ of 550 books
26. 2.125 of \$40000
27. $\frac{19}{20}$ of 1440 tons
28. .16⅔ of 3600 tons
29. $\frac{9}{17}$ of \$850
30. .90 of 2000 lb.
31. $\frac{3}{8}$ of \$7216
32. .0575 of \$60000
33. $\frac{12}{7}$ of 49 bbl.
34. 5.875 of 800 miles
35. $\frac{7}{15}$ of \$75000
36. .625 of \$48000

Finding what fractional or decimal part one number is of another.

> ## What decimal part of 800 is 40?
>
> STATEMENT: What decimal part of 800 = 40?
> SOLUTION: ? × 800 = 40?   .05
>   40 ÷ 800 = .05   800)‾40.00‾

In the above example the product and one factor are given to find the other factor.

Estimate the answer before solving:

1. What decimal part of 80 is 8?

2. What fractional part of 700 is 350?

3. One thousand pounds is what fractional part of a ton?

4. Thirty-five cents is what decimal part of one dollar?

5. Three hundred seventy-five dollars is what fractional part of one thousand dollars?

6. The area of a rectangle is $6\frac{1}{2}$ sq. ft. If the rectangle is 13 ft. long, what is its width?

7. Mr. Harper drew out $585 of the $5850 which he had deposited in the bank. What fractional part of his deposit did he withdraw?

8. Mr. Clark's field containing 4 acres is divided into building lots, each containing $\frac{1}{4}$ of an acre. One building lot is what fractional part of the field?

9. Mr. Sullivan sold 13.5 tons of coal from a bin containing 67.5 tons. What fractional part of the coal in the bin did he sell?

10. What decimal part of two gallons is a pint?

11. What fractional part of $6000 is $300?

Finding the number of which another is a given fractional or decimal part.

---

36 is .3 of what number?

STATEMENT: 36 = .3 of what number?

SOLUTION: 36 ÷ .3 = 120   120

                                3)360

In the above example the product and one factor are given to find the other factor.

Estimate the answer before solving:

1. $850 is .5 of how many dollars?

2. 49 pounds is ¼ of how many pounds?

3. Three hundred four is twenty hundredths of what number?

4. Four gallons of a mixture of soap and water is water. If twenty-five hundredths of the mixture was water, how many gallons were there of the mixture?

5. Sixty dollars was six hundredths of a sum of money. What was the sum of money?

6. If a field of seven acres is one tenth of John's father's farm, how many acres are there in the farm?

7. Change .33⅓ of a yard to inches.

8. Of a shipment of 40 tons of cabbage 8 tons were not sold. How many hundredths of the shipment were sold?

9. Find three one hundredths of $7000.

10. One tenth of a carload of grain weighs 3 tons. How many tons of grain are there in the car?

Review of Principles and Processes

1. A fraction always indicates what operation?

2. What is cancellation?

3. Cancellation shortens what processes?

4. When the factors of a number are known, how may the number be found?

5. When a number and one of its two factors are known, how may the other factor be found?

6. How may an improper fraction be changed to a whole or mixed number?

7. How may yards be changed to inches?

8. How may fractions be multiplied?

9. When the dimensions of a rectangle are known, how may its area be found?

10. When the area and one dimension of a rectangle are known, how may the other dimension be found?

11. When one dimension of a rectangle is given in inches and the other in feet, what must be done in order to find the area in square inches? In square feet?

12. Name five sums of money that are aliquot parts of $1.

13. When is a fraction in its simplest form?

14. What name is given to numbers which are to be added?

15. Which is larger, the minuend or the subtrahend? The minuend or the remainder?

16. If the denominator of a fraction is increased is the value of the fraction increased or diminished?

Mental Tests

1

1. 9 times $1\frac{1}{3}$ = ?
2. $\frac{3}{4}$ of 12 + $\frac{2}{3}$ of 9 = ?   **3.** What is $\frac{2}{3}$ of 11?
4. Find distance around a table 12 ft. long and 8 ft. wide.
5. What will 4 oranges cost at 30¢ a dozen?
6. 16 is what part of 24?
7. What is $\frac{1}{2}$ of $6\frac{1}{2}$?   **8.** $9 \times ?$ = 63.
9. Draw a line $4\frac{3}{4}$ inches long.   **10.** $6 + 5 + 4 + 2 + 3 + 7$ = ?

2

1. 15 is what part of 45?
2. Draw a line $2\frac{1}{4}$ inches long.
3. Find cost of 3 oranges at 60¢ a dozen.
4. $7 + 4 + 2 + 7 + 6 + 7$ = ?   **5.** Find $\frac{1}{2}$ of $8\frac{1}{2}$.
6. How many inches are there in 2 yards?
7. If $\frac{1}{3}$ of a number is 6, what is the number?
8. A rectangular garden is 55 feet long and 35 feet wide. Find the distance around it.   **9.** $\frac{1}{3} \times \frac{3}{22}$ = ?
10. The product of two numbers is 48; one of the numbers is 3. What is the other?

3

1. $16 \times ?$ = 4.   **2.** $6 + 5 + 8 + 3 + 6 + 8 + 2$ = ?
3. Find the distance around a square flower bed 16 feet on a side.
4. $\frac{1}{2} \times \frac{2}{17}$ = ?   **5.** Find cost of 7 apples at 36¢ a dozen.
6. How many inches are there in $3\frac{1}{4}$ feet?
7. $\frac{1}{4}$ of my money is 12 dollars. How much money have I?
8. What is $\frac{3}{4}$ of 5?   **9.** 36×9 = ?
10. Draw a line $5\frac{1}{2}$ inches long.

4

1. $? \times 12 = 3$.

2. Find cost of $1\frac{1}{2}$ pounds of fish at $22\not c$ per pound.

3. 8 is what part of 48?   **4.** $\frac{1}{5}$ of what equals 3?

5. If six oranges cost 42 cents, what will seven oranges cost?

6. The product of two numbers is 48. One factor is 3. What is the other?

7. If $\frac{1}{4}$ of a pound of butter costs 12 cents, what is the price per pound?

8. $\frac{1}{5}$ of $35 + \frac{1}{3}$ of $27 = ?$ **9.** $6 + 4 + 7 + 2 + 1 + 8 + 5 = ?$

10. What is $\frac{1}{2}$ of $5\frac{1}{2}$?

5

1. $23 \times 8 = ?$ **2.** $30 \times ? = 10$.

3. 7 is what part of 56?

4. A table is 12 feet long and 8 feet wide. How many feet is it around it?

5. A window pane is 15 inches square. How many inches is it around it?

6. $\frac{2}{3}$ of what $= 20$?   **7.** $6 \times 2\frac{1}{3} = ?$

8. $\frac{1}{2} + \frac{1}{3} = ?$

9. When grapefruit are 4 for a quarter dollar, how many can be bought for $1\frac{1}{4}$ dollars?

10. How many feet are there in $2\frac{1}{3}$ yards?

6

1. $\frac{1}{2} + \frac{2}{3} = ?$ **2.** $8 + 5 + 6 + 4 + 2 + 7 = ?$

3. 16 is what part of 24?   **4.** $8 \times 7\frac{1}{2} = ?$

5. 4 feet 7 inches are how many inches?

6. What is $\frac{1}{3}$ of $\frac{1}{4}$?

7. How many ounces are there in $1\frac{1}{2}$ pounds?

8. Find the cost of 9 oranges at $40\not c$ a dozen.

9. At 3 for 5 cents, how many apples will 25 cents buy?

10. Find $\frac{3}{8}$ of 10.

True-and-False Test

1. The product of two or more numbers is found by multiplication. True or false?

2. Moving the decimal point two places to the right has the same effect as multiplying the number by 10. True or false?

3. Moving the decimal point three places to the left is the same as dividing by 1000. True or false?

4. If the units' place of a number is zero or five, it can be divided by five. True or false?

5. A number which has no factor except itself and one is a prime number. True or false?

6. Annexing a zero to an integer multiplies the integer by one hundred. True or false?

7. Annexing a zero to a decimal has no effect upon the decimal. True or false?

8. The numerator of a fraction is always less than the denominator. True or false?

9. One half of a whole number is equal to one fourth of twice that number. True or false?

10. The product of three factors contains five decimal places. One of the factors has three decimal places and the other one. Then, the third factor has one decimal place. True or false?

11. Multiplying a number by $.33\frac{1}{3}$ is the same as dividing the number by 3. True or false?

12. The product of a whole number and an improper fraction is less than the number. True or false?

13. If $\frac{1}{2}$ of a number is 12, then twice the number is 24. True or false?

Percentage

Percentage is computing in hundredths.

Per cent is another name for hundredths.

The **sign of percentage** is % and is read *"per cent"* or *"hundredths."*

The **number of hundredths** is the **rate** or rate **per cent.**

1. Mr. Jones earns $240 a month and pays $\frac{1}{5}$ of it for rent. How much rent does he pay?

2. Mr. Henderson earns $250 a month. He pays .20 of his wages for rent. How much is his rent?

3. Mr. Cole earns $300 a month. His rent is 20% of his income. How much rent does he pay monthly?

4. Henry saves $\frac{1}{4}$ of his wages. He earns $7 a week. How much does he save weekly?

5. One week Henry earned only $6. He put .25 of it in the savings bank. How much did he put in the bank that week?

6. Mary saves 25% of her allowance of $3 a week. How much does she save a week?

7. In a certain city $\frac{1}{3}$ of the money raised by tax is spent in support of the public schools. How many cents of each dollar of tax is used for schools?

8. In that city Mr. Carr paid a tax of $48. How much did he pay for the support of the schools?

9. Mr. Walrath had $6000 in the bank. He withdrew $66\frac{2}{3}\%$ of the money to make a payment on his home. How much did he withdraw?

10. Florence missed 10% of the words in her spelling test of 100 words. How many words did she spell correctly?

Percentage

$1\% = .01$	$12\frac{1}{2}\% = .12\frac{1}{2}$ or $.125$
$9\% = .09$	$\frac{1}{2}\% = .00\frac{1}{2}$ or $.005$
$10\% = .10$	$10\frac{7}{10}\% = .10\frac{7}{10}$ or $.107$
$90\% = .90$	$33\frac{1}{3}\% = .33\frac{1}{3}$
$100\% = 1.00$	$8\frac{1}{4}\% = .08\frac{1}{4}$ or $.0825$
$125\% = 1.25$	$\frac{1}{8}\% = .00\frac{1}{8}$ or $.00125$

NOTE. — Care should be taken to express the decimal rate per cent properly, as hundredths. Every fractional part of 1% must be written at the right of the hundredths' place.

Express decimally:

1. 7%	6. $6\frac{1}{4}\%$	11. 101%	16. $\frac{1}{2}\%$
2. 6%	7. $12\frac{1}{2}\%$	12. 110%	17. $\frac{3}{4}\%$
3. 2%	8. $15\frac{3}{4}\%$	13. 250%	18. $\frac{2}{5}\%$
4. 12%	9. $37\frac{1}{2}\%$	14. 200%	19. $\frac{5}{8}\%$
5. 78%	10. $4\frac{5}{8}\%$	15. $127\frac{1}{2}\%$	20. $\frac{18}{20}\%$

Express with the sign %:

21. $.15$	24. $.201$	27. $.37\frac{1}{2}$	30. 1.22
22. $.15\frac{1}{2}$	25. 2.01	28. $.422$	31. 5
23. $.154$	26. 3	29. $.04\frac{5}{8}$	32. 5.2

How do you reduce a common fraction to a decimal?

33. Express $\frac{2}{3}$ as hundredths with the sign %.

SOLUTION : $\frac{2}{3} = 2 \div 3 = .66\frac{2}{3}$ or $66\frac{2}{3}\%$.

Express as hundredths with the sign %:

34. $\frac{1}{2}$	37. $\frac{4}{5}$	40. $\frac{3}{5}$	43. $\frac{3}{50}$
35. $\frac{1}{4}$	38. $\frac{1}{3}$	41. $\frac{1}{6}$	44. $\frac{1}{25}$
36. $\frac{3}{8}$	39. $\frac{1}{8}$	42. $\frac{3}{10}$	45. $\frac{1}{20}$

Change to hundredths:

1. 50%
2. $33\frac{1}{3}$%
3. $87\frac{1}{2}$%
4. 200%
5. 91%
6. $66\frac{2}{3}$%
7. 7%
8. 29%
9. 38%

10. 69%
11. 38%
12. 19%
13. 200%
14. 98%
15. 76%
16. 93%
17. 10%
18. 1%

19. 67%
20. 500%
21. 75%
22. 36%
23. 47%
24. 36%
25. 72%
26. 59%
27. 300%

28. 82%
29. 45%
30. 86%
31. 95%
32. 74%
33. 86%
34. 400%
35. 26%
36. 600%

37. 300%
38. 78%
39. 281%
40. 39%
41. 79%
42. 144%
43. 35%
44. 78%
45. 100%

Change to a decimal:

46. $20\frac{1}{2}$%
47. $15\frac{3}{4}$%
48. $3\frac{1}{4}$%
49. 275%
50. 50%
51. 40%
52. 25%

53. $41\frac{1}{2}$%
54. $12\frac{1}{2}$%
55. $6\frac{1}{4}$%
56. $83\frac{1}{3}$%
57. $62\frac{1}{2}$%
58. 87%
59. 43%

60. $14\frac{2}{7}$%
61. 10%
62. 33%
63. 59%
64. 64%
65. 40%
66. 30%

67. 68%
68. 2%
69. 82%
70. 20%
71. 38%
72. 8%
73. 19%

74. $87\frac{1}{2}$%
75. 32%
76. $\frac{1}{2}$%
77. 42%
78. 32%
79. 88%
80. 27%

Change to a decimal:

81. 200%
82. 49%
83. $33\frac{1}{3}$%
84. 40%
85. $16\frac{2}{3}$%
86. $8\frac{1}{3}$%
87. $66\frac{2}{3}$%
88. $37\frac{1}{2}$%
89. 90%

90. $\frac{1}{2}$%
91. 75%
92. $62\frac{1}{2}$%
93. 98%
94. 22%
95. 300%
96. 50%
97. 68%
98. 79%

99. 7%
100. $8\frac{1}{2}$%
101. 35%
102. $\frac{7}{8}$%
103. 36%
104. 27%
105. 76%
106. 2%
107. $\frac{3}{4}$%

108. $\frac{3}{8}$%
109. 62%
110. 29%
111. 38%
112. 65%
113. 39%
114. $\frac{1}{4}$%
115. $\frac{1}{8}$%
116. $\frac{3}{20}$%

Master this table:

$5\% = \frac{1}{20}$	$25\% = \frac{1}{4}$	$62\frac{1}{2}\% = \frac{5}{8}$
$6\frac{1}{4}\% = \frac{1}{16}$	$30\% = \frac{3}{10}$	$66\frac{2}{3}\% = \frac{2}{3}$
$8\frac{1}{3}\% = \frac{1}{12}$	$33\frac{1}{3}\% = \frac{1}{3}$	$70\% = \frac{7}{10}$
$10\% = \frac{1}{10}$	$37\frac{1}{2}\% = \frac{3}{8}$	$75\% = \frac{3}{4}$
$12\frac{1}{2}\% = \frac{1}{8}$	$40\% = \frac{2}{5}$	$80\% = \frac{4}{5}$
$16\frac{2}{3}\% = \frac{1}{6}$	$50\% = \frac{1}{2}$	$87\frac{1}{2}\% = \frac{7}{8}$
$20\% = \frac{1}{5}$	$60\% = \frac{3}{5}$	$90\% = \frac{9}{10}$

Cover the above table and see how quickly you can give the fraction equal to each of the following:

1. 50%
2. 35%
3. $12\frac{1}{2}\%$
4. 40%
5. $37\frac{1}{2}\%$
6. 250%
7. $87\frac{1}{2}\%$
8. 70%
9. $33\frac{1}{3}\%$
10. $62\frac{1}{2}\%$
11. 75%
12. 125%
13. 150%
14. 20%
15. 175%
16. $8\frac{1}{3}\%$
17. 10%
18. 90%
19. $66\frac{2}{3}\%$
20. 100%
21. $16\frac{2}{3}\%$
22. 25%
23. $133\frac{1}{3}\%$
24. $6\frac{1}{4}\%$
25. 800%
26. 300%
27. $62\frac{1}{2}\%$
28. 300%

Find $37\frac{1}{2}\%$ of \$800. $37\frac{1}{2}\% = \frac{3}{8}$; $\frac{3}{8}$ of \$800 = ?

Using fractions, find:

29. 50% of 248 pounds
30. $66\frac{2}{3}\%$ of 900 days
31. $16\frac{2}{3}\%$ of \$96
32. 200% of 345 inches
33. $8\frac{1}{3}\%$ of 48 yards
34. $33\frac{1}{3}\%$ of 99 books
35. 250% of 56 quarts
36. $6\frac{1}{4}\%$ of 456 square miles
37. $12\frac{1}{2}\%$ of 900 bushels
38. 125% of 800 days
39. $37\frac{1}{2}\%$ of \$500
40. 150% of \$1000
41. 30% of \$325
42. $87\frac{1}{2}\%$ of \$840
43. $87\frac{1}{2}\%$ of \$2400
44. 5% of \$4000

Finding a Per Cent of a Number

> What is 35% of 800?
>
> STATEMENT: 35% of 800 = ?
> SOLUTION: .35 × 800 = 280

In the above example two factors are given to find the product.

Find:

1. $12\frac{1}{2}$% of $480
2. 25% of 392 lb.
3. 20% of $85
4. 75% of 100 miles
5. $62\frac{1}{2}$% of $500
6. 60% of 180 days
7. $37\frac{1}{2}$% of $1000
8. $16\frac{2}{3}$% of 90 bushels

9. $66\frac{2}{3}$% of 300 minutes
10. $33\frac{1}{3}$% of $1000
11. 40% of 450 bushels
12. $66\frac{2}{3}$% of 200 miles
13. 80% of 500 feet
14. 50% of 498 lb.
15. 1% of 5280 ft.
16. 5% of 800 yd.

Find:

17. 24% of $228
18. 15% of $86.80
19. 25% of $582.30
20. 75% of 1780 pounds
21. 50% of $1998
22. 33% of 58 miles
23. 52% of 482 bushels
24. 99% of 1660 tons
25. 58% of $75

26. 125% of 3856 ft.
27. 200% of $1896
28. $112\frac{1}{2}$% of 492 yd.
29. 35% of 3286 miles
30. 150% of $1810
31. 38% of 103
32. $87\frac{1}{2}$% of 906 rods
33. $133\frac{1}{3}$% of 1925
34. 35% of 679

Written. Find :

1. 66⅔% of 900 tons
2. 65% of $600
3. 5% of 500 apple trees
4. 25% of $800
5. 87½% of $6500
6. 75% of 2745
7. 90% of 550
8. 8⅓% of $62.76
9. 37½% of 10,000 bushels
10. 4½% of $275.50
11. 5¾% of $2500
12. 91% of $185.45

13. 31% of 5280 in.
14. 50% of 144 sq. ft.
15. 16% of 135 in.
16. 112½% of $864
17. 225% of $3564
18. 1¼% of 728 miles
19. 8.2% of $2840
20. ⅛% of 680,700
21. 2½% of 2150
22. 11.4% of $126
23. 8% of 47 lb.
24. 2.6% of $100

25. Mr. Hood sold 33⅓% of his crop of potatoes. He raised 996 bushels. How many bushels did he sell?

26. Sixty-five per cent of the members of a church are women. The membership is 1800. How many are women?

27. An automobile selling for $1400 cost the dealer 83% of that sum. What did it cost him?

28. There are 40 pupils in John's grade, of whom 90% passed. How many pupils passed? How many failed?

29. Twenty per cent of a trip of 800 miles was over macadam road. Find the number of miles of macadam road.

30. John's father drove his car 8400 miles in one year and 75% as far the previous year. How far did it travel the previous year?

Note. — Answer as many questions as possible in the following mental drills in the time indicated. Score 5 for each correct answer.

I	2
4 Minutes	3 Minutes
$\frac{1}{3}$ of 963 = ?	25% of 800 = ?
$\frac{1}{4}$ of 1608 = ?	$33\frac{1}{3}$% of 600 = ?
$\frac{3}{8}$ of 320 = ?	$12\frac{1}{2}$% of 400 = ?
$\frac{11}{12}$ of 96 = ?	$37\frac{1}{2}$% of 240 = ?
$\frac{7}{8}$ of 88 = ?	20% of 500 = ?
$\frac{2}{3}$ of 180 = ?	$83\frac{1}{3}$% of 60 = ?
$\frac{1}{9}$ of 270 = ?	$87\frac{1}{2}$% of 80 = ?
$\frac{1}{6}$ of 360 = ?	$62\frac{1}{2}$% of 160 = ?
$\frac{1}{8}$ of 640 = ?	200% of 21 = ?
$\frac{2}{5}$ of 225 = ?	$66\frac{2}{3}$% of 21 = ?
$\frac{5}{8}$ of 320 = ?	5% of 900 = ?
$\frac{3}{16}$ of 64 = ?	6% of 600 = ?
$\frac{7}{12}$ of 144 = ?	$16\frac{2}{3}$% of 48 = ?
$\frac{9}{10}$ of 90 = ?	$2\frac{1}{2}$% of 200 = ?
$\frac{7}{16}$ of 32 = ?	150% of 22 = ?
$\frac{5}{12}$ of 60 = ?	$\frac{1}{2}$% of 800 = ?
$\frac{7}{10}$ of 110 = ?	$\frac{1}{4}$% of 400 = ?
$\frac{3}{2}$ of 50 = ?	$\frac{3}{5}$% of 1000 = ?
$\frac{5}{4}$ of 200 = ?	$\frac{1}{8}$% of 6400 = ?
$\frac{5}{3}$ of 90 = ?	$\frac{1}{10}$% of 200 = ?

To the Teacher. — Let all pupils start and stop at a signal given by you. By using these drills frequently a marked improvement in speed and accuracy will be noted. Place similar exercises on the blackboard for added drill.

Finding What Per Cent One Number Is of Another

1. What per cent of 400 is 60?

STATEMENT: What per cent of 400 is 60?
SOLUTION: $60 \div 400 = .15$ or 15%. *Ans.*

In the above example the product and one factor are given, to find the other factor.

Oral

2. What per cent of 18 is 9? **4.** ? (%) of 24 = 6

3. What per cent of 18 is 6? **5.** 3 is ? (%) of 12?

Written

6. ? (%) of 120 = 6 **9.** $25.60 is ? (%) of $320

7. ? (%) of $141.10 = $28.22 **10.** $7.20 is ? (%) of $180

8. ? (%) of 56 bu. = 14 bu. **11.** ? (%) of $200 = $12

12. The Hamilton school baseball team played 24 games and won 18 games. What per cent of the games played were won by this team?

STATEMENT: What per cent of 24 games are 18 games?
  ? × 24 = 18
SOLUTION: $18 \div 24 = .75$ or 75%. *Ans.*

13. What per cent of $38 is $24.70?

Reading hundredths instead of per cent, the question is, "How many hundredths of $38 is $24.70?"

STATEMENT: What per cent of $38 is $24.70?
  ? × 38 = 24.70
SOLUTION: $24.70 \div $38 = .65 or 65%. *Ans.*

14. What per cent of $240 is $80?

15. Seven bushels are what per cent of 8 bushels?

STATEMENT: 7 bushels are ?% of 8 bushels.
  7 " = ? × 8
SOLUTION: 7(product) ÷ 8 (factor) = ? (factor)

Before dividing, to find the rate per cent, arrange the dividend and divisor so that the dividend contains two more decimal places than the divisor. This may be done by annexing zeros to one or the other of these terms, as may be necessary.

If the quotient is not exact when two decimal places have been reached, express the remainder as a common fraction, in the quotient.

16. One hundred fifty is what per cent of 900?

17. What per cent of $113 is $39.55?

18. Find what per cent 495 years is of 825 years.

19. Find what per cent 12.96 feet is of 96 feet.

20. Mr. Adams works 8 hr. every day. He works what per cent of a ten-hour day?

21. Your father bought 10 T. of coal. At Christmas, he had used 4 T. What per cent of the coal had he used?

22. If 1 T. of sugar beets contains 200 lb. of sugar, what per cent of the weight of the beets is sugar?

23. A ton of coal contains 180 pounds of ash. What is the percentage of ash?

24. In a grade of 48 pupils 44 passed. What per cent of the pupils passed?

25. Of the 365 days in the year 52 are Sundays. What per cent of the days of the year are Sundays?

26. A 9 by 12 rug is placed on a floor 12 ft. by 15 ft. What per cent of the floor was covered by the rug?

What per cent of:

1. 20 is 10?   5. 100 is 90?   9. 2 is 1?

2. 48 is 12?   6. 72 is 12?   10. 3 is 1?

3. 16 is 2?   7. 12 is 9?   11. 6 is 3?

4. 45 is 15?   8. 24 is 16?   12. 6 is 5?

13. ? (%) of 512 = 64   19. $18 = ? (%) of $24

14. ? (%) of $18.40 = $4.60   20. 36 = ? (%) of 48

15. ? (%) of $1.80 = $.60   21. $2.40 = ? (%) of $720

16. ? (%) of $2.36 = $1.18   22. 63 lb. = ? (%) of 72 lb.

17. ? (%) of $9.60 = $8.40   23. 12 ft. = ? (%) of 144 ft.

18. ? (%) of $1.92 = $.32   24. 144 ft. = ? (%) of 12 ft.

25. There were 50 words in the spelling lesson and Charlotte missed two. What per cent of the words did she spell correctly?

26. Out of 25 words, Charles missed one. What per cent of the words did Charles miss?

27. Edith had 7 examples right. If there were 8 in the lesson, what per cent did she have right?

28. Mr. Smith pays $150 a year for fuel. That is what per cent of his salary of $3000?

29. Thomas had saved $128. He paid $16 for a suit of clothes. What per cent of his money did he expend for clothing?

30. One pint is what per cent of one gallon?

31. A U. S. marine whose weight when he enlisted was 160 lb. wrote to his mother that he had gained 20 lb. in weight. What per cent of his former weight had he gained?

32. What per cent of $345 is $115?

Finding the Number of Which Another Number is a Given Per Cent

1. 60 is 15% of what number?

STATEMENT: $60 = 15\%$ of what?
SOLUTION: $60 \div .15 = 400.$ *Ans.*

In the above example the product and one factor are given to find the other factor.

2. 25% of ? = 64

3. 6% of ? = $12

4. 16% of ? = 80 horses

5. 40 is 75% of ?

6. 1% of ? is 41

7. 24 is 10% of ?

8. 18 = 90% of ?

9. $250 is 5% of ?

10. Mr. Archer puts 20% of his wages in the bank. If he puts $18 in the bank every month, what are his monthly wages?

STATEMENT: 20% of (monthly wages) is $18
.20 × ? = 18
SOLUTION: $18 \div .20 = 90.$ $90. *Ans.*
Notice that the STATEMENT is given in the problem.

11. Donald gave his mother $3.75, which was 75% of his week's wages. How much a week did he receive?

12. Walter planted 300 tomato plants which was $33\frac{1}{3}\%$ of the total number to be planted. How many tomato plants were there in all?

13. There were 45 tons of coal in a car. If this was $12\frac{1}{2}\%$ of the amount ordered, how many tons were ordered?

14. Thirty-seven and one-half per cent of the grain in a certain mixture is corn. If there are 300 pounds of corn, what is the weight of the mixture?

15. There are six quarts of water in a mixture which is 30% water. How many quarts are there of the mixture?

In the following problems give the *Statement of the Problem* and the *Solution*.

Observe that the *Statement* can be found in the problem itself.

1. James had $5 for Christmas shopping. He spent $.75 for a baseball bat. How many hundredths of his money did he spend?

2. Mr. Smith's salary is $2800 a year. He saves $700. How many hundredths of his salary does he save?

3. 9 quarts are how many hundredths of 45 quarts?

4. 1175 pupils were promoted from the eighth grade of a city school last year, 1034 of them entered the high school. How many hundredths entered the high school?

5. By selling a house at 23% profit, the owner gains $920. Find the cost.

STATEMENT OF PROBLEM: 23% of the cost is $920,
or,   23 × ? = $920.
Observe that we use the × sign, which means "of," and we use the sign =, which means "is." Observe also that $920 is a product and .23 one of its factors. How may the other factor be found?
SOLUTION: $920 ÷ .23 = $4000. *Ans.*

6. .65 of a certain number is 897. What is the number?

7. When 35 hundredths of Pauline's earnings are $1.40, what amount does she earn?

8. By selling an auto at 27% profit, Mr. Wood gains $405. What did the car cost him?

9. A car load of potatoes was bought at 50 cents a bushel. If the freight and handling cost 10 cents a bushel, what must be the selling price to gain 25% on the total cost?

Problems

1. 10% of what number is 5?

2. 1% of what number is 12?

3. 25% of what number is 2?

4. 25 is 5% of what number?

5. $1 is 50% of what?

6. 20% of what number is 8?

7. 42 is 21% of what number?

8. 14 is 2% of what number?

9. 80 is 125% of what number?

10. 120% of what number is 6?

11. $12\frac{1}{2}$% of what number is 8?

12. 9 is 90% of what number?

13. 10% of what number is 9?

14. 8% of what number is 25?

15. 4% of what number is 200?

16. $2000 is 50% of what?

17. 6% of what number is $180?

18. $600 is 75% of what?

19. 15% of what number is 75?

20. 130% of what number is 260?

21. 150% of what number is 30?

22. 20 is 8% of what number?

23. 3 is 1% of what number?

24. 1% of what number is 20?

25. 28% of what number is $1120?

26. 75% of what number is $3000?

27. 32% of what number is 96?

28. 17% of what number is $340?

29. 30% of what number is $1.80?

30. 300% of what number is 75?

31. Mr. Dunbergh has received a 10% increase in wages, amounting to $35 per month. What wage does he now receive per year?

32. Mr. Dey found that his sales for Jan. amounted to $8750. Feb. they increased 4%, March 7% over January and April decreased 4% under January. Find the total amount of sales for these four months.

33. Mr. Wilson deposits 40% of his salary in the bank each month. If he deposits $140 monthly, what is his yearly salary?

34. Mr. Williams has 40 acres of timber land. This is 25% of all his land. How many acres has he?

35. A man borrowed some money and paid $75 for the use of it. If that was 5% of the sum borrowed, how much was borrowed?

36. It costs a man $1200 to support his family for a year. If this is 80% of his salary, what is his salary?

37. 60% of a class were boys. If there were 21 boys, how many pupils were there in the class?

38. A man bought a lot and built a house on it. The lot cost $800, which was 20% of the cost of the house. How much did the house cost? How much did the house and lot cost?

39. A house rents for $630, which is 9% of its value. Find its value.

40. Dr. Smith sold his motor car for $1860, which was .66⅔ of its cost. What did it cost?

41. Mr. Dingle's salary is increased $200, or 10%. What was his former salary?

42. Mr. Hurd borrows money for a year, and pays $15, or 5% for the use of it. How much does he borrow?

43. If $300 will pay 25% of a debt, how much is the debt?

44. A grocer gains 8¢ a pound on coffee, or 20% of what it cost him. What did it cost per pound and for how much per pound did he sell it?

45. By selling a gas stove at 20% profit, I gained $16. What did the stove cost?

46. If the increase in the price of coal over last year is $2.50, or 20%, what was the price last year?

47. A baseball team played 18 games and won 12 of them. What per cent of the games did it win?

48. In a graduating class there were 18 boys and 24 girls. What per cent of the class are boys?

49. There are 1200 books in the school library, of which five per cent are biography. How many books are biography?

50. Mr. Adams had $720 in the bank, he drew out $468. What per cent remained in the bank?

51. What per cent of 30 is .05?

52. James solved eight of the ten examples in the lesson correctly. What should be his rating per cent?

53. Wallace's paper in arithmetic was rated at 85%. If there were twenty examples in the lesson, how many did he solve incorrectly?

54. Of the 50 pupils registered in a schoolroom 10 were absent. What per cent of the pupils were in school?

55. Charles was marked 94% in spelling. He missed three words. How many words were there in the lesson?

56. Milton has completed eight of the twelve sentences assigned. How many more sentences must he finish before he has accomplished 75% of the assignment?

57. How many minutes are there in $33\frac{1}{3}$% of an hour?

58. A market gardener sells 15% of his crop of 580 bushels of tomatoes at $1 per bushel, and the remaining at $.75 per bushel. How much does he receive for his crop?

59. A magazine containing 220 pages devoted 77 pages to advertisements. What per cent of this magazine is advertisements?

60. Find 120% of $960.

61. A city newspaper has a daily circulation of 52,344 copies. Of this number 13,086 are mailed. What per cent are mailed?

62. The capital and surplus of a bank are $2,500,000. If $500,000 is surplus, what per cent is capital?

63. The assets of a bank are $8,000,000 and its liabilities are $4,000,000. Its liabilities is what per cent of its assets?

64. An apprentice is paid $66 a month and a barber $120 a month. What per cent of a barber's pay does the apprentice receive?

65. 80% of a 30-ton carload of grain is corn. How many tons of corn are there in the car?

66. A house valued at $6000 rents for $45 a month. The yearly rent is what per cent of the value?

67. A store valued at $30,000 is rented so as to realize 12% on the investment. What is the rent per month?

68. Milton's father uses 5% of his salary for charity. He gives $240 a year to charity. What is his yearly salary?

69. 120% of a number is 6. What is the number?

70. A house is sold for $9180, which is 90% of the cost. What was the cost of the house?

71. Seven is 5% of what number?

72. 15% of the weekly output of a factory is sold at $900. Find the value of the weekly output.

73. A store is insured for $49,000, which is $87\frac{1}{2}$% of its value. What is its value?

74. On an investment of $4000 a man makes $400. Find the return in per cent on his investment.

75. $2120 is 106% of what sum?

76. How many square rods are there in $87\frac{1}{2}$% of an acre?

77. 16% of 640 A. is how many acres?

78. A store with its stock costs $54,000. If 13% of this amount was paid for the store, what was the cost of the stock?

79. 6% of what sum is $60?

80. $12\frac{1}{2}$% of a farm was forest. There were 140 acres of cleared land. Determine the number of acres in the farm.

81. $33\frac{1}{3}$% of the pictures in a certain collection were rented. If 180 pictures were not rented, find the total number of pictures in the collection.

82. Thirty per cent of the books in a library are loaned. If 7000 volumes are on the shelves, how many volumes belong to the library?

83. A certain company made 40% on its investment during last year. Its investment was $40,000. How much did it make?

Percentage Drill

Without copying the figures, write as many answers as possible in 5 minutes.   Score 5 for each correct answer. Keep results and compare with later trials.   Use this drill frequently.

A

25% of 800 = ?
150% of 400 = ?
$12\frac{1}{2}$% of 320 = ?
$33\frac{1}{3}$% of 660 = ?
20% of 750 = ?
$37\frac{1}{2}$% of 240 = ?
$66\frac{2}{3}$% of 420 = ?
100% of 139 = ?
75% of 80 = ?
300% of 26 − ?
1% of 300 = ?
$\frac{1}{2}$% of 200 = ?
$\frac{1}{3}$% of 600 = ?
$\frac{1}{8}$% of 800 = ?
$\frac{3}{8}$% of 800 = ?

B

$14\frac{2}{7}$% of 700 = ?
1% of 700 = ?
60% of 800 = ?
175% of 1200 = ?
$16\frac{2}{3}$% of 1200 = ?
1% of 1200 = ?
$\frac{5}{6}$% of 1200 = ?
$\frac{2}{7}$% of 210 = ?
180% of 60 = ?
$\frac{5}{8}$% of 1600 = ?
7% of 300 = ?
$87\frac{1}{2}$% of 1600 = ?
$\frac{4}{5}$% of 1000 = ?
$\frac{7}{8}$% of 1600 = ?
$137\frac{1}{2}$% of 800 = ?

C

?% of 400 = 200
?% of 400 = 100
?% of 400 = 4
?% of 400 = 1
?% of 900 = 300
?% of 900 = 30
?% of 1000 = 10
?% of 1000 = 50
?% of 1000 = 200
?% of 1000 = 700

?% of 900 = 3
?% of 900 = 1200
?% of 500 = 100
?% of 500 = 400
?% of 500 = 750
?% of 500 = 2000
?% of 1600 = 160
?% of 1600 = 80
?% of 1600 = 400
?% of 1600 = 1000

D

? % of 800 is 100	? % of 300 is 100
? % of 100 is 800	? % of 30 is 20
? % of 10 is 20	? % of 48 is 12
? % of 20 is 15	? % of 48 is 24
? % of 15 is 20	? % of 48 is 16
? % of 40 is 8	? % of 75 is 25
? % of 40 is 10	? % of 25 is 75
? % of 40 is 30	? % of 42 is 7
? % of 40 is 15	? % of 36 is 9
? % of 12 is 6	? % of 25 is 20
? % of 12 is 12	? % of 20 is 25
? % of 12 is 15	? % of 60 is 12

E   ## F

64 is 50% of ?	22 is $12\frac{1}{2}$% of ?
72 is 100% of ?	17 is $33\frac{1}{3}$% of ?
40 is $66\frac{2}{3}$% of ?	26 is $16\frac{2}{3}$% of ?
32 is $12\frac{1}{2}$% of ?	31 is 25% of ?
32 is 125% of ?	33 is $37\frac{1}{2}$% of ?
10 is 1% of ?	45 is $62\frac{1}{2}$% of ?
10 is 10% of ?	28 is $87\frac{1}{2}$% of ?
10 is 100% of ?	45 is 20% of ?
600 is 150% of ?	9 is $8\frac{1}{3}$% of ?
300 is 150% of ?	64 is 75% of ?
45 is 150% of ?	36 is 60% of ?
24 is 150% of ?	12 is 40% of ?
24 is 15% of ?	10 is 80% of ?
36 is 10% of ?	63 is 90% of ?
75 is 10% of ?	63 is 30% of ?
12 is 6% of ?	63 is 60% of ?
30 is 6% of ?	36 is 6% of ?
25 is 5% of ?	36 is 3% of ?
25 is 50% of ?	36 is 9% of ?

Profit and Loss

Problems of profit and loss are problems of percentage involving gain or loss.

The profit (or the loss) is the product of two factors, the **cost** and the **rate per cent**.

The profit (or loss) divided by either factor (cost or rate) gives the other factor.

Compute profit or loss upon the cost unless the problem directs otherwise.

Expenses attending the cost of goods, such as interest on the investment, freight, insurance, cartage, rent, etc., are properly included in the cost and are called **overhead**.

When the cost of any article includes a proper share of the overhead the gain computed is called the **net gain**.

The following expressions are commonly understood to mean that the gain is 10% of the cost:

At a profit of 10%; at 10% gain; at 10% above cost; at an advance of 10%.

1. 10% of $80 = ?   4. 6% of $200 = ?
2. 5% of $60 = ?   5. 25% of $480 = ?
3. 12½% of $640 = ?   6. 75% of $12 = ?

7. (? per cent) of $80 = $8   9. (? per cent) of $12 = $3
8. (? per cent) of $10 = $6   10. $6 = (? per cent) of $12

11. $60 = (? per cent) of $240
12. $18 = (? per cent) of $24

13. 50% of ? = $30   18. 33⅓% of ? = 20
14. 25% of ? = $6   19. 30% of ? = $120
15. 12½% of ? = $4   20. 15% of ? = $120
16. 20% of ? = 40   21. 10% of ? = $120
17. 16⅔% of ? = 50   22. 5% of ? = $120

23. A contractor gained $12\frac{1}{2}\%$ on a job of grading that cost him $2448. How many dollars did he gain?

$12\frac{1}{2}\%$ of $2448 = ?$ $\frac{1}{8}$ of $2448 = ?$

24. A stock of paper costing $2345 was damaged by water so that it had to be sold at a loss of 15%. What was the loss? What was the selling price?

25. A man bought a city lot for $2400 and sold it so as to gain 20%. How much did he receive for the lot?

26. The whole of anything is what per cent of it?

The cost of an article is 100% of the cost. The gain is 10% of the cost. The selling price, which is the sum of the cost and the gain, is what per cent of the cost?

27. An article that cost $8 was sold at a gain of 10%. Find the selling price.

$100\% + 10\% = 110\%.$
110% of $8 = selling price.

28. A fruit dealer lost 40% on a shipment of peaches that cost him $200. What was the selling price?

$100\% - 40\% = 60\%.$ 60% of $200 = ?$

29. A book that cost $5 was sold at a gain of 25%. What was the selling price? What was the gain?

30. A grocer paid 80 cents a bushel for potatoes and sold them at a profit of 20 cents a bushel. What per cent did he gain?

What per cent of $.80 is $.20?

31. If a merchant sells, for $15, goods that cost $12, what part of the cost does he gain? What per cent of the cost does he gain?

What is the profit? $?\%$ of $12 =$ the profit.

32. What per cent is gained on carpets bought at 90 cents a yard and sold at $1.25 a yard? Make and solve another problem like this one.

33. Cloth that cost $2 a yard was sold for $3 a yard. What was gained on a yard? What per cent of the cost was gained?

34. A dealer bought potatoes at 60¢ a bushel and sold them at 48¢ a bushel. What was the loss on a bushel? What per cent of the cost was lost?

35. A hardware merchant bought 75 hundred-pound kegs of nails for $262.50. When he sells them at 4¢ a pound, what per cent profit does he make?

36. An implement dealer gained 18% by selling a reaper for $36 more than he paid for it. Find its cost.

18% of ? = $36.

37. A furniture dealer sold a desk at a gain of 25%. He gained $5. What did the desk cost?

38. A grocer makes a profit of 10% by selling sugar at 70 cents per hundredweight above cost. At what price per pound does he sell it? Make and solve another problem like this one.

39. A merchant lost $250 by selling damaged goods at a loss of 25%. What was the cost? What was the selling price?

40. By selling a piano at a profit of 40% Mr. Failing gained $92. What was the cost of the piano?

41. An agent gained $.09 by selling binding twine 25% above cost. What did it cost him?

42. A real estate dealer buys a house and lot for $4500. He pays $150 for painting and decorating, $180 for plumbing, and $100 for grading and walks. He wishes to sell the property and make a profit of 12½%. At what price must he sell it?

43. When I sell a fur coat for $48, I make $16. What did the coat cost me? My profit is what part of the cost? What per cent of the cost? It is what per cent of the selling price?

44. A confectioner bought a bill of goods for $1500 and sold them at an advance of $33\frac{1}{3}\%$. What was the selling price? What was the profit?

45. A dealer bought a shipment of cotton for $5600, but during a fire it was so damaged that he was compelled to sell it for $3500. What was his rate of loss?

46. A shoe dealer sold a bill of goods costing $400, and lost $16 in bad debts, but made a net profit of 26% in the sale. At what price did he sell?

47. By selling flour at a loss of 15%, a grocer lost $37.50. What was the cost of the flour? What was the selling price?

48. In a city department store goods were sold in a year costing $240,000. If the profits averaged $37\frac{1}{2}\%$ of the cost, what were the profits? How much was received from the sales?

49. A huckster buys sweet corn at $1.75 per hundred ears and sells it at 30¢ a dozen. What per cent profit does he make?

50. A speculator paid $7500 for 50 horses. He sold 30 of them at $140 a head and the rest at $210 a head. What per cent of profit did he make?

51. A horse dealer bought a span of horses for $240 each. He sold them so as to gain 20% on one and lose 20% on the other. What were the selling prices?

52. Interview a grocer, a dry goods merchant, and other tradesmen, to learn the rates of profit in their lines. Bring facts to school and use these for problems.

53. By selling goods at $1600 I gain 25%. What is my gain?

100% of the cost plus 25% of the cost = what per cent of the cost?

STATEMENT : 125% of the cost is $1600.
                    1.25 ×   ?   = $1600.

54. A produce dealer sold potatoes at $2.20 a barrel, thereby gaining 10%. What did they cost per barrel?

55. On an article that sold for $2.40 the dealer gained 20%. What was the cost? What was the gain?

56. A man sold his farm at $32 per acre, thereby losing 20%. What price per acre did he pay for the farm?

100% of the cost less 20% of the cost = what per cent of the cost?

STATEMENT : 80% of the cost is $32.
                    .80 ×   ?   = $32.

57. On an article that sold for $180 the dealer lost 10%. What was the cost? How much was lost?

58. John sold his skates for $.63, which was 10% less than they cost. How much did they cost?

59. By selling a piano for $189 the owner lost 10%. At what price must he have sold the piano to gain 10%?

60. A man sold a house and lot for $4800, thereby gaining 20%. How much did the house and lot cost?

61. Mr. Odell sold his automobile for $450, thereby losing 40%. What did it cost?

62. A merchant received $875,000 for goods sold in one year. If his profits averaged 37½%, what did he pay for the goods sold that year? How much were his profits?

63. A real estate dealer desired to sell a city lot that cost him $2800. His asking price was 25% above the cost. He sold it finally at 90 per cent of his asking price. What was the selling price?

For various reasons many merchants are adopting the plan of computing their gain or loss on the selling price. Unless specified *in the problem*, however, compute gain or loss upon the *cost*.

An article costing $100 is sold for $125. The gain is what per cent of the selling price?

$125 − $100 = $25 gain.

$25 ÷ $125 = 20%.

The per cent of gain *on the selling price* is 20%.

1. What advantage is it to the merchant to estimate the gain on the selling price rather than on the cost of the article?

2. May the rent of the store, the clerk hire, the interest on the money invested, and the store expenses be considered as a part of the cost?

3. What are the two ways in which you may interpret the following statement made by a merchant? "I am selling these articles at a gain of 20%."

4. Find the per cent of gain on the selling price in the following transactions:

(*a*) Shoes costing $8 a pair sell for $12.

(*b*) A coat costing $24 sells for $30.

(*c*) A table costing $50 sells for $80.

5. For what must the following articles be sold in order that a merchant may gain 20% on the selling price of each article?

(*a*) An automobile costing $1000.

(*b*) A house costing $8000.

(*c*) A rug costing $120.

(*d*) A coat costing $60.

6. What per cent of the cost is equal to 20% on the selling price?

7. A chair costing $80 is sold for $100. What is the rate of gain computed on the selling price? On the cost?

8. A house bought at $7500 is sold at $8000. Find the rate of gain computed on the selling price.

9. An automobile brings $1500 when sold at a gain of $33\frac{1}{3}$% on the selling price. What was the cost?

10. When a piano is sold for $1000, a profit of 20% is made on the selling price. What was the gain?

11. A rug costing $120 is sold at a gain of $80. What per cent of the selling price was gained?

12. A lot costing $1200 is sold for $900. What is the loss per cent computed on the selling price? What is the loss per cent computed on the cost?

13. A shipment of goods is bought for $2000 and sold at a gain of 20% computed on the selling price. Find the gain and the selling price.

14. A farm costing $8000 is sold at a gain of 20% of the selling price. Find the gain and the selling price.

15. At what price must a rug costing $22.50 be sold in order that the gain may be 25% of the selling price?

16. A merchant sells a table for $36 and gains $33\frac{1}{3}$% of the selling price. What per cent does he gain on the cost?

17. A watch is sold for $64 at a gain of $37\frac{1}{2}$% computed on the selling price. What was the gain per cent on the cost?

18. Frank's father bought an old house for $4,000. He spent $600 for repairs, $120 in taxes, $240 in interest and $40 in advertising. He sold the house at a gain of 20% on the cost. What was the gain on the selling price?

Commission

Much of the business of the world is transacted by people who do not own the property which is being bought or sold, or the money that is handled. People who produce or make goods do not often sell them directly to the people who use them. Sometimes the goods are sold first to a jobber or wholesaler who employs men to travel about and sell them to retailers or consumers.

A person who transacts business for another is an **agent**.

Agents are known by various names according to the kind of business transacted by them. Those who buy and sell merchandise on commission are called commission merchants or commission brokers; those who buy and sell stocks and bonds are called stock brokers. Can you mention other kinds of agents?

When an agent is paid for his services a certain per cent of the value of the goods which he buys or sells, or of the money involved in the transaction, this compensation is called **commission** or **brokerage**.

Commission for buying goods is computed as a certain per cent of the cost of the goods; commission for selling goods is computed as a certain per cent of the selling price of the goods; commission generally is computed as a certain per cent of the money handled, or the value of the property with which the agent deals. The principal exception to this rule is brokerage for buying and selling stocks and bonds, which will be treated later.

A newsboy is an agent. He sells Sunday papers which cost him 8¢ for 10¢. His commission is 25% of the cost or 20% of the selling price.

A quantity of goods delivered to a commission merchant to be sold is called a **consignment**.

The party sending a consignment of goods to be sold by a commission merchant is the **consignor**.

The party to whom a consignment of goods is delivered for sale is the **consignee**.

The account rendered by a commission merchant to the shipper is called **account-sales**.

The sum received from the sale of goods, after all expenses, such as commission, freight, and cartage, have been deducted, is called the **proceeds of sales**.

The party who employs an agent is called the **principal**.

---

1. A college student sold 200 books at $3 apiece during a summer vacation. What was his commission, at 40%?

2. A real estate agent received $80 for selling a house. His *commission* was 2%. What was the selling price of the house?

STATEMENT: $80 = 2% of selling price.

3. A lawyer received $30 *for collecting* $200. What was the rate of his commission?

STATEMENT : $30 = ? % of $200.

4. A commission merchant sold 1000 pounds of butter at 25 cents a pound, retained his commission of 10%, and sent the remainder to his principal. What did his commission amount to? How much did the principal receive?

5. An auctioneer sold, on 10% commission, household goods to the amount of $700. What were the net proceeds of the sale?

6. An agent receives $50 for selling $1000 worth of goods. What is his rate of commission?

7. An agent receives $120 commission for selling goods on a commission of 10%. What was the selling price of the goods?

Find the commissions for the following amounts, at the per cents standing at the tops of the columns :

5%	10%	12½%	33⅓%
8. 40¢	**12.** $50	**16.** $800	**20.** $300
9. 60¢	**13.** $100	**17.** $400	**21.** $30
10. $1.00	**14.** $500	**18.** $1600	**22.** $9.00
11. $2.00	**15.** $1000	**19.** $2400	**23.** $900

24. When an agent sells goods on 20% commission, what per cent of the selling price of the goods does the principal receive?

25. A commission merchant gets 2¢ a dozen for selling eggs at 40¢ a dozen. This is equivalent to what per cent commission?

26. A collector's commission is 5%. How much must he collect daily to earn $4 a day?

27. A collector working on 10% commission must collect how many dollars in order that his principal may receive $180? (90% of ? = $180.)

28. A commission merchant's commission is 10%. He makes a sale, takes out his commission, and returns $900 to the consignor. What is the selling price?

29. An agent collected a sum of money, took out his commission of 20%, and paid the remainder, which was $40, to his employer. What sum was collected?

30. What is an architect's commission at 5% on a school building costing $101,000?

31. A real estate agent sold a farm for $8000, receiving 5% commission. How much was left for the owner?

32. A rent collector's commission is 4%. If he collects $4000 per month, how much will he pay over to the owners?

33. An agent's fee for collecting is 3%. If his commission is $86.25, how much has he collected?

34. What is an agent's rate of commission if he receives $223 for buying produce to the amount of $5575?

35. What is a broker's commission at $\frac{1}{8}$% for buying $500,000 of bonds?

36. An agent is paid 5% for collecting $235.75. How much does he pay over to his employer?

37. What is an agent's commission for selling 6840 lb. of butter at 35¢ a pound, commission 2%?

38. What is an agent's commission at $4\frac{1}{2}$% for selling 850 barrels of flour at $7.25 a barrel?

39. A commission merchant sold a consignment of goods for $2470, took out his commission of 8%, paid $28 freight and $5 storage, and sent the remainder to the consignor. How much did the consignor receive?

40. An agent receives 6% commission for buying wool at 21 cents a pound. What is his commission for buying 50 tons of wool?

41. An agent's commission for selling 479 books at $3.50 apiece was $670.60. Find the rate of his commission.

42. A lawyer procured a loan for an improvement company, charging $1\frac{1}{2}\%$ commission. His commission was $4500. What was the amount of the loan?

43. A farmer sells his produce through a commission merchant in the city. If the merchant's commissions average $9\frac{1}{2}\%$, how many dollars' worth of produce must the farmer sell in order to receive $1810 net proceeds?

44. A fruit selling agency charged 25¢ a box for selling apples. What was its commission on 2500 boxes sold at $1.25 a box, 3420 boxes sold at $1.75, and 1940 boxes sold at $1.62?

45. A jobber employed a man to sell goods, at a salary of $250 a month, and paid his traveling expenses amounting to $2950 a year. If he sold $85,000 worth of goods in a year, the expense of selling the goods was what per cent of the sales?

46. A dealer in typewriters receives 35% commission, out of which he pays freight charges, averaging $2.25 for each machine. How much does he clear by selling 100 typewriters at $103 each?

47. An agent took grocery orders on a commission of $12\frac{1}{2}\%$. He sold goods amounting to $1325, took out his commission, paid freight charges amounting to $30.75, and sent the remainder of his collections to his principal. What were the net proceeds of the sale?

48. A real estate agent sold my property in Boston, took out his commission of 2%, and remitted to me the remainder, which was $5880. What was the amount of his commission? 98% of (the sales) = $5880.

49. A manufacturer in Pittsburg sells his products through a commission house in Philadelphia, paying 8% commission. What is the selling price of goods for which the manufacturer receives $6440 net proceeds?

Commission House Business

Mr. J. Souter is a dealer in farm produce in Canastota. He sends the produce to T. G. Boyce, a commission merchant in New York, to be sold on a commission of 8%. The commission merchant, after selling the goods at market prices, mails to the shipper an **Account-Sales** stating the amount of sales for each item, and the expenses, including his commission, with a check for the difference between the amount of sales and the expenses, which is the **net proceeds** of the sale.

Mr. Souter at different times made the following shipments to Mr. Boyce, which he sold. Find the commission and net proceeds of each.

		SHIPMENTS		EXPENSES
1.	Dec.	2000 bbl. apples	@ $5	$36
2.	Jan.	3000 lb. wool	@ 75¢	$49
3.	Aug.	600 lb. veal	@ 20¢	$15
4.	Oct.	1000 tons hay	@ $18	$75
5.	Sept.	250 crates plums	@ $2	$10
6.	Nov.	1200 bbl. potatoes	@ $4.50	$46
7.	Feb.	1400 bu. onions	@ $1.25	$50
8.	July	1000 doz. eggs	@ 40¢	$30

Find the net proceeds of the following commission house transactions:

9. 6050 lb. cotton @ 14¢. Cartage and storage, $12. Commission, 3%.

10. 4000 bu. wheat, @ $2.25. Cartage and insurance, $150. Commission $\frac{1}{4}$¢ per bushel.

11. 2000 lb. lard @ 25¢. Cartage and storage, $40. Commission, 5%.

12. 500 bbl. pork @ $35. Cartage and insurance, $50. Commission, 4%.

13. Mr. J. P. McGuire of Utica shipped the following to A. D. Cox & Co., commission merchants, New York, to be sold on a commission of 8% of the amount of sales.

> 2000 lb. wool
> 52 tons hay
> 1000 bbl. potatoes

Messrs. Cox & Co. sold the wool at 65¢ per pound, the hay at $20 per ton, and the potatoes at $4 per barrel. The expense of carting was $54, and for insurance was $15. How much was their commission, and what were the net proceeds remitted to Mr. McGuire?

Find the net proceeds of the following commission sales:

	SHIPMENTS		EXPENSES
14.	1000 crates peaches	@ 80¢	Cartage, $36
	1000 bu. onions	@ $1.25	Insurance, $6.25
	2000 bbl. cabbages	@ $1.50	Storage, $14.50
	500 qt. blackberries	@ 18¢	Commission, 8% of amount of sales
15.	1000 bu. corn	@ $1.75	Cartage, $64
	2000 bu. wheat	@ $2.20	Storage, $31
	1500 bu. oats	@ $.90	Commission, 5% of amount of sales
16.	600 crates beans	@ $2.15	Insurance, $10.15
	400 crates beets	@ $3.00	Cartage, $30.00
	800 boxes apples	@ $2.25	10 % commission, on sales.

17. The Oneonta Creamery Co. shipped to a commission merchant in New York 1200 lb. butter and 1600 lb. cheese to be sold on a commission of 5%.

The butter was sold at 40¢ a pound, and the cheese at 25¢ a pound. The expenses were $26 for cartage and $8.75 for storage. How much was due the Creamery Company after deducting the commission and other expenses?

Problems

1. An agent sells a house for $8500. What is his commission at 4%?

2. On a sale of fruit amounting to $885 an agent is given a commission of $2\frac{1}{2}$%. Find his commission.

3. On a sale of $4000 an agent receives $120. What is the rate of commission?

4. Find the rate of commission an agent receives when his commission is $350 on sales amounting to $10,000.

5. An agent's commission is $2\frac{1}{2}$%. If his sales amount to $100,000 a year, what is the amount of his commission?

6. An agent received $208.20 as his commission on the sale of an auto for $3470. What was the rate of commission?

7. A commission merchant received $10 as his commission at 5% on a sale of butter. What was the value of the butter?

8. Eggs sold at a commission of 2% yield $4 commission. Find the selling price of the eggs.

9. An agent sold wheat at a 3% commission, and sent the owner $9700. What was the agent's commission?

10. The net proceeds of a sale of cotton were $9898, after a commission of 2% had been deducted by the agent. What was the selling price of the cotton?

11. For what must a book be sold so that the agent may return $2.70 to the publishers after deducting a commission of 10%?

12. The net proceeds from a sale of fruit at 5% commission are $702.05. What was the commission?

13. An agent charges $280 for collecting $8000. What rate does he charge?

14. An agent sells 200 pounds of butter for a farmer, charging 4% commission. If he remits $115.20, what was the selling price of the butter per pound?

15. Mr. Brown pays Mr. Smith $52.25 for collecting a bill. If the rate of commission is $2\frac{3}{4}\%$, what was the amount of the bill?

16. How much is an architect's commission at $4\frac{1}{2}\%$ on a house costing $12,000?

17. An agent sold property valued at $8000 at a commission of $240. What was his rate of commission?

18. The commission on a sale was $150. If the rate was 3%, what was the amount of the sale?

19. For collecting a sum of money an agent receives 4% commission. If he receives $160, what was the amount of the collection?

20. A broker charged $\frac{3}{8}\%$ for selling $24,000 worth of bonds. How much did he send his principal?

21. What sum must an agent send his employer after deducting his commission of $3\frac{1}{4}\%$ on a sale of $28,000?

22. An agent finds his commission at $\frac{1}{4}\%$ for buying bonds to be $50. How much money must his principal send him to cover both the brokerage and the cost of the bonds?

23. How many bonds at $100 each can an agent buy for $801, including brokerage of $\frac{1}{8}\%$?

24. An architect's commission is 6% on a contract of $415,000. What is his commission?

25. John receives one cent for selling a copy of the Saturday Evening Post at 5¢. What is his rate of commission?

Commission

In these examples, state what is given and what is required;
estimate each answer before solving.

	SELLING PRICE	AGENT'S COMMISSION		NET PROCEEDS TO PRINCIPAL
		In %	In Dollars	
1.	$600	10%	?	?
2.	$100	?	$8	?
3.	$600	?	?	$570
4.	?	5%	$40	?
5.	?	10%	?	$360
6.	?	?	$20	$380
7.	$800	5%	?	?
8.	$300	?	$15	?
9.	$1000	?	?	$900
10.	?	9%	$45	?
11.	?	20%	?	$400
12.	?	?	$50	$450
13.	$2000	2%	?	?
14.	$700	?	$49	?
15.	$150	?	?	$135
16.	?	12½%	$25	?
17.	?	25%	?	$300
18.	?	?	$100	$400
19.	$64	12½%	?	?
20.	$32	?	$4	?
21.	$400	?	?	$300
22.	?	20%	$60	?
23.	?	12½%	?	$490
24.	?	?	$80	$560

Trade Discount

Any reduction or allowance on an account, a debt, or a price is a **discount**.

A **price list** is a published list of prices of articles for sale. The **list price** is the price given in a price list.

A reduction from the list price of goods is a **trade discount**.

A discount for cash payment is sometimes called a **cash discount**. In the trade a cash discount is usually made in consideration of a bill being paid within a certain time, the terms being stated in the bill. A discount because of the quantity of goods sold is sometimes called a **quantity discount**.

A 10% reduction from a price is called "a 10% discount," "10% off," or "$\frac{1}{10}$ off."

The total amount charged in a bill is the **gross price**.

The gross price less all discounts is the **net amount**.

When two or more discounts are made from the price of an article, they are called **successive discounts**.

The first discount is a certain per cent of the list price, the second a certain per cent of the remainder, the third a certain per cent of the second remainder, and so on.

Find the discount of each of these list prices at the rate placed above each column:

10%		25%		33⅓%		5%		12½%
1. $2.00	6. $40	11. $30	16. 40¢	21. $16
2. $5.00	7. $60	12. $15	17. 80¢	22. $24
3. $8.00	8. $80	13. $45	18. 20¢	23. $64
4. $11.00	9. $100	14. $60	19. $1.00	24. $96
5. $50.00	10. $1000	15. $1.20	20. $2.00	25. $80

Problems

1. The whole of anything is what per cent of it?

2. When an article is sold at a discount of 10% from the list price, it is sold for what per cent of the list price?

3. I bought Longfellow's poems listed at $1.50, the bookseller allowing me 20% off. How much did I pay?

4. I can buy a bicycle for $40 and pay for it in 30 days, or obtain a discount of 2% by paying cash. How much will I save by paying cash? What is the cash price?

5. A man bought a bill of goods at 10% discount. He paid $180 for them. What per cent of the list price did he pay? What was the list price?

6. By paying cash for a bill of goods I obtained a discount of 2%, thereby saving $2. What was the amount of the bill?

7. A merchant bought from a jobber goods listed at $2000, receiving a discount of 40%. What was the entire discount? What did he pay for the goods?

8. A merchant bought a bill of goods at ⅓ off. What was the discount on goods listed at $90? What was the net price?

9. What is the net price of goods listed at $200 and bought at a discount of 30%? What is the discount?

10. The net price of a bill of goods is $12. The rate of discount is 40%. What is the list price? What is the discount?

11. The net price of a bill of goods is $30. The rate of discount is 40%. What is the discount?

12. Goods listed at \$3241 are sold at a discount of 30%. What is the discount?   30% of \$3241 = ?

13. Goods listed at \$3241 are sold at a discount of 30%. What is the net price?   70% of \$3241 = ?

14. What is the discount on a catcher's mitt listed at \$7.20, $\frac{1}{10}$ off?

15. Find the net price of bacon listed at 40¢ a pound, less $\frac{1}{5}$.

16. A snare drum was marked \$9.60 but was sold at $12\frac{1}{2}$% discount. What was the sale, or net price?

17. An article costs a merchant \$2. What must be the marked price so that a discount of 20% may be given from the marked price and the merchant still make 20% on the cost?

18. Mr. Fox paid \$2000 for a car. He gave it a marked price of \$3000 and sold it at a discount of 20%. Find his gain per cent.

19. A merchant bought a tractor for \$960. It is marked \$1560. At what discount can he sell the tractor so that he may make a profit of 30%?

20. What was the first cost of a Victrola which when sold at a discount of 30% from the list price of \$330, yields a gain of 10%?

21. I bought a chair at a sale for \$6.40, at a discount of 20%. What was the list price?   80% of ? = 6.40.

22. A man bought goods at 15% discount. What was the list price of goods that cost him \$59.50?

23. The net price of a purchase of stationery at $\frac{1}{10}$ off was \$4.50. What was the list price?

24. Net price, \$1.28, rate of discount, 20%. What is the list price?

25. When goods are selling $\frac{1}{4}$ off from list price, what is the list price of goods sold at $1.50?

26. Miss Geyer paid cash for goods, and was allowed a 2% discount for cash. She saved $1.80 by paying cash. What was the amount of her purchase?   2% of ? = $1.80.

27. A merchant saved $4.50 by paying cash, thus obtaining a discount of $1\frac{1}{2}$% on a bill of goods. What was the amount of the bill?

28. Mr. J. J. Hogan could buy a bill of furniture for $520 on credit, or at 5% off for cash. What was the cash price?

29. A fruit dealer sold me ten barrels of apples at $2.50 a barrel. They arrived in poor condition and he discounted the bill 20%. How much did I pay?

30. The list price of baseball suits is $4.75 each. Our team needs 11 suits. How much must we pay for them at 20% discount?

31. A suit marked $48 was sold late in the season for $40. The reduction was what per cent of the marked price?

32. Mr. Johnson's store caught fire, and his goods were damaged by smoke and water, so that he sold them at 65% below cost. What did he receive for 38 yd. of lace that cost $.25 a yard? What was the cost of a coat that sold for $7? How much did he lose on a table that cost $15?

33. I saw straw hats in a window marked as follows: $1.50, $4.50, $1.20, $2.70, $2.25. How much would be taken off from the price of each one if they were marked down $33\frac{1}{3}$%?

34. $2 union suits are marked down 25%. At what price are they sold?

Trade Discount

For the following examples, state what is given and what is required; estimate the answer before solving.

	Cost	Per Cent of Gain Computed on the Cost	Discount from the Marked Price	Marked Price
1.	$16	25%	20%	?
2.	$240	12½%	10%	?
3.	$360	25%	10%	?
4.	$816	33⅓%	12%	?
5.	$1000	?	40%	$2000
6.	$600	?	27½%	$900
7.	$400	?	25⅓%	$600
8.	$1500	?	20%	$2500
9.	$840	25%	?	$1500
10.	$900	33⅓%	?	$1500
11.	$1600	20%	?	$2400
12.	$480	5%	?	$800
13.	?	33⅓%	20%	$1000
14.	?	40%	30%	$6000
15.	?	12%	20%	$11,200
16.	?	20%	10%	$600
17.	$4000	30%	10%	?
18.	$6000	?	20%	$10,000
19.	$900	33⅓%	?	$1600
20.	$60	25%	20%	?
21.	$300	10%	?	$363
22.	?	40%	20%	$3500
23.	?	20%	50%	$20,000
24.	?	50%	50%	$36,000

25. How much do I save on a $30 overcoat by waiting until it is marked down 16⅔%?

Successive Discounts

There are two ways of treating successive discounts. For example, let it be required to find the net price of a bill of goods listed at $400, on which successive discounts of 15%, 10%, and 5% are allowed.

15% of $400 = $60.	*First discount.*
$400 − $60 = $340.	*First discount price.*
10% of $340 = $34.	*Second discount.*
$340 − $34 = $306.	*Second discount price.*
5% of $306 = $15.30	*Third discount.*
$306 − $15.30 = $290.70	*Net price.*

Or

The net price is 95% of 90% of 85% of $400. Find the net price in this way and compare results.

The latter method is the more direct and, in most cases, the shorter.

List price $1.00.   Find net price.   Allow discounts of:

1. 10 and 5 per cent.
2. $12\frac{1}{2}$ and 5 per cent.
3. 15 and 5 per cent.
4. 20 and 10 per cent.
5. 20, 10, and 5 per cent.
6. 25 and 5 per cent.
7. 25 and 10 per cent.
8. 25, 10, and 5 per cent.
9. 30 and 5 per cent.
10. 30 and 10 per cent.
11. 15 and 10 per cent.
12. $16\frac{2}{3}$ and 10 per cent.
13. 20 and 5 per cent.
14. $33\frac{1}{3}$, 10, and 5 per cent.
15. 40 and 5 per cent.
16. 40 and 10 per cent.
17. 40, 10, and 5 per cent.
18. 40 and 20 per cent.
19. 40, 20, and 5 per cent.
20. 45 and 10 per cent.

Find the net prices of the following bills of goods:

	List Price	Discounts		List Price	Discounts
21.	$240	2%, 10%, 8%	24.	$312.50	10%, 10%, 10%
22.	$300	10%, 5%, 2%	25.	$214	2%, 10%, 20%
23.	$870	30%, 5%, 2%	26.	$300	15%, 10%, 5%

27. Steel screws are listed at $6 a gross, and successive discounts of 30%, 40%, 15%, and 5% are allowed. What must be paid for 40 gross?

28. Find the net price of goods listed at $720, and discounted at 5%, 10%, and 20%.

29. Two merchants have the same kind of goods marked at the same price. One offers discounts of 25%, 20%, and 5%. The other offers discounts of 5%, 20%, and 25%. Which is the better offer?

30. Two merchants have goods exactly alike, listed at $200. One offers discounts of 20%, 10%, and 10%. The other offers a single discount of 37%. Which is the better offer, and how much better?

31. $144 was sufficient to pay a bill on which discounts of 20% and 10% were given. What was the amount of the bill before the discounts were made?

STATEMENT: 90% of 80% of the amount = $144. When the product of three factors and two of the factors are given, how may the remaining factor be found?

32. What is the list price of a bill on which discounts of 10%, 10%, and 5% make the net price $153.90?

33. Two successive discounts reduced to $108 the price of an article listed at $160. One of the discounts was 25%. What was the other?

STATEMENT: ——% of 75% of $160 = $108.

When the product of three factors and two of the factors are given, how may the remaining factor be found? That factor subtracted from 100% is the required discount.

34. What discount, in addition to one of 20%, will reduce a price from $50 to $39.20?

35. What list price will give a net price of $113.40 when discounts of 30%, 10%, and 10% are made?

Successive Discounts

For the following examples, state what is given and what is required; estimate the answers before solving.

	LIST PRICE	DISCOUNTS TO DEALER	COST TO DEALER	PRICE TO CUSTOMER	GAIN PER CENT
1.	$5020	5%; 10%	?	$5677.45	?
2.	$1480	20%; ?	$888	$1110	?
3.	?	33%	$6780	$8136	?
4.	$20,000	25%; 20%	?	?	25%
5.	$12,080	$33\frac{1}{3}$%; ?	$6040	List	?
6.	$5440	25%; 3%	?	$4947	?
7.	$640	$12\frac{1}{2}$%; $12\frac{1}{2}$%	?	?	20%
8.	$880	25%; 10%	?	?	$33\frac{1}{3}$%
9.	?	10%; 10%	$9720	$12,150	?
10.	$10,040	5%; ?	$9462.42	$10,354.90	?
11.	$10770	$33\frac{1}{3}$%; 2%	?	$7915.95	?
12.	?	20%; 25%	$6000	List	?
13.	$3600	10%; 10%	?	?	25%
14.	?	26%; 5%	$1140	$1368	?
15.	$12,720	$12\frac{1}{2}$%; 7%	?	$12,419.88	?
16.	$990	10%; ?	$801.90	$1002.375	?
17.	$12,456	1%; ?	$10,790.01	$13,487.51	?
18.	$330	10%; 10%	?	$334.125	?
19.	$6360	$12\frac{1}{2}$%; ?	$5174.95	$6209.99	?
20.	?	$33\frac{1}{3}$%; 20%	$400	$760	?
21.	$6040	$33\frac{1}{3}$%; 25%	?	List	?
22.	$48	25%; $33\frac{1}{3}$%	?	?	50%

23. A bill of goods listed at $640 is sold at discounts of 10% and 10%. Find the net cost.

24. An office desk was sold at successive discounts of $33\frac{1}{3}$% and 10% for $36. What was the list price?

Bills and Discounts

1. The following bill shows three items discounted at different rates. Observe that these discounts have been *reckoned out* in the bill.

<table>
<tr><td>TERMS:
2%. 10 days.
—
60 days, net.</td><td colspan="3">Binghamton, N. Y. 5/18/18.
BABCOCK, HINDS & UNDERWOOD
WHOLESALE HARDWARE
SOLD TO O. Smeader, Onango, N. Y.</td></tr>
</table>

5# 3 × ¼ *W. B. Rivets*	$ .20	$1.00	
less 33⅓ %			$ .67
½ *doz. Sink Collars*	.07½ ea.		.45
½ " *2000 Spring Balances*	1.50	.75	
less 10 %			.68
½ " ½" *Petroleum Faucets*	11.00	5.50	
less 50% and 10 %			2.48
1 *Keg 3d Galv. Wire Nails*			6.90
			$11.18 Net Amt.

Interpretation of the above bill.

Item 1. — 5 lb. Rivets @ 20¢ = $1.00. $1.00 less 33⅓%
= $.67 net.

Item 3. — ½ doz. Spring Balances @ $1.50 = $.75.
$.75 less 10% = $.68 net.

Item 4. — ½ doz. ½ in. Petroleum Faucets @ $11 = $5.50.
$5.50 less 50% and 10% = $2.48 net.

Items 2 and 5 are not discounted, and are, therefore, net.
The terms, 2% 10 days, 60 days net, mean that if the bill is paid within 10 days or by May 28th a cash discount of 2% will also be allowed.   This is computed on the net amount of the bill.   2% of $11.18 = $.22. $11.18 − $.22 = $10.96.   But if not paid within 10 days, no cash discount is allowed and the net amount remains $11.18.

THE ONEONTA GROCERY CO., Importers

WHOLESALE GROCERS.   CONFECTIONERY
50 Broad St.

ONEONTA, N.Y., *Apr. 18, '28.*

Sold to *E. S. Manwarring*

R. R. to Onango, N. Y.

TERMS. — Net Cash.   30 days.
If paid within 10 days, 2% cash discount will be allowed on this bill.

2 Bx.	*Pep't Neccos*	$ .90		
2 "	*Wint. "*	.90		
2 "	*Sterling Pep't Gum*	.65		
2 "	*Wrig. Spea. Gum*	.67		
2 M	*Ca'mels*	6.00		
1 Bx.	*Lunch Creams,* 24½#	.18		

2. Extend the items, foot the bill, and find the net amount if it is paid on or before Apr. 28, 1928.

3. If the above bill is not paid until May 17th, what amount must be paid?

4. If there had been a trade discount of 10% and 10% on the 5th item of the above bill, what would have been the net amount, if paid within 10 days from date?

5. The terms of Butler Bros., Wholesalers, New York, are 2% 10 da., 1% 30 da., net 60 da.

What is the amount to be paid for the following, if paid within 10 days of the date of the bill?

½ doz. rubber balls @ $2.10 a doz.   1 Jardiniere, $.45. 1 doz. nut picks, $.75.   1 toy kitchen set, $.89.   1 toilet set, $5.00.

If not paid till the expiration of 30 days, what is the net amount?

6. The following goods were purchased of Butler Bros., New York, by a city retailer, Aug. 6, 1918:

2 Fringed Wilton Rugs, 9 × 12, @ $75. 2 doz. Silk Taffeta Umbrellas, @ $33 per doz. 10 pieces Silk Moire Ribbon, 10 yd. in the piece, @ $2.40 per yard. What sum will settle the bill Sept. 5? Oct. 5?

Fill out the bill, supplying the name of a retailer whom you know, extend the items, foot, and compute the net amount.

7. A dealer in auto supplies sold 1 doz. Klaxon Horns at $2.67 each, $\frac{1}{2}$ doz. Electric Head Lamps at $5.75 each, and $1\frac{1}{2}$ doz. Trouble Lamps at $9 per doz. His terms are 10, 10, and 5. What amount will settle the bill?

8. A bookseller bought a bill of school books from D. C. Heath & Co. amounting to $675. What was the net amount? Terms, $\frac{1}{6}$ off.

9. What amount will settle for these goods within 10 days? terms, 2% 10 days:

3 Porcelain Kitchen Sinks, $32.85 each.

10. Make out a bill for the following items. Foot it and compute the net amount, supplying the name of the wholesaler and the buyer.

10 Steamer Trunks @ $7.20.
2 Wardrobe Trunks @ $31.50.
180 Leather Suitcases @ $3.85. Terms, $\frac{1}{5}$ off.

What is the net amount of each of the following?

11. 1 doz. Couch Hammocks @ $15.50 each. Terms, 2% 10 da. Paid within 10 days.

12. 1 doz. Bicycle Saddles at $24 per doz. Discounts 10% and 10%.

13. $\frac{1}{2}$ doz. Middy Blouses @ $24 per doz. Paid in 60 days. Terms, 2% 10 da., 1% 30 da., net 60 da.

Insurance

Many years ago, people had not learned to share risks with one another as they do now by means of insurance. If a man's house burned, it was a complete loss to him. If one's property was stolen and not recovered, he alone bore the loss. And so with all risks; each person carried his own, alone.

Finally, people learned that by combining in large groups, each member of the group could pay into the treasury a small sum regularly, and then when a loss occurred to one of the group, the accumulated contributions of all in the group would be sufficient to repay the unfortunate one for his loss, and the burden was not heavy upon any one of the group. Such a plan of sharing losses is **insurance**.

The insurance business is generally carried on by companies that make a contract with the party insured by which they agree to reimburse him for his losses, up to a certain amount, and he agrees to pay to the company a specified sum whether he suffers loss or not. In this sense, the insurance business is a sort of legalized lottery.

The insurance company must, of course, charge the insured much more than merely his share of the risk; because it must pay the salaries of its officers and clerks, the fees of its agents, the rent of its offices, and many other expenses.

Some large establishments "carry their own insurance." For example, the school departments of many cities do not insure their school buildings in any company, but pay into an insurance fund of their own a certain sum each year, and thus accumulate an amount sufficient to meet the loss when a fire occurs in one of the school buildings.

In this way, such cities save the "overhead" expense of salaries, etc., that insurance companies must meet. Does your school department carry its own insurance?

Among the commonest kinds of insurance are **life** insurance, **fire** insurance, **accident** insurance, **marine** insurance, and **liability** insurance.

There are many other kinds of insurance, named according to the kind of risk assumed by the insurer, such as health, boiler, plate glass, automobile, burglary, etc.

Can you mention some kind of insurance that is not named here?

The written or printed document that contains the terms of an insurance contract is called an **insurance policy**. The sum which the insurer agrees to pay is called the **face of the policy**. The sum paid by the insured to the insurer is called the **premium**.

Life insurance policies are in force for a term of years or during the life of the insured; but the premium is usually paid in annual, semi-annual, or quarterly installments. Installments after the first are called **renewals**.

Most other kinds of insurance policies are for a shorter time, and the premium is paid in one sum when the policy is issued.

Accident policies are usually made out for one year, though some special kinds, like travelers' accident policies, are sold for shorter periods.

Fire insurance policies are usually for three years.

The premium on a fire insurance policy is computed at a certain sum for each $100 of insurance, or a certain per cent of the face of the policy, this single rate covering the entire time for which the policy is given.

The premiums on life insurance policies are generally computed at a certain sum for each $1000 of the face of the policy, the sum varying according to the age of the insured when the policy was issued, and according to the conditions of the contract.

Jan. 3, 1933.

Problems

1. *a.* A wooden dwelling house in a city was insured for three years for $3500, the rate of premium being $.65 on $100 of insurance for three years. Find the premium.

b. How much did the owner pay in premiums in twelve years at this rate?

c. The rate of premium for brick dwellings in the same city is 55¢ on $100 for three-year policies. Find the premium for $4200 of insurance on a brick dwelling in that city.

d. The insurance agent who wrote the policy in question *c* received as his commission 25% of the premium. Find the agent's commission.

2. A schoolhouse in a Western city is insured for three years for $28,000, at $\frac{3}{4}$%. The agent's commission is 20% of the premium. Find the agent's commission.

3. *a.* The premium for insuring a mill, in a small village, for $2000, amounted to $75 a year. What was the annual rate of premium?

STATEMENT: ── % of $2000 = $75.
Which term (factor or product) is to be found?

b. What was received by the agent who wrote three annual policies on this mill, his commission being 15% of the premiums?

4. A merchant's stock of goods is insured for $\frac{4}{5}$ of its value, for three years, at $\frac{4}{5}$%. If the stock is worth $7500, what is the annual expense for insurance?

5. I pay $28.50 for three years' insurance, the rate of premium being $\frac{3}{5}$%. How much insurance have I?

STATEMENT: $\frac{3}{5}$% of $── = $28.50.

6. The premium for insuring my house, at 70¢ per $100, is $38.50. What is the face of the policy?

7. A machine shop is insured for three years at a cost of $114. If the rate is $1\frac{1}{2}\%$, what is the face of the policy?

8. An agent received $5.25 as his commission for insuring a house for $\frac{4}{5}$ of its value. The rate of premium was $\frac{3}{4}\%$ and the agent received 25% of the premium.

a. What was the premium?

b. What was the face of the policy?

c. What was the value of the house?

9. How many dollars of insurance must an agent secure in order that he may obtain $46.35, if his commission is 15% of the premiums and the premiums are $1\frac{1}{5}\%$ of the insurance?

10. A man had an accident insurance policy which cost him $25 a year. After he had paid three years' premiums, he was injured by an accident and received $20 a week for six weeks.

a. The man received how much more than he paid?

b. If the agent received 30% of the premiums, how much did the insurance company lose by insuring this man?

c. If the company insured ten other men for the same time at the same rate, and none of them made any claim for injuries, how much more did the company receive from the eleven men than it paid out on account of the one man's injuries?

11. A house worth $3600 was insured for $\frac{2}{3}$ of its value, and the contents, worth $2800, were insured for $\frac{1}{2}$ of their value. The rate of insurance was 65¢ on $100. The house and contents were entirely destroyed within a year.

a. What did the company lose by insuring the property?

b. What did the owner lose by the fire?

12. Property worth $48,600 is insured for $\frac{5}{6}$ of its value at a cost of $364.50. What is the rate?

13. A man took out a $5000 ten-year endowment life insurance policy, on which the semi-annual premium was $55.95 per $1000 of the face of the policy. If he lived ten years after taking the policy, and paid all the premiums when due, how much did he pay to the company?

14. A merchant has his stock of goods insured for $18,000 at $2\frac{1}{4}\%$ for three years, his building for $12,500 at 2% for three years, one boiler at $15 a year, an elevator at $35 a year, and plate glass at $12 per year, with 30% off, on the plate glass. How much does his insurance cost in three years?

15. The three-year insurance rate for wooden dwellings in a small town was $1.35 per hundred dollars of insurance. The town put in a water system and bought modern fire-fighting apparatus. The rate was then reduced to $.75 per hundred dollars. If $500,000 of fire insurance was carried by home owners of that town, how much was saved in three years? Why should the insurance rate be higher for a planing mill than for a dwelling?

Automobile Insurance

Owners of automobiles have their cars insured against loss by fire or theft. Owners also purchase insurance against loss by having to pay damages for injury to persons or property caused by their machines. The last is called liability insurance.

16. Mr. Randall paid $17 a year to insure his car against fire and theft. He paid $28.25 a year public liability insurance and $7.05 a year for insurance against property damage. What was the entire insurance cost of his car?

17. Mr. Baker can get property damage insurance for his car for $6.15 and public liability insurance for $24.50. How much would he save by getting both together for $30.60?

Taxes

1. Who pays the policemen, firemen, and other employees of the city?

2. Who pays for the electric light in your street?

3. Who paid for the pavement in your street?

4. Who pays the salaries of the Governor and other officers of your state?

5. Does the sheriff of your county receive a salary? If so, from what source does the money come?

6. From what source is money obtained to pay the senators and representatives who compose our Congress?

7. From what source is money obtained for the support of the public schools? For building bridges and sewers? For cleaning and repairing streets and roads?

8. How are colleges and universities supported?

9. Find out, if you can, all of the uses made of the money which your father pays in taxes upon his property.

10. Does a person who rents, but does not own, property contribute to the support of the city, county, and national governments? If so, in what way?

Money required for public uses, and levied upon property, incomes, business, or persons, is a **tax**.

It was formerly the custom, especially in rural communities, to require each male citizen to pay a fixed sum, called a *poll tax*, for certain public uses. This method of taxation has been abandoned by most states.

The amount of tax to be levied upon any piece of property depends upon the entire amount to be raised, and the value of this particular piece of property in comparison with the entire value of all the property upon which the tax is levied.

The valuation of property upon which taxes are to be levied is made by men appointed or elected for that purpose and known as **assessors.**

The assessors make a list of all the taxable property in the territory to be taxed, with their estimate of the value of each piece. This is the **assessment roll.**

When a tax is to be levied, a list is made, including all items of expense to be provided for in the levy. This list is called the **tax budget.** From the total of the budget is deducted all of the income (for licenses, fines, sales of privileges, etc.) to find the **net amount** of the budget.

The decimal obtained by dividing the *net amount* of the budget by the *total amount of the assessment roll* is the **tax rate.** This decimal is seldom exact, but is carried to three, four, or five places. It gives an approximation that is close enough.

For example, the total assessed valuation of a school district is $3,742,000, and the school budget is $28,000. The quotient of 28,000 ÷ 3,742,000 is .00748+. In this case .0075 would be taken as the tax rate. It would be mentioned as " 7½ mills " or as " 7½ mills on a dollar." The school tax on a property assessed at $5000 would be .0075 × $5000, or $37.50.

What is the amount of the school tax budget for this year in your school district?

What is the school tax rate?

What is the county tax rate in your county?

What is the total assessed valuation of the property in your school district?

Problems

1. The money to be raised by tax in a town is $9000. The property of the town is valued at $600,000. What is the tax rate?

STATEMENT: —— of $600,000 = $9000.
SOLUTION: 9000 ÷ 600,000 = .015, tax rate, *Ans.*

2. The tax rate of a county is .003 and the property is valued at $24,567,800. What is the amount of the tax budget?

SOLUTION: .003 of $24,567,800 = $73,703.40, *Ans.*

3. When it requires a tax rate of .0132 to raise $264,000 in taxes, what is the valuation of the property taxed?

STATEMENT: .0132 of —— = $264,000. How may the required factor be found?

4. The tax budget of a township is $12,000. The assessed valuation of the property in the township is $1,200,000.

a. What is the tax rate?   ($12,000 = —— of 1,200,000)

b. Mr. A has property in this township assessed at $25,000. What is his tax?

c. Mr. B pays $15 taxes. What is the valuation of his property?   ($15 = .01 of ——)

5. A man's city taxes were $40 on property valued at $2000. What was the tax rate?

6. The tax budget of a town is $4900.

a. The tax rate is .007. What is the valuation of the property?

b. How much are the taxes of a man in this town, who owns property assessed at $4000?

7. The tax rate of a county is .0025. The tax budget is $75,000. What is the value of the property?

8. The school tax in a village having property to the amount of $3,000,000 was $9000.

a. What was the school tax rate?

b. What amount did a man pay whose property was assessed at $15,000?

c. Mr. Jones's school tax was $12. What was the valuation of his property?

9. The property of a town is assessed at $1,000,000, and the rate is .01. What is the amount raised by tax?

10. A man's property is assessed at $4000. The city tax rate is .014, the county rate is .004, and the state rate .002. The poll tax is $1.50. What is this man's entire tax?

11. If the rate for county and state taxes together is .005, what is my bill for state and county taxes on an assessment of $9000?

12. The assessed valuation of the property in a county is $70,000,000. The tax rate is 3 mills on a dollar.

a. How much money will be raised by the tax?

b. The county has an income from various sources amounting to $40,000. After all the taxes and other income have been collected and all the expenses have been paid, $5000 remains. What are the expenses of the county?

13. What is the rate when $24 will pay the tax on property assessed at $1200?

14. Let each pupil find out the assessed valuation of the house in which he lives, and the amount of the last tax paid. From those, find the tax rate. Find out, if possible, what is done with the money raised by tax, and what would be the rate for each purpose, on $1000 of valuation.

City Tax Budget for One Year

Interest	$ 49,755.44
Comptroller	11,620
City Treasurer	18,450
Department Public Instruction (School Funds)	463,780
Library Fund	35,000
Art Museum	5,000
Department Charities and Correction	85,129
Municipal Lodging House	4,071
Veteran Relief	8,000
City Engineer	35,959
Public Buildings and Grounds	15,000
Department Public Works (General Office)	14,462
Parks and Cemeteries	47,000
Walks and Sidewalk Repair	5,000
Street Cleaning	91,542
Collecting Garbage and Ashes	86,455
Street Repairs, Sewers, and Bridges	64,120
Municipal Baths	4,000
Public Markets	3,382
Lighting Fund	114,000
Boiler Inspector	900
Department of Law	13,720
Municipal Court	11,978
Police Court	6,000
Department of Public Safety (General Office)	7,520
Police Department	162,730
Fire Department	205,080
Health Department	55,925
Department of Taxes and Assessments	19,200
Executive Department	8,400
City Clerk	9,000
Civil Service Board	2,600
Election and Primary Fund	16,000
Printing and Publishing Fund	7,500
Sealer of Weights and Measures	1,200
Common Council	16,450
Smoke Inspector	1,200
Plum Street Bridge	6,000
Other Expenses	139,879
Total	$
Less Income from Licenses, etc.	246,228
Net Total	$

From the city tax budget on page 80,

1. Find the total expenses of the city for the year.

2. Find the net total of the tax budget.

3. Find the tax rate, correct to four places of decimals, the assessed valuation of the real property in the city being $89,000,000 and of the personal property $9,000,000.

4. Find the amount of A's city tax on $15,000 of personal property and $5000 of real property.

5. In this city the county and state taxes are paid together, and the rate is .00363682. What is A's county and state tax?

6. Mr. B's county and state taxes, computed by the above rate, amount to $65.46276. He pays $65.47. What is the valuation of his property?

7. Mr. C owns two pieces of property in this city, one valued at $600 and the other at $3200. What is the entire amount of his city, county, and state taxes?

8. The valuation of property in a town is $1,500,000, and the rate is $\frac{1}{5}\%$. What is the tax?

9. The tax to be raised in a village is $37,500. The valuation of the taxable property is $2,500,000.

a. What is the rate?

b. What will be A's tax on $15,000 real estate and $3000 personal property?

c. What is the valuation of property on which the tax is $37.50?

10. The property of a town is assessed at $1,250,000. The tax to be raised is $15,325. What is B's tax, if his property is assessed at $2500?

11. The officers of a town find that all the town expenses for a year will amount to $46,000. The tax-roll shows real estate valued at $2,000,000, and personal property at $300,000. What is the tax rate?

COMPARISON OF THE TAX BUDGET OF THE CITY OF SYRACUSE FOR
THE YEARS 1914 AND 1924

ASSESSED VALUATION	1914	1924
Real	$129,030,777.00	$227,294,021.00
Personal	4,730,550.00	301,265.00
Special Franchise	8,067,540.00	8,392,555.00
Total	$141,828,867.00	$235,987,841.00

TAX BUDGET		
Administration	252,882.11	562,809.28
Bureau of Street Repairs, Sewers, Etc.	105,858.50	130,308.49
Bureau of Street Cleaning	115,598.18	180,982.82
Bureau of Garbage and Ashes	122,558.30	300,950.99
Department of Parks	36,052.50	112,737.59
Bureau of Police	237,371.84	531,873.30
Bureau of Fire	257,450.61	662,360.75
Department of Health	80,011.97	182,784.17
Department of Charities	113,763.92	249,891.24
Department of Public Instruction	607,979.40	1,580,326.69
Public Library	45,000.00	89,516.00
Bureau of Water	341,203.30	705,301.52
Miscellaneous	809,671.21	2,234,624.46
Total	$3,125,401.84	$7,524,467.34
Less Miscellaneous Receipts	635,281.85	1,518,983.98
Amount of Tax Budget	$2,490,119.99	$6,005,483.36
Plus 1% Pursuant to Law	24,901.20	60,054.83
Total to be Raised by General Tax	$2,515,021.19	$6,065,538.19
Rate per Thousand Dollars	$17.733	$25.7028

From the city tax budget, page 82 :

1. Find the per cent of increase in assessed valuation of real property between 1914 and 1924.

2. What is the tax rate for the year 1914?

3. What is the tax rate for the year 1924?

4. Mr. Bond's property was assessed for $4800. What was the tax in 1924?

5. What is the valuation of a piece of property on which $1285.14 tax is paid in the year 1924?

6. Mr. Kelley's property was assessed for $2800 in 1914 and for $5800 in 1924. What was the amount of his tax in 1914 and in 1924?

7. What was the per cent of decrease in personal assessed valuation from 1914 to 1924?

8. Mr. Brown's house was valued at $15,000. What was his city tax in 1924?

9. Mr. Coon owns two pieces of property, one valued at $3875 and the other at $4870. What taxes did he pay in the year 1924? What would he have paid in 1914 if the valuation had been the same as in 1924?

10. What was the per cent of increase of the tax per thousand in 1924 over that in 1914?

11. What was the per cent of increase of expenditures for public instruction in 1924 over 1914?

12. Find the taxes paid in 1924 on the property assessed as follows :

(a) $6000	(b) $8000	(c) $4000	(d) $7000
(e) $9200	(f) $7600	(g) $6800	(h) $15,000
(i) $16,000	(j) $300,000	(k) $19,500	(l) $3400
(m) $14,000	(n) $11,300	(o) $2500	(p) $1900

Problems with Numbers Omitted

1. I bought a house for $——, spent $—— for repairs, and sold it for $——. How much did I gain?

SOLUTION: The gain may be found by adding the cost of the house and the amount spent for repairs and subtracting that sum from the selling price.

2. Three members of a family earn respectively $——, $——, and $—— a week. Their living expenses are $—— a week.

a. How much can they save in one week?

b. How much can they save in one year?

3. A merchant bought a piece of cloth for $—— and sold it so as to gain ——% of the cost. How much did he gain? For how much did he sell it?

4. A grain merchant bought corn at ——¢ a bushel and sold it at ——¢ a bushel. What per cent of the cost did he gain? What per cent of the selling price?

5. Mr. Hurd sold goods on a commission of —— per cent of the selling price. What was his commission on goods sold for $——?

6. What must be paid for —— hundred feet of lumber at $—— per M?

7. Find the cost of —— inches of cloth at $—— per yard.

8. A man sells goods on a commission of ——% of his sales. How many dollars' worth of goods must he sell per week to earn $—— a day?

9. A quantity of corn shrank —— per cent in weight from October to May, and then weighed —— pounds. How much did it weigh in October?

10. An agent received $—— for selling a house. This was ——% of the selling price. Find the selling price.

11. Anna earned $—— and gave her mother $——. She gave her mother what per cent of her earnings?

12. Frank earned $—— a year while in college. His college expenses amounted to $—— a year. He earned what per cent of his expenses?

13. Mr. Alvord spent ——% of his salary and had $—— left. What was his salary?

14. A merchant made a profit of ——% on the cost of cloth which he sold for $—— a yard. What was the cost per yard?

15. By selling a suit for $——, the merchant lost ——% of the selling price. What did the suit cost?

16. What per cent is gained on land bought at $—— an acre, and sold at $—— an acre?

17. A commission merchant sold —— lb. of butter at ——¢ a pound, retained his commission of ——%, and sent the remainder to his principal. How much did he send to his principal?

18. A canning club received $—— for a case of canned peaches containing —— cans. They paid —— for each can and —— for the fresh fruit. How much per can did they receive for their labor?

19. A merchant bought —— articles listed at —— each. He received ——% discount. What did they cost him?

20. The list price of an article is —— dollars. On sale a reduction of ——% is given. How many dollars will the article cost if bought at this sale?

Mental Tests

1

1. Find $\frac{1}{6}$ of 60.

2. Find 200% of 20.

3. What is .10 of 200?

4. What is $33\frac{1}{3}\%$ of 90?

5. How many buttons are there in $\frac{1}{4}$ of a gross?

6. What will 500 ft. of lumber cost at $40 per M?

7. What will 18 eggs cost at 50¢ per doz.?

8. Add $\frac{1}{2}$ and $\frac{1}{4}$.

9. Change $66\frac{2}{3}\%$ to a common fraction.

10. How many pints are there in $\frac{3}{8}$ of a gallon?

2

1. Change $\frac{1}{4}$ to per cent.

2. $\frac{1}{3}$ equals what per cent?

3. Change $\frac{20}{100}$ to per cent.

4. $2\frac{1}{2}$ ft. = how many inches?

5. How many bolts are there in $\frac{3}{4}$ of a gross?

6. How many pecks are there in 3 bu. 1 pk.?

7. Find the cost of 200 ft. of lumber at $50 per M.

8. If $10 will buy 5 books, how many can you buy for $12?

9. Add $\frac{1}{2}$ and $\frac{3}{4}$.

10. Subtract $\frac{1}{3}$ from $\frac{3}{4}$.

3

1. Change 3 gal. to pints.

2. 1 mi. = how many feet?

3. Find .05 of 200.

4. Change 32 pt. to gallons.

5. Find 1% of $800.

6. $\frac{1}{8}$ = what per cent?

7. Change 150% to a fraction.

8. Subtract $\frac{3}{4}$ from $1\frac{1}{4}$.

9. At $30 per M find the cost of 1500 ft. of lumber.

10. What will $\frac{3}{4}$ of a yard of cloth cost at $1 per yard?

4

1. From $10 take 6\frac{1}{4}$.

2. 20% of a ton = ? lb.

3. Find 250% of 100.

4. $\frac{1}{4}$ mi. = how many rods?

5. $\frac{1}{8}$ A. = how many square rods?

6. Change $2\frac{1}{2}$ lb. to ounces.

7. What will 10,000 shingles cost at $4 per M?

8. How many square feet are there in a rug 9 ft. by 12 ft.?

9. At 9¢ per lb. what will 2 cwt. of flour cost?

10. Subtract $\frac{5}{8}$ from $1\frac{1}{8}$.

5

1. Write 1918 in Roman numerals.
2. $\frac{11}{12}$ of 144 = ?
3. $\frac{3}{4}$ hr. = how many minutes?
4. $3\frac{1}{4} \div 13$ = ?
5. 6% of $600 = ?
6. Change 4 lb. to ounces.
7. What is .5 of 5?
8. 60% of $60 = ?
9. $\frac{1}{4}$ of .8 = ?
10. $\frac{1}{4}$ gal. = ? gills

6

1. Change $\frac{11}{16}$ to hundredths.
2. Write $796 in words.
3. What are the prime factors of 81?
4. If two eggs cost 8¢, what will $1\frac{1}{2}$ doz. cost?
5. 18 is 50% more than what number?
6. How many pounds are there in 20% of a ton?
7. If .3 of Roy's money is $300, how much has he?
8. 12 is what decimal part of 16?
9. $5\frac{1}{2}$% of $1000 = ?
10. 87% of $1000 = ?

7

1. What will 3 pk. of apples cost at $1.60 per bushel?
2. Find the cost of $2\frac{1}{4}$ lb. of rice at 12¢ per lb.
3. From Jan. 1 to Nov. 1 is how many months?
4. 24 is 25% more than what number?
5. $4\frac{1}{2}$% of $600 = ?
6. What are the prime factors of 70?
7. Write $1049 in words.
8. If one yard of cloth costs 75¢, how many yards can be bought for $4?
9. At 3¢ per mile, what will it cost to travel 31 miles?
10. At 20¢ per cwt., what will it cost to ship 1 T. of feed?

8

1. Hay at $20 per T. brings $50. How many tons are sold?
2. Find $4\frac{1}{4}$% of $400.
3. Write $938 in words.
4. What change should be received from $2.00 when a purchase of $1.43 is made?
5. A jar of butter weighing $10\frac{1}{2}$ pounds is sold for $5.25. What is the price per pound?
6. At $8 per ton, what will 1000 pounds of coal cost?
7. Change $8\frac{1}{3}$ feet to inches.
8. What is 40% of $120?
9. Write $\frac{3}{8}$ as a %.
10. Find .03 of $400.

9

1. Find the cost of 10 quarts of milk at 7¢ a pint.

2. Find the interest on $600 for 2 years at 6%.

3. How many pieces 6 inches long can a carpenter cut from a board 7½ feet in length?

4. Potatoes were 30 cents a peck. Find the cost of 1½ bushels.

5. After using an automobile costing $2000 for 2 years, the owner was offered $800 by a dealer in second-hand cars. Compute the per cent of depreciation.

6. Find 125% of $400.

7. A boat marked $84 was reduced 33⅓% at the end of the season. Find the selling price.

8. Mrs. Smith purchased 2 pounds of crackers at 15 cents a pound and 1½ dozen of rolls at 24 cents a dozen. How much change did she receive from a dollar?

9. A boy bought a bicycle for $15 and made repairs costing $5. He sold the bicycle for $25. What rate of profit did he make?

10. Subtract ¾ yd. from 1⅛ yd.

10

1. Grapefruit were sold 6 for 25¢. At that rate what will 2 dozen cost?

2. What is the interest on $10 for 6 months at 4%?

3. A boy shined shoes for 10 cents a shine. On July 4th, he gave 75 shines. Allowing $1.50 for running expenses, find the amount received for the day's work.

4. An agent sold $800 worth of goods, receiving a commission of 20%. Find the proceeds.

5. Earning 25 cents daily, how long will it take to earn a pair of shoes costing $4.50?

6. Find the cost of ½ dozen handkerchiefs when the price of two such handkerchiefs is 25 cents.

7. Add ½, ⅔, and ¾.

By selling a lot for $2100, an agent made 16⅔% on his investment. What was his investment?

9. At what rate will $1200 earn $1344 in 2 years?

10. Three pecks of apples cost $1.20. At the same rate what will $2\frac{1}{2}$ bushels cost?

11

1. It takes 4 packages of crêpe paper for a costume. At 18 cents a package find the cost of 2 costumes.

2. Find the cost of 6 quarts of molasses when 1 gallon cost $1.25.

3. An agent receives a commission of 6% for buying wool at 21 cents a pound. What amount of money does he receive for buying 50 tons of wool?

4. At 40 cents a dozen what will 78 buttons cost?

5. What is the interest on $450 for 6 mo. at $4\frac{1}{2}$%?

6. An advertisement of a sale offers a dress listed at $16 for $12. Compute the rate of discount.

7. Find the cost of 2 tons of coal when 1000 lb. cost $6.25.

8. An engine travels 8 miles in 12 minutes. How far will it go in 1 hour?

9. A discount of $2 was given on a $24 suit. What was the rate of discount?

10. A house worth $5000 is insured for $\frac{4}{5}$ of its value. The rate is $5.50 on $1000 for a three-year policy. What is the premium on this policy for three years?

12

1. A man can do a piece of work in 8 days. In how many days can 4 men to it if working at the same rate?

2. At the rate of 5¢ an ounce, what will 1 pound of candy cost?

3. A boy earns $12\frac{1}{2}$¢ an hour for work. How much will he earn in 16 hours?

4. A girl spent $400 but saved 20% of her money. How much money had she at first?

5. In a class of 54 children, 18 are on the honor roll. What per cent are not honor students?

6. 6 is 1% of what number?

7. Cloth costing $3 a yard is sold at a gain of 20%. How much is gained on 5 yards?

8. A man sold his potatoes for 80¢ a bushel.   He received $160 from one sale.   How many bushels did he sell?

9. Change 32 pints to pecks.

10. 81 is what per cent of 108?

13

1. Cloth that cost $4 a yard became damaged so that it had to be sold for $3 a yard.   What per cent of the cost was the loss?

2. At 64¢ a lb. how much does 14 oz. of tea cost?

3. 21¢ is paid for ¾ yd. of ribbon.   How much is 1 yard worth?

4. How much is saved by buying a lamp at a reduction of 30% from the regular price, $12?

5. A boy earned $10.25 in one week during vacation.   How much would he earn at that rate in 2 months?

6. A man bought a horse for $200 and sold it for 90% of the cost. For how much did he sell the horse?

7. Find the cost of 18 eggs at 60¢ a doz.

8. What will 3 pk. of turnips cost at $1.60 per bu.?

9. 1 lb. of coffee costs 60¢.   How many pounds can be bought for $2.70?

10. 5 yds. of ribbon cost $1.   What will 7 yds. cost?

14

1. What is 7½% of $400?

2. A man bought goods listed at $100 and received a 5% discount. How much did he pay?

3. Find the cost of 500 lbs. of coal at $12 per T.

4. A man bought milk at 30¢ a gal. and sold it at 10¢ a qt.   What was his profit?

5. Cloth costing $2 per yd. is sold at a gain of 20%.   How much will a merchant gain on 10 yards?

6. I spell 20 words out of 25 correctly.   What per cent of the words are wrong?

7. A pole measured 150 in. long.   How many feet long was it?

8. 1 lb. of coffee costs 60¢.   How many pounds can be bought for $2.40?

9. In an orchard of 320 trees 25% were plum.   How many plum trees were there?

10. ¾ doz. of oranges cost 75¢, what will ½ doz. cost?

15

1. How many packages of peanuts each containing 1 pint are filled up from ½ bu. of peanuts?

2. A coat that cost $25 was sold for $30. What was the gain per cent?

3. At 30¢ a peck how many bushels of apples can be bought for $12?

4. A man had 80 dollars. How many dollars had he after his money was increased by 25% of that number?

5. What will 1 doz. grapefruit cost at 3 for 25¢?

6. A girl read 70 pages of a book containing 280 pages. What per cent of the book did she read?

7. Find the cost of 2 lb. 4 oz. of meat at 40¢ per lb.

8. How much must be paid for 200 lb. of corn at $40 per T.

9. A boy gave to the Red Cross 50 cents, or 20% of all he had earned. How much money had he earned?

10. $3000 is ¾ of Mr. Smith's money. How much money has he?

16

1. How many 4-oz. packages of cinnamon can be put up from 2 lb. of cinnamon?

2. What is the cost of the milk per week for a family using 2 quarts of milk daily at 10 cents a quart?

3. A boy bought a bicycle for $40 and received a 2% cash discount. How much did he save?

4. At 60¢ a lb. how much will 8 oz. of tea cost?

5. What is the discount on a victrola listed at 60 dollars if 16⅔% is given?

6. The coal man put 4½ T. of coal in my cellar. How many trips did he make if he carried 3000 lbs. to a load?

7. There are 132 bananas in a bunch. How much is it worth with bananas selling at 40¢ a dozen?

8. A 5% discount is given on goods listed at $20. What is the selling price?

9. John had 220 chickens and sold 75% of them. How many did he have left?

10. How many pencils at the rate of 3 for 5¢ can be bought for 25¢?

17

1. Find the cost of 5 gal. of milk at 12¢ a quart.

2. What is the cost of 2 bushels of potatoes at 25¢ a peck?

3. A good walker can average $4\frac{1}{4}$ miles per hour. How far can he walk in 90 minutes at that average?

4. At 60¢ a lb. how much candy can be bought for 15¢?

5. A coat was sold at a discount of 10% from the list price, $50. How much did it cost?

6. What is the cost of 3000 lbs. of hay at $20 per T.?

7. 2 lb. 8 oz. of candy is given to 5 boys. How many ounces will each boy have when the candy is divided equally?

8. How many pint bottles could a milkman fill with 4 gal. of milk?

9. A grocer bought 5 bushel-crates of cranberries at $3 per crate with a 10% discount. How much did he pay?

10. Goods costing $320 were sold at a discount of 25%. How much was saved?

18

1. $\frac{2}{3}$ of a yard of cloth costs $1.50. What is the price per yard?

2. A merchant buys a pocketknife for 50¢ and sells it at a gain of 20¢. What per cent does he gain?

3. How much will 2 doz. gloves cost at $1\frac{1}{2}$ per pair?

4. Find the cost of $1\frac{1}{2}$ bu. of pears at 40¢ a peck.

5. A man bought a suit at 20% off. The suit was marked $50. How much did he pay for it?

6. A secondhand book was sold for 90¢, which was $37\frac{1}{2}$% of its cost. What was the cost?

7. One yard of cloth costs 75¢. How many yards can be bought for $4?

8. 2 eggs cost 8¢. What will $1\frac{1}{2}$ doz. cost?

9. When writing paper is marked 50¢ a box, how much must be paid for 3 boxes bought at a discount of $33\frac{1}{3}$%?

10. By selling tea at a gain of 8¢ a lb., a grocer gained 10% of the cost of the tea. What was the cost?

19

1. Find $\frac{1}{5}$ of 45.   **2.** What is 5% of 400?   **3.** Add $\frac{1}{2}$ and $\frac{3}{8}$.

4. How many quarts are there in $\frac{1}{4}$ of a bushel?

5. Change 60% to a fraction in lowest terms.

6. How many gallons are there in 48 quarts?

7. If 3 yards of cloth cost 30¢, what will $8\frac{1}{2}$ yards cost?

8. Find the cost of 60 tons of coal at $12 per ton.

9. What is the interest on $400 for two years at 6%?

20

1. Find $\frac{1}{8}$ of 40.   **2.** What is 37% of 100?   **3.** Subtract $\frac{1}{4}$ from $\frac{3}{8}$.

4. How many quarts are there in $\frac{3}{8}$ of a bushel?

5. What will 3 pounds 4 ounces of meat cost at 40¢ per pound?

6. Find the cost of $\frac{3}{4}$ of a yard of wire at 2¢ an inch.

7. Find the interest on $500 for 3 years at 5%.

8. What is the cost of $8\frac{3}{4}$ tons of coal at $12 per ton?

9. What is the amount of $600 for 4 years at 6%?

10. One is what per cent of four?

21

1. What is $\frac{3}{11}$ of 11?   **2.** Find 75% of 44.

3. A house was bought for $4000 and sold for $5000. What was the gain per cent?   **4.** Change 10 bushels to quarts.

5. A merchant lost $33\frac{1}{3}$% on goods costing him $1200. How much money did he lose?

6. How many square rods are there in $\frac{1}{4}$ of an acre?

7. Subtract $\frac{3}{4}$ from $\frac{5}{6}$.   **8.** Find $12\frac{1}{2}$% of $64.

9. What is the interest on $800 for 1 year 6 months at 4%?

10. Change 10 square feet to square inches.

22

1. One factor 25%; the product $100. Find the other factor.

2. Cost = $36; Rate of gain = 25%; selling price = ?

3. If $\frac{3}{4}$ of a dozen oranges cost 75¢, what will $\frac{1}{2}$ dozen cost?

4. Find the amount of $1000 for 4 months at 6%.

5. 40 is what decimal part of 60?   **6.** Find 3% of 300.

7. How many pounds are there in 20 oz.?

8. What must be paid for 200 pounds of corn at $40 per ton?

9. Marked price $84; selling price $72; find the per cent of discount.   **10.** 4000 ÷ 2000 = ?

23

1. A book sold for 90¢ after a discount of 10% had been made. What was the marked price?

2. A discount of 12% was made on an article marked $1. Find the discount.

3. When the marked price is $20 and the discount is 10%, what is the selling price?

4. An article costing $2 is marked so as to gain 100%. Find the marked price.

5. The marked price of a hat is $4 but it is sold for $3. What is the rate of discount?

6. The list price of a coat is $10. It is sold at a discount of 20%. What is the net selling price?

7. A discount of 10% is given on a desk. If the discount is $2, what is the marked price?

8. The marked price of a table is 40% above cost. If the marked price is $14, what was the cost?

9. The cost of a suit is $20. It is marked at a gain of 25%. What is the marked price?

10. A house is sold at a discount of 20% from the list price. The net price is $8000. What was the list price?

24

1. A commission of 3% is charged for selling $100 worth of hay. What is the commission?

2. If an agent receives $6 for collecting a $100 debt, what is his rate of commission?

3. An agent's commission of 5% is $10. What is the amount of the sale?

4. The net proceeds of a sale of $100 is $94. What is the rate of commission?

5. The net proceeds of a sale are $97, after a commission of 3% had been deducted by the agent. What was the agent's commission?

6. What must be paid an agent for collecting a debt of $1000 at a commission of 5%?

7. What per cent of discount is given when an article marked $1000 is sold for $900?

8. When the discount of $40 is 10% of the marked price, what is the marked price?

9. A stove costing $40 is marked at a gain of 25% on the cost. What is the marked price?

10. A stove costing $40 is sold at a loss of 20%. Find the selling price.

Completion Test

Fill each blank space with one word to complete the statement:

1. The amount of sales multiplied by the rate of the commission equals ——.

2. When buying, the total cost is secured by —— the purchase price, the commission, and any other expenses connected with the purchase.

3. When selling, the proceeds are found by —— the commission, and any other expenses incident to the sale —— the selling price.

4. The product of the amount of sales and the rate of commission equals the ——.

5. The amount of sales equals the commission —— by the rate of commission.

6. The rate of commission equals the commission —— by the sales.

7. Make an original problem for the *above statements.*

8. If the denominator of a fraction is increased, the value of the fraction is ——.

9. When the area and one dimension of a rectangle are known, the other dimension may be found by —— the area by the given dimension.

Tests of Accomplishment

1

1. Twenty hundredths of 5000 men are how many men?

2. $\frac{1}{10}$ of my salary is $220. What is my salary?

3. What part of $3200 is $800?

4. Reduce 3600 inches to feet.

5. A city lot is 40′ by 150′. What is the perimeter?

6. A floor 18′ by 15′ contains how many square yards?

7. A blackboard 3′ × 4′ contains how many square inches?

8. How much is $12\frac{1}{2}\%$ of 4800 lb.?

9. Seventy-five dollars is what % of $1500?

2

1. Mr. Ray subscribed for a $500 Liberty bond, $\frac{1}{10}$ to be paid each month. How much had he paid in 3 months?

2. James sold 20 papers, which was $\frac{4}{5}$ of the number that he bought. How many did he buy?

3. In a spelling lesson of 20 words, Lucy spelled 18 words correctly. How many hundredths were spelled correctly?

4. How many days are there in 10 years, allowing for 2 leap years? How many hours?

5. A field is 15 rd. wide, and 3 times as long. How many rods of fence will be required to enclose it?

6. A floor is 24 ft. by 30 ft. How many tiles 8 in. square will be required to cover it? (Cancel.)

7. A room is 18 ft. long, 15 ft. wide, and contains 2700 cu. ft. How high is it?

8. A plumber earns $2000 a year and saves 25% of it. How much does he save?

3

1. In a southern city of 60,000 people 33⅓ hundredths are negroes. What is the negro population?

2. If $60 is ⅘ of my bank balance, how much have I in the bank?

3. Mr. Dix pays $300 for the use of $5000 for a year. How many hundredths of $5000 does he pay?

4. If a man steps 2½ ft. at each step, how many miles will he cover in taking 4224 steps?

5. A steamer sails 480 knots in a day. How many miles does she sail? (1 knot = nearly 1⅛ miles.)

6. A roll of carpet ¾ yd. wide contains 60 yd. How many square yards of floor surface will it cover?

7. What must be paid for 14 tons of bran at $1.60 per hundred pounds?

8. A farmer having 400 acres of land sold 75% of it. How many acres were unsold?

9. If 800 bushels of potatoes are 80% of my crop, how much is my entire crop?

10. What per cent of 20 bu. are 16 pecks?

4

1. ⅖ of the pupils in a school of 240 pupils are girls. How many of the pupils are boys?

2. How many bushels are there in 35,842 dry pints?

3. Mr. Knapp had 900 white leghorn chickens, and sold 33⅓% of them. How many did he have remaining?

4. $160 is ⅝ of how many dollars?

5. A house worth $5000 rents for $500 a year. The rent is what fraction of the value of the house?

6. Both sides of a road are fenced with wire for a distance of 100 rods. What did it cost at 2¢ a foot?

7. Find 69½% of $1600.

8. $150 is 5% of a sum of money that I borrowed. How much money did I borrow?

9. At the close of school, 450 pupils out of 500 pupils were promoted. What per cent of them failed?

10. The floor of a room is 12′ by 18′. Find the cost of finishing and varnishing this floor at $.35 a square foot.

5

1. A farmer having 320 acres sold $\frac{3}{20}$ of them to one man and $\frac{1}{4}$ to another. How many acres remained?

2. If a milkman buys 20 gal. of milk for $10 and sells it at 15¢ a quart, how much does he gain?

3. Mr. York sold a horse for $225, which was 75 hundredths of what it cost. What did it cost?

4. A field is 24 rd. by 60 rd. What is the perimeter in feet?

5. My salary is $2400 a year and my expenses $1800. My expenses are what part of my salary?

6. A close board fence, 6½ ft. high, surrounds a lot 450 ft. by 380 ft. The fence contains how many sq. yards?

7. Find the number of acres in a rectangular farm 280 rd. long and 60 rd. wide.

8. From a training camp of 320 officers, 20% were sent away at one time and 40% at another. How many remained?

9. Mary answers 9 of her 10 questions correctly. What per cent of them are answered correctly?

10. What is 87½% of $9600?

6

1. At $12\frac{1}{2}$¢ each, what is the cost of 64 melons?

2. How many melons at $12\frac{1}{2}$¢ each can be bought for $1600?

3. At $16\frac{2}{3}$¢ a can, what will 72 cans of corn cost?

4. $37\frac{1}{2}$% of 480 acres is how many acres?

5. Multiply 64 by $.87\frac{1}{2}$.

6. Divide 2100 by $.33\frac{1}{3}$.

7. 25% of 40 = ? $66\frac{2}{3}$% of $999 = ? 75% of 4000 = ?

8. $1800 ÷ 90% = ? $4400 ÷ 110% = ? (Estimate first)

7

1. There are how many feet in $\frac{3}{40}$ of a mile?

2. When a gross of pens are bought for 75¢ and sold at 2 for 3 cents, what is the gain?

3. How many rods of fence are required to enclose a mile square of land?

4. The Declaration of Independence was signed on July 4, 1776. How many years, months, and days have elapsed since that date?

5. How many quarts are there in $87\frac{1}{2}$% of a bushel?

6. A rectangular field is 64 rd. long and 20 rd. wide. How many sq. rods does it contain?   How many acres?

7. What must be paid for 8600 bricks at $35 per M?

8. Find the interest on $965 for 3 years at 6%.

9. Mr. Glen's salary now is $2400, which is 20% more than it was last year.   What was it last year?

10. After selling 20% of his hens, Mr. Knapp had 400 left.   How many had he at first?

8

1. Selling price $220, rate of profit 10%. Find the cost.

2. Market price $50, discount 20%. What is the selling price?

3. List price $150, discounts 15%, 5%. Find the selling price.

4. How much is 8% profit on goods that cost $2000?

5. Profit $10. Rate of profit 25%. Find the cost.

6. Cost $80, profit $20. What is the rate of profit?

7. What is the interest on $500 at 6% for $2\frac{1}{2}$ years?

8. One pint is what % of one gallon?   (Prove it.)

9. Find the perimeter of a square 26.8 ft. on a side.

9

1. What is the profit on a typewriter bought at $75, and sold at 25% profit?

2. By selling goods at a gain of $12\frac{1}{2}$% I make a total profit of $800. Find the cost of the goods.

3. Find the rate of profit on wagons bought at $1000 and sold at $1250.

4. A merchant sold goods for $1700 at a 15% loss. What was the cost of the goods?

5. At a marked-down sale, a lady bought a set of $50 furs at a discount of 16%. What did she pay?

6. Bought books, marked $48.20. Discounts 10%, 5%, 5%. Find the net price.

7. If an agent sells 250 bbl. of flour @ $11.50, on 5% commission, what are the commission and net proceeds?

8. In a rectangular field 160 rd. by 62 rd. there are how many acres?   (Use cancellation.)

10

1. Mr. Foster bought a quantity of wheat for $2400, and sold it at a loss of 6%. What was the loss?

2. At a fire sale a merchant lost $600 by selling goods at 20% below cost. What was the cost?

3. If a cow is bought for $80, and sold for $70, what is the per cent of loss?

4. Mr. Jones sold his automobile for $800, and thereby lost 25%. What was its cost?

5. The list price of some goods is $540, and the cash discount is $90. What is the rate of discount?

6. Knives listed at $108, and Yale locks for $36; discount 40%, 10%, 5%. Find net price.

7. If an agent receives 5% for collecting $675, how much must he pay over to his employer?

8. What are the interest and amount of $1500 at $5\frac{1}{2}$% for 2 years?

9. A farmer sold $33\frac{1}{3}$% of a flock of 660 hens. How many hens remained unsold?

10. A rectangular lot 98 ft. by 120 ft. is sold at $2.25 a sq. ft. Find the selling price.

11

1. A room is $15' \times 18'$. Find the cost of flooring at 40¢ per sq. ft.

2. A purchasing agent receives $446 for buying $11,150 worth of goods. Find the rate of commission.

3. A note for $700 was dated Mar. 1, 1924. What was due Mar. 1, 1925, interest at 6%?

4. Our school has 960 pupils. 144 are in the 6th grade. What % of them are in the 6th grade?

5. If you buy oranges at 4¢ each, and sell them at 25% profit, for how much do you sell them?

6. Charles sold his skates for 72¢ and thereby lost 10%. What did he pay for the skates?

7. If eggs are bought for 50¢ per dozen, and sold for 60¢, what is the rate of profit?

8. The marked price of a fur coat is $104. The selling price is $91. What is the rate of discount?

9. Mr. Barnes sold 50 acres of land for $2760 at a loss of 8%. What was the cost per acre?

10. On July 1, I bought goods marked $275, paying for them July 30. Terms, 10%, 30 da., net 60 da. What did I pay?

12

1. Mrs. Fisher bought a dining table for $68, a wicker chair for $15, and 6 dining chairs at $4 each. Discount $4\frac{1}{2}$%. Find the net price.

2. On Sept. 2 a merchant bought rugs marked $330, and bedsteads marked $240. Discount 15%, 10%, 5%. Find the net price.

3. By selling boots for $206.40, a merchant gained 20%. What did they cost him?

4. How many tons of iron are there in 3500 lb. of iron?

5. A clothier buys cloth at $1.50 per yard and sells at a profit of 15%. What is the selling price?

6. By selling damaged goods at a 10% loss, I lose $1800. Find the selling price.

7. A grocer buys tea at 25¢ and sells it at $37\frac{1}{2}$¢. What is his rate of profit?

8. My agent remits $5890, after selling my house, at 5% commission. What is the selling price and the commission?

9. Find the interest and amount of $4150 at 5% for $\frac{1}{2}$ year.

SEVENTH GRADE — SECOND HALF

Interest

1. Mr. Horton owns four houses which he rents; one to Mr. Gordon, one to Mrs. Mosher, one to Mrs. Teal and one to Mr. Clark. Each of these tenants pay him $40 a month rent. How much rent does he receive each month from these houses?

2. How much rent would Mr. Gordon pay in three months?

3. How much rent would Mrs. Mosher pay in six months?

4. If Mr. Horton were to change the rent to $45 a month, what amount of money would Mrs. Teal pay for two months' rent?

5. Mr. Clark borrowed $100 from Mr. Horton. He kept it a year and then returned it. He paid Mr. Horton an additional $6 for its use. Money paid for the use of money is interest. Had Mr. Clark borrowed $200 and kept it 2 years, how much interest would he have paid at the same rate?

6. If I borrow money at the rate of $5 for the use of $100 for one year, what per cent of the money borrowed do I pay annually?

7. At the rate of 5% per annum, what will be the interest on $1000 for 1 year?

8. What would be the interest on $1000 at 5% for 2 years?

9. What would be the interest on $2000 at 5% for 2 years?

10. What would be the interest on $1000 at 6% for $\frac{1}{2}$ year?

Find the interest at 6% on $100 for:

1. 1 yr.	**4.** 2 yr.	**7.** $\frac{1}{2}$ yr.	**10.** $4\frac{1}{2}$ yr.
2. 3 yr.	**5.** 6 yr.	**8.** $1\frac{1}{2}$ yr.	**11.** $3\frac{1}{2}$ yr.
3. 5 yr.	**6.** 4 yr.	**9.** $2\frac{1}{2}$ yr.	**12.** $5\frac{1}{2}$ yr.

In examples 1–12 find the interest at 6% on $200.

Find the interest at 6% for 1 yr. on:

13. $100	**16.** $500	**19.** $50	**22.** $150
14. $200	**17.** $250	**20.** $25	**23.** $125
15. $300	**18.** $400	**21.** $75	**24.** $175

In examples 13–24 find the interest at 6% for 2 years.

Find the interest on $100 for 1 yr. at:

25. 5%	**27.** 3%	**29.** $2\frac{1}{2}$%	**31.** $4\frac{1}{2}$%
26. 4%	**28.** 2%	**30.** $3\frac{1}{2}$%	**32.** $5\frac{1}{2}$%

Find the interest at 4% on:

33. $100 for 1 yr.; for 2 yr.; for 5 yr.; for $2\frac{1}{2}$ yr.

34. $300 for 1 yr.; for 3 yr.; for 2 yr.; for $2\frac{1}{2}$ yr.

35. $200 for 1 yr.; for 2 yr.; for 4 yr.; for $3\frac{1}{2}$ yr.

36. $500 for 1 yr.; for 3 yr.; for 5 yr.; for $2\frac{1}{2}$ yr.

37. $800 for 1 yr.; for 2 yr.; for 3 yr.; for 5 yr.

In examples 33–37 find the interest at 6%; at 5%.

Interest is money paid for the use of money.

Principal is money for the use of which interest is paid.

Rate is the per cent of the principal taken as interest for one year.

Amount is the sum of principal and interest.

Legal rate is the rate fixed by law.

In a majority of states, the legal rate is 6%.

1. What is the interest on $2000 for 3 yr. at 7%?

$2000	*Principal*
.07	*Rate*
$140.00	*Interest for 1 yr.*
3	
$420	*Interest for 3 yr.*

The **interest** *is the product of three factors;* viz. *the principal, the rate, and the time in years.*

After the above method of solution has been *thoroughly mastered, the computation of interest may be shortened by cancellation.*

$$\frac{7}{\cancel{100}} \times \$\cancel{2000}^{\,20} \times 3 = \$420$$

The following examples should be solved by both methods, the cancellation method being used as a check upon the other solution.

Find the interest on :

First *estimate* the answer.

2.	$380 at 6% for 2 yr.	**16.**	$50 at 6% for $\frac{1}{2}$ yr.
3.	$470 at 7% for 3 yr.	**17.**	$80 at 6% for $\frac{1}{6}$ yr.
4.	$590 at 5% for 2 yr.	**18.**	$300 at 6% for $1\frac{1}{2}$ yr.
5.	$286 at 5% for 6 yr.	**19.**	$900 at 6% for $\frac{1}{3}$ yr.
6.	$950 at 4% for 4 yr.	**20.**	$340 at 6% for $2\frac{1}{2}$ yr.
7.	$290 at 6% for 2 yr.	**21.**	$725 at 4% for $3\frac{1}{2}$ yr.
8.	$184 at 5% for 3 yr.	**22.**	$234 at 5% for $1\frac{1}{2}$ yr.
9.	$364 at 5% for 2 yr.	**23.**	$75 at 6% for $\frac{1}{6}$ yr.
10.	$282 at 4% for 4 yr.	**24.**	$750 at 6% for $\frac{1}{6}$ yr.
11.	$198 at 6% for 5 yr.	**25.**	$750 at 3% for $\frac{1}{6}$ yr.
12.	$389 at 3% for 2 yr.	**26.**	$2500 at 4% for $\frac{1}{2}$ yr.
13.	$250 at 4% for 3 yr.	**27.**	$5500 at 3% for 2 yr.
14.	$685 at 3% for 3 yr.	**28.**	$8000 at 4% for $\frac{1}{2}$ yr.
15.	$900 at 3% for 4 yr.	**29.**	$3500 at 5% for $1\frac{1}{2}$ yr.

1. Find the interest on $350 at 4% for 3 yr. 6 mo.

$350	*Principal*
.04	*Rate*
14.00	*Interest for 1 yr.*
$3\frac{1}{2}$	*3 yr. 6 mo. = $3\frac{1}{2}$ yr.*
7	
42	
$ 49	*Interest for 3 yr. 6 mo.*
350	*Principal*
$399	*Amount*

BY CANCELLATION

$$\frac{\overset{2}{\cancel{4}}}{\cancel{100}} \times \$\overset{3.50}{\cancel{350}} \times \frac{7}{\cancel{2}} = \$49. \quad \textit{Interest}$$

NOTE. — Observe how 100 and 350 are cancelled.

$ 49	*Interest*
350	*Principal*
$399	*Amount*

Find the interest and amount :

First *estimate* the answer.

2. $150 at 6% for 2 mo.

3. $370 at 6% for 2 mo.

4. $725 at 6% for 2 mo.

5. $396 at 4% for 3 mo.

6. $962 at 4% for 3 mo.

7. $372 at 3% for 4 mo.

8. $846 at 3% for 4 mo.

9. $325 at 4% for 9 mo.

10. $296 at 3% for 2 yr.

11. $729 at 6% for 2 yr. 6 mo.

12. $386 at 4% for 1 yr. 3 mo.

13. $900 at 3% for 2 yr. 6 mo.

14. $845 at 6% for 9 mo.

15. $1250 at 5% for 2 yr. 6 mo.

1. Find the interest on $434.50 at $3\frac{1}{2}\%$ for 2 yr. 6 mo.

$434.50	*Principal*
.035	*Rate*
217250	
130350	
15.20750	*Interest for 1 yr.*
15.208	*Interest to nearest mill*
$2\frac{1}{2}$	
7604	
30416	
$38.020	*Interest for 2 yr. 6 mo.*
434.50	
$472.52	*Amount*

NOTE. — Final results in interest are usually expressed to the nearest cent.

BY CANCELLATION

NOTE. — Observe that $\dfrac{3\frac{1}{2}}{100} = \dfrac{7}{200}$.

$$\frac{7}{200} \times \overset{2.1725}{\cancel{\$434.50}} \times \frac{5}{2} = \$38.02. \quad Interest$$

$38.02	*Interest*
434.50	*Principal*
$472.52	*Amount*

Find the interest and amount :

First *estimate* the answer.

1. $482 at $3\frac{1}{2}\%$ for 2 yr.

2. $796 at $3\frac{1}{2}\%$ for 3 yr.

3. $840 at $4\frac{1}{2}\%$ for 1 yr. 6 mo.

4. $900 at $4\frac{1}{2}\%$ for 3 yr. 6 mo.

5. $836 at $4\frac{1}{2}\%$ for 2 yr. 4 mo.

6. $324 at $4\frac{1}{2}\%$ for 6 mo.

7. $866 at $5\frac{1}{2}\%$ for 2 yr.

8. $380 at $5\frac{1}{2}\%$ for 3 yr. 6 mo.

9. $400 at $3\frac{1}{2}\%$ for 1 yr. 1 mo.

10. $500 at $5\frac{1}{2}\%$ for 7 mo.

1. Find the interest on $350 at 4% for 3 yr. 10 mo. 15 da.

NOTE. — In computing interest 30 days is considered a month. 12 months is equal to 360 days.

$350	*Principal*	10 mo. 15 da. $= 10\frac{1}{2}$ mo.
.04	*Rate*	
$14.00	*Interest for 1 yr.*	$10\frac{1}{2}$ mo. $= \dfrac{10\frac{1}{2}}{12} = \dfrac{21}{24}$ yr. $= \dfrac{7}{8}$ yr.
$3\frac{7}{8}$		3 yr. 10 mo. 15 da. $= 3\frac{7}{8}$ yr.
12.25		
42		
$ 54.25	*Interest for 3 yr. 10 mo. 15 da.*	
350		
$404.25	*Amount*	

BY CANCELLATION

$$3 \text{ yr. } 10 \text{ mo. } 15 \text{ da.} = 1395 \text{ da.}$$

$$\frac{\cancel{4}}{\cancel{100}} \times \cancel{\$350} \times \frac{\cancel{1395}}{\cancel{360}} = \$54.25. \quad Interest$$

$ 54.25	*Interest*
350.	*Principal*
$404.25	*Amount*

Find the interest :

First *estimate* the answer.

2. $300 at 5% for 1 yr. 5 mo. 12 da.

3. $900 at 4% for 1 yr. 7 mo. 11 da.

4. $360 at 7% for 1 yr. 2 mo. 7 da.

5. $840 at 6% for 2 yr. 15 da.

6. $485.50 at 4% for 1 yr. 3 mo.

7. $125.50 at $4\frac{1}{2}$% for 1 yr. 4 mo.

8. $240 at $5\frac{1}{2}$% for 8 mo. 15 da.

9. $540 at 5% for 1 yr. 4 mo. 10 da.

10. $632.50 at 6% for 2 yr. 2 mo. 15 da.

11. $792.30 at 4% for 3 yr. 1 mo. 10 da.

Written. Find the interest :

First *estimate* the answer.

	PRINCIPAL	RATE	TIME
1.	$4320	$3\frac{1}{2}\%$	2 yr. 6 mo.
2.	$720	5%	1 yr. 8 mo.
3.	$1081.08	6%	6 mo. 20 da.
4.	$5000	$4\frac{1}{2}\%$	2 yr. 8 mo.
5.	$901.80	6%	1 yr. 4 mo.
6.	$1200	$4\frac{1}{2}\%$	2 yr. 2 mo.
7.	$620.40	$5\frac{1}{2}\%$	3 mo. 10 da.
8.	$1250	5%	6 mo. 15 da.
9.	$1500	$4\frac{1}{2}\%$	2 yr. 9 mo.
10.	$275	6%	2 mo. 21 da.
11.	$396	5%	1 mo. 9 da.
12.	$444	4%	2 yr. 6 mo.
13.	$84.50	7%	2 yr. 5 mo.
14.	$16.75	6%	7 mo.
15.	$336	5%	15 da.
16.	$300	3%	1 yr. 2 mo. 15 da.
17.	$42.20	$4\frac{1}{2}\%$	1 yr.
18.	$50	4%	9 mo. 20 da.
19.	$35.50	7%	1 yr. 5 mo.
20.	$691	5%	1 mo. 3 da.
21.	$640.50	6%	10 mo. 26 da.
22.	$105.10	6%	48 da.
23.	$300	7%	4 mo. 3 da.
24.	$900	4%	273 da.

Finding Difference of Time between Two Dates

Find the number of years, months, and days from Oct. 15, 1927, to May 7, 1929.

SOLUTION

yr.	mo.	da.
1929	5	7
1927	10	15
1	6	22

1 yr. 6 mo. 22 da. *Ans.*

May is the fifth month.
October is the tenth month.
Say "15 and 22 (write 22) = 37 (30 + 7).
10 and 1 = 11.
11 and 6 (write 6) = 17 (12 + 5).
1927 and 1 = 1928.
1928 and 1 (write 1 = 1929)."

Written

1. What is the amount of $700 when placed at interest at 5% from Nov. 21, 1927, to June 3, 1929?

1929 yr.	6 mo.	3 da.
1927	11	21
1 yr.	6 mo.	12 da.

Diff. in Time

$$\frac{5}{100} \times \frac{\overset{7}{700}}{1} \times \frac{\overset{46}{552}}{\underset{\underset{6}{30}}{360}} = \$53.67 \; \textit{Interest}$$

$700.00
  53.67
$753.67 *Amount. Ans.*

Find the amount of

2. $250 from April 7, 1925, to Oct. 19, 1926, at 6%.

3. $5000 from Sept. 15, 1925, to May 21, 1927, at 6%.

4. $348 from July 25, 1922, to March 11, 1924, at 5%.

5. $1000 from Jan. 28, 1927, to Jan. 21, 1929, at $5\frac{1}{2}$%.

6. $875 from Sept. 30, 1928, to Feb. 24, 1929, at $4\frac{1}{2}$%.

7. $3980 from March 2, 1921, to July 2, 1923, at $4\frac{1}{2}$%.

8. $600 from Oct. 12, 1919, to April 12, 1921, at 7%.

9. $1350 from Aug. 25, 1927, to Dec. 5, 1928, at 5%.

The method of finding the time between dates is shown on page 110.

Find the interest:

First *estimate* the answer.

1. $2000 at 4½% from May 22, 1929, to March 10, 1931.

	yr.	mo.	da.
Mar. 10, 1931 =	1931	3	10
May 22, 1929 =	1929	5	22
	1	9	18

2. $35 at 6% from Jan. 1, 1927, to June 10, 1929.

3. $850.25 at 4% from Aug. 5, 1927, to April 15, 1930.

4. $392 at 3% from March 4, 1926, to May 10, 1928.

5. $400 at 3½% from Feb. 2, 1928, to July 7, 1930.

6. $750 at 3½% from April 1, 1919, to Oct. 1, 1920.

7. $290 at 4½% from July 1, 1928, to Jan. 1, 1930.

8. $3000 at 4½% from Jan. 1, 1926, to Oct. 16, 1929.

9. $950 at 5½% from Dec. 10, 1918, to Jan. 1, 1920.

10. $200 at 5½% from May 1, 1928, to Jan. 1, 1930.

11. On July 6, 1929, William Winter obtained a loan of $800 at 6%, promising to pay it with interest on Oct. 24, 1929. What was the amount due?

12. Fort & Co., on July 10, 1924, purchased hay to the value of $1200.   They pay half cash, and agree to pay the remainder with interest at 6% on Dec. 30, 1924.   Find the amount due.

13. If I borrow $1280 on June 5, 1926, what amount will I owe Nov. 5, 1926, interest at 5%?

The Six Per Cent Method

For a long time the legal rate of interest in many states has been 6%. The number 6 is an exact divisor of 12, which is the number of months in a year, and of 30, which is the number of days in a month. For these reasons there has come into general use the following method of computing interest, known as the " six per cent " method.

At 6% the interest on $1.00

for 1 year is $.06
for 1 mo. is $.005
for 1 da. is $.000⅙

1. Find the interest on $284.40 for 1 yr. 6 mo. 15 da. at 6%.

The interest on $1 for   1 yr.   = $.06
for   6 mo. = $.03
for 15 da.   = $.0025
for 1 yr. 6 mo. 15 da. = $.0925

The interest on $284.40 for 1 yr. 6 mo. 15 da. is the product of $284.40 and $.0925, which is $26.307. $26.31.   *Ans.*

Find the interest at 6% on

2. $200 for 1 yr. 4 mo. 12 da.

3. $850 for 2 yr. 6 mo. 18 da.

4. $2000 for 1 yr. 8 mo. 24 da.

5. $2500 for 4 yr. 2 mo. 6 da.

6. $3000 for 1 yr. 3 mo. 15 da.

7. $400 from Jan 1, 1928, to Sept. 7, 1929.

8. $560 from July 3, 1928, to Dec. 15, 1929.

9. $650 from Mar. 4, 1929, to June 22, 1930.

10. $1000 from Feb. 10, 1929, to Nov. 22, 1930.

11. $2800 from Nov. 12, 1928, to Apr. 2, 1929.

1. Find the interest on $375.50 for 2 yr. 5 mo. 7 da. at 6%.

The interest on $1 for 2 yr. $\quad = \$.12$
$\quad\quad\quad\quad\quad$ for 5 mo. $= \$.025$
$\quad\quad\quad\quad\quad$ for 7 da. $\quad = \$.001\frac{1}{6}$
$\quad\quad$ for 2 yr. 5 mo. 7 da. $= \$.146\frac{1}{6}$

The interest on $375.50 for 2 yr. 5 mo. 7 da. is the product of 375.50 and $.146\frac{1}{6}$ which is $54.8855+. $54.89 *Ans.*

Find the interest at 6% on :

2. $265.24 for 3 yr. 3 mo. 3 da.

3. $582.63 for 6 mo. 24 da.

4. $347 for 1 yr. 5 mo. 17 da.

5. $356.24 for 1 yr. 2 mo. 15 da.

6. $287.15 for 2 yr. 11 mo. 22 da.

7. Find the interest on $3000 for 1 yr. 3 mo. at 5%.

The interest on $1 at 6% for 1 yr. $\quad = \$.06$
$\quad\quad\quad\quad\quad\quad\quad$ for 3 mo. $= \$.015$
$\quad\quad\quad\quad\quad\quad$ for 1 yr. 3 mo. $= \$.075$
$\quad\quad 3000 \times \$.075 = \$225.00$ interest at 6%
$\quad\quad \frac{1}{6}$ of $225 = \quad \$37.50$ interest at 1%
$\quad\quad$ By subtraction $\quad \$187.50$ interest at 5% *Ans.*

NOTE. — First find the interest at 6%. To find the interest at 5%, subtract $\frac{1}{6}$ of it; at 4%, subtract $\frac{1}{3}$ of it; at 7%, add $\frac{1}{6}$ of it, at $4\frac{1}{2}$%, subtract $\frac{1}{4}$ of it, etc.

Find the amount of the following :

8. $6000 at 5% for 1 yr. 3 mo. 6 da.

9. $2640 at 7% for 2 mo. 18 da.

10. $3450 at 4% for 2 yr. 6 mo. 20 da.

11. $6300 at 8% for 2 yr. 24 da.

12. $7500 at 9% for 2 yr. 7 mo. 17 da.

13. $3000 at $4\frac{1}{2}$% for 2 yr. 11 mo.

14. $347.40 at 5% for 2 mo. 15 da.

15. A note for $600 was dated Mar. 1, 1923. What was due Aug. 5, 1924, interest at 5%?

The Sixty-Day Method

The interest on $1 at 6% for 60 da. is $.01 which is 1% of the principal. Therefore to find the interest on any sum of money at 6% for 60 da. take 1% of it. This is easily done by *pointing off two decimal places* from the right; *e.g.*

The interest for 60 da. at 6% on $845 is $8.45; on $3958.30 is $39.58, etc.

From the interest for 60 da. it is easy to find the interest for other short periods: *e.g.*

The interest on $4236 for 60 da. is $42.36
  for 30 da. it is ½ of $42.36 or $21.18
  for 10 da. it is ⅙ of $42.36 or $7.06
  for 15 da. it is ¼ of $42.36 or $10.59
for 90 da. it is $42.36 (for 60 da.) + $21.18 (for 30 da.) or $63.54
for 80 da. it is $63.54 (for 90 da.) − $7.06 (for 10 da.) or $56.48, etc.

This method is also called the "banker's" method. It is a modification of the "six per cent" method.

Find the interest at 6% on $8424 for:

1. 60 da.	**4.** 10 da.	**7.** 120 da.	**10.** 80 da.
2. 30 da.	**5.** 15 da.	**8.** 105 da.	**11.** 25 da.
3. 90 da.	**6.** 45 da.	**9.** 130 da.	**12.** 50 da.

Find the interest at 6% on :

13. $3663 for 60 da.
14. $4242 for 30 da.
15. $6200 for 90 da.

16. $2400 for 10 da.
17. $3600 for 40 da.
18. $4200 for 100 da.

Compute the amount, at 6%, of :

19. $2433 for 4 mo.
20. $167.40 for 2 mo. 15 da.
21. $143.40 for 3 mo. 20 da.
22. $875.22 for 5 mo. 10 da.
23. $324.85 for 4 mo. 25 da.

The Method by Days

This is a modification of the " six per cent " method.
It is based on the fact that the interest on $1 for 6 days
at 6% is $.001.   To compute the interest by this method
move the decimal point in the principal three places to
the left. This gives the interest for 6 days. Multiply
that interest by ⅙ of the number of days.

1. What is the interest on $1575.25 from Jan. 9, 1924,
to March 15, 1924, at 6%?

22 da. left in Jan.	$1.57525	The interest for 6 da.
29 da. in Feb.	11	
15 da. in March	$17.32775	
66 da. *Term of Interest*		$17.33 is the interest for 66 da.

Compute the interest at 6% on

2. $600 from April 21 to Aug. 3.

3. $845.60 from Sept. 1 to Dec. 24.

4. $570 from April 25 to Aug. 13.

5. $473.70 from June 1 to July 31.

6. $1857 from Nov. 30 to Dec. 31.

7. $900 from Dec. 18, 1923, to Feb. 21, 1924.

8. $388 from Dec. 18, 1926, to Feb. 21, 1927.

9. $188 from Dec. 19, 1925, to March 1, 1926.

10. $4200 from Jan. 7, 1927, to March 9, 1927.

11. $5610 from Jan. 7, 1928, to March 9, 1928.

12. $34.32 from July 5, 1925, to Sept. 5, 1925.

13. $34.32 from June 5, 1926, to Aug. 5, 1926.

14. $6420 from April 10, 1928, to June 9, 1928.

15. $342.30 from May 9, 1925, to Aug. 7, 1925.

16. $363.30 from April 10, 1929, to July 10, 1929.

Estimating Answers in Interest

Estimate the interest on $8899 at 4% for 1¾ years.

Think, $8899 is almost $9000. 4% of $9000 is $360, which is the interest for one year.

¾ of $360 is $270. $270 + $360 = $630.

The interest for 1¾ years is a little less than $630.

Exercise I			Exercise II		
PRINCIPAL	RATE	TIME	PRINCIPAL	RATE	TIME
1. $1,200	6%	2 yr.	1. $14,000	6%	4 mo.
2. $4,350	5%	1 yr.	2. $2,400	6%	5 mo.
3. $4,200	6%	½ yr.	3. $8,900	4%	1¼ yr.
4. $12,000	5%	½ yr.	4. $9,000	6%	75 da.
5. $8,300	6%	2 mo.	5. $10,000	4%	1½ yr.
6. $7,500	6%	60 da.	6. $16,400	6%	30 da.
7. $10,800	6%	90 da.	7. $3,700	6%	15 da.
8. $14,200	6%	30 da.	8. $7,725	6%	75 da.
9. $11,600	3%	2 mo.	9. $10,650	5%	6 mo.
10. $12,300	3%	60 da.	10. $6,250	5%	3 mo.
11. $6,500	3%	90 da.	11. $1,375	5%	9 mo.
12. $3,200	4%	90 da.	12. $13,265	6%	8 mo.
13. $8,400	4%	9 mo.	13. $3,625	6%	1 yr. 2 mo.
14. $13,500	4%	6 mo.	14. $2,750	4¾%	1 yr.
15. $9,000	4½%	1 yr.	15. $1,575	6%	10 mo.
16. $5,000	5%	2 yr.	16. $8,750	5%	½ yr.
17. $4,250	6%	60 da.	17. $720	6%	60 da.
18. $10,500	3%	90 da.	18. $360	6%	1 yr. 3 mo.
19. $2,500	5%	2 mo.	19. $145	6%	1 yr. 11 mo.

Problems

Find the amount of:

1. $2850 for 6 da. at 6%; for 1 da.; for 10 da.

2. $4815 for 2½ yr. at 4%; at 5%; at 6%.

3. $700 for 30 da. at 6%.

4. $450 for 45 da. at 5%.

5. $1380 for 82 da. at 4½%.

6. $3000 for 2 mo. 20 da. at 6%.

7. $6540 for 1 yr. 15 da. at 5%.

8. $2700 for 1 yr. 2 mo. 12 da. at 4%.

9. $450 for 1 yr. 6 mo. 6 da. at 5½%.

10. $280 for 2 yr. 2 mo. 17 da. at 3%.

11. $519.16 for 173 da. at 5%.

12. $249.83 for 1 yr. 5 mo. 14 da. at 6%.

13. $750 for 2 yr. at 6%.

14. $375 for 1 yr. 6 mo. at 6%.

15. $500 for 2 yr. at 3½%.

16. $625 for 6 mo. at 4%.

17. $342.40 for 1 yr. 3 mo. at 4½%.

18. $279.75 for 1 yr. 2 mo. at 6%.

19. $640 for 1 yr. 9 mo. at 5½%.

20. $2060 for 2 yr. 4 mo. 6 da. at 6%.

21. $3090 from Jan. 5, 1925, to July 17, 1925, at 6%.

22. $2500 from Dec. 31, 1927, to Mar. 1, 1928, at 4%.

23. $250 from July 3, 1927, to Apr. 21, 1929, at 6%.

24. $327 from Mar. 11, 1924, to Feb. 11, 1925, at 5%.

Find the interest and the amount:
First estimate the answers.

1. $900 for 2 years at 6%.

2. $1200 for 5 years at 6%.

3. $1400 for 6 months at 6%.

4. $1800 for 4 months at 6%.

5. $1600 for 3 months at 6%.

6. $2100 for 1 year 4 months at 5%.

7. $240 for 2 years 3 months at 4%.

8. $1500 for 2 years 8 months at 3%.

9. $600 for 2 months at 6%.

10. $36 for 3 years 2 months at 5%.

11. $540 for 2 years 10 months at 4%.

12. $6600 for 10 months at 3%.

13. $4800 for 1 month at 6%.

14. $6000 for 7 months at 5%.

15. $9600 for 11 months at 3%.

16. *Complete the following:*

(a) Money paid for the —— of money is interest.

(b) Money for the use of which interest is paid is the ——.

(c) The sum of the —— and —— is the amount.

(d) The rate of interest is always expressed in ——.

Decide whether true or false:

17. Interest on $600 for 9 months at 4% = $\frac{3}{4}$ of $24.

18. Interest on $450 for 6 months at $4\frac{1}{2}$% = .045 × $450.

19. The interest subtracted from the amount = principal.

20. The interest for one year is found by multiplying the amount by the rate.

21. Add the interest and principal for the amount.

INTEREST

Problems in Interest

Optional

1. If you have three factors given, how do you find the product?

2. What is the interest on $50 at 6% for 2 yr.?

Notice that in this example you have given *three factors.*

The **interest** is the product of three *factors*, the **principal**, the **rate**, and the **time**.
The principal is the *number* of dollars.
The rate is always expressed in *hundredths*.
The time is the *number* of years.

3. If you had given a product and two of three factors, how do you find the other factor?

4. $3 \times 2 \times ? = 24$ 7. $50 \times \frac{6}{100} \times ? = 6$

5. $6 \times ? \times 5 = 90$ 8. $? \times \frac{6}{100} \times 2 = 12$

6. $4 \times ? \times 3 = 48$ 9. $200 \times ? \times 3 = 36$

Find the rate and test your answer :

10. At what rate will $250 yield $50 interest in 4 years?

STATEMENT: $250 \times ? \times 4 = 50.$
SOLUTION: $50 \div (4 \times 250) = .05$ or 5%. *Ans.*

11. What is the rate when the interest of $250 for 4 years is $60?

12. Mr. Sweet received $123.75, which was the interest for 5 years on a debt of $450. What was the rate?

13. If $28.80 is paid for the use of $960 for 6 months, what is the rate per cent?

14. At what rate per cent must $1440 be loaned for 10 months to yield $54?

15. At what rate will $840 amount to $924 in 2 years?

16. At what rate must $2800 be loaned, so that, in 2 years 3 months, it will amount to $3052?

Find the principal and test your answer :

17. What sum will yield $84.60 interest in 3 yr. at 6%?

STATEMENT: ? $\times \frac{6}{100} \times 3 = 84.60$.

SOLUTION: $84.60 \div (3 \times \frac{6}{100}) = 470$. $470. *Ans.*

18. What principal at 6% will gain $60 interest in 4 years?

19. What sum invested at 5% will yield a yearly income of $1000?

20. What principal in 3 yr. 6 mo. at 5% will yield $105?

21. What principal at 6% will amount to $310 in 4 years?

? $\times (\frac{6}{100} \times 4) + \frac{100}{100} = 310$.   ? $\times \frac{124}{100} = 310$. $310 \times \frac{100}{124}$ = $250. *Ans.*

22. What principal at 6% will amount to $515 in 6 months?

23. What sum will yield $220 interest in 2 yr. 9 mo. at 4 per cent?

Find the time and test your answer :

24. How long must $800 be at interest at 4% to yield $48 interest?

STATEMENT: $800 \times \frac{4}{100} \times ? = 48$.

SOLUTION: $48 \div (800 \times \frac{4}{100}) = 1\frac{1}{2}$. 1 yr. 6 mo. *Ans.*

25. In what time will $250 gain $60 interest at 6%?

26. In what time will $400 yield $55 interest at $5\frac{1}{2}$%?

27. The face of a note was $900, the rate of interest 5%, and the interest $67.50. What was the time?

28. In what time will $450 amount to $486 at 4%?

29. In what time will $800 amount to $1600 at 5%?

30. Mr. Tracy received $9.73 interest at $3\frac{1}{2}$% on a loan of $556. What was the time?

31. A note of $1730 drew interest at 6% until the principal and interest amounted to $1885.70. What was the time in years?

1

What is the interest?   (5 min.)

	PRINCIPAL	RATE	TIME		PRINCIPAL	RATE	TIME
1.	$100	4%	1 yr.	6.	$1000	5%	3 yr.
2.	$100	5%	2 yr.	7.	$500	4%	2 yr.
3.	$200	6%	2 yr.	8.	$1000	6%	$\frac{1}{2}$ yr.
4.	$300	6%	2 yr.	9.	$1000	6%	3 mo.
5.	$1000	5%	1 yr.	10.	$2000	4%	1 yr. 3 mo.

2

Give the answers.   (10 min.)

	PRINCIPAL	RATE	TIME	INTEREST	AMOUNT
1.	$1000	6%	1 yr.	?	?
2.	$1000	6%	?	$120	?
3.	$1000	?	3 yr.	$120	?
4.	$2000	?	4 yr.	$200	?
5.	$3000	5%	?	$150	?
6.	$4000	4%	2 yr.	?	?
7.	$4000	?	1 yr.	?	$4120
8.	$4000	?	1 yr.	?	$4240

3

Give the answers.   (10 min.)

	PRINCIPAL	RATE	TIME	INTEREST	AMOUNT
1.	$1000	6%	1$\frac{1}{2}$ yr.	?	?
2.	$1500	5%	2 yr.	?	?
3.	?	6%	1 yr.	$30	?
4.	?	4%	2 yr.	$80	?
5.	?	5%	3 yr.	$300	?
6.	$200	4$\frac{1}{2}$%	1 yr.	?	?
7.	?	?	2 yr.	$100	$1100
8.	?	?	3 yr.	$240	$2240
9.	$300	6%	?	?	$336

4

	Cost	Gain	Selling Price		Cost	Loss	Selling Price
1.	$200	10%	?	**11.**	$400	10%	?
2.	$500	?	$550	**12.**	$600	?	$540
3.	?	10%	$440	**13.**	?	10%	$90
4.	$600	25%	?	**14.**	$880	5%	?
5.	$800	?	$1000	**15.**	$800	?	$700
6.	?	20%	$500	**16.**	?	5%	$950
7.	$460	50%	?	**17.**	$160	$12\frac{1}{2}$%	?
8.	$900	?	$1200	**18.**	?	$12\frac{1}{2}$%	$875
9.	?	50%	$600	**19.**	$1000	20%	?
10.	$660	$33\frac{1}{3}$%	?	**20.**	$1600	?	$1200

Mental Tests

1

1. $\frac{3}{8}$ = what per cent?

2. 35¢ = what per cent of $1?

3. $3\frac{1}{4}$ T. = ? hundredweight.

4. 2 cwt. = what per cent of a ton?

5. Find 6% of $600.

6. 40 sq. rd. = what per cent of an acre?

7. 80% of a ton is how many pounds?

8. 15 is $\frac{3}{4}$ of what number?

9. Cost $80, gain 25%. Find gain.

10. Cost $90, loss $33\frac{1}{3}$%. Find loss.

2

1. Cost $60. Loss 20%. Find selling price.

2. Cost $70. Gain 10%. Find selling price.

3. $\frac{1}{2}$% of 100 = ?

4. 20 = 5% of what number?

5. 4 ounces = ? % of a pound.

6. 36 sq. ft. = ? sq. yd.

7. 4 is what decimal part of 20?

8. 30 is $\frac{1}{6}$ less than what number?

9. Write five thousand four and four hundredths.

10. After deducting 2% commission, how much is left from a sale amounting to $400?

3

1. What is 2% of $1600?

2. How many cubic feet are there in $3\frac{1}{3}$ cu. yd.?

3. $5 is paid for $1000 insurance. What is the rate per cent?

4. What is the cost of 2 lb. 4 oz. of meat at 40¢ per pound?

5. 15 is what per cent of 45?

6. An agent charged $30 for selling $600 worth of produce. What rate of commission did he charge?

7. On a sale of $3000 a commission of 1% is charged. What is the commission?

8. If 2 bbl. of flour cost $23, what will 5 bbl. cost?

9. Change $\frac{2}{5}$ to a decimal.

10. At $.16$\frac{2}{3}$ each, how many day-old chickens can be bought for $10?

4

1. A man lost $\frac{1}{3}$ of his money and had $60 left. How much had he at first?

2. At $3\frac{1}{2}$%, what is the commission on $1000?

3. An agent receives $50 on a sale of $2000. What is the rate of commission?

4. What will 200 feet of lumber cost at $16 per M?

5. Write $\frac{7}{8}$ as per cent.

6. Write $66\frac{2}{3}$% as a fraction.

7. How many tons are there in 40,000 pounds?

8. How many board feet in a plank 20 ft. by 1 ft. by 2 in.?

9. Goods are sold at 110% of the cost. What is the gain per cent?

10. Goods are sold at 95% of the cost. What is the loss per cent?

5

1. A man makes a profit of $20 on goods costing $200. What is his gain per cent?

2. What is the interest on $500 for 2 months at 6%?

3. I borrow $700 for 1 year at 6%. How much must I pay back at the end of the year to settle the debt?

4. A lawyer collected 75% of a debt of $360. How much did he collect?

5. What will 1000 pounds of feed cost at $50 per ton?

6. If 4 pounds of butter cost $2.20 what will 10 pounds cost?

7. Find the interest on $4000 for 3 mo. at 6%.

8. 20% profit is made on an article costing $10. What was the gain?

9. 8 is what per cent of 64?

10. 10 is what decimal part of 20?

6

1. Find the interest on $1200 for 1 yr. 3 mo. at 4%.

2. How many quarts are there in $1\frac{1}{2}$ pk.?

3. What is 50% of half a dollar?

4. What is the interest on $1600 for 8 mo. at 6%?

5. What rate of interest must be charged in order that $1000 shall amount to $1060 in one year?

6. 50 is 20% of what number?

7. For how many years must $100 be at interest at 5% to amount to $120?

8. Find the interest of $150 for 3 yr. at 6%.

9. Find the amount of $300 for 4 years at 5%.

10. $5 \div .5 = ?$

Review Tests in Interest

What is the interest on $4000 for 1 year at

1. 6%	**3.** 4%	**5.** $3\frac{1}{2}$%	**7.** $5\frac{1}{2}$%	**9.** $7\frac{1}{4}$%
2. 3%	**4.** 5%	**6.** $4\frac{1}{2}$%	**8.** 8%	**10.** $4\frac{1}{4}$%

I.

Find the interest :

First estimate the answers.

1. On $8000 for 3 years at 6%.
2. On $6000 for 5 months at 6%.
3. On $4500 for 7 months at 6%.
4. On $10,000 for 90 days at 6%.
5. On $7500 from May 21, 1919, to May 21, 1920 at 4%.
6. On $3000 for 9 months at 4%.
7. On $1800 for 90 days at 6%.
8. On $5000 for 30 days at 6%.
9. On $2000 for $1\frac{1}{2}$ years at 3%.
10. On $4000 for 1 year 2 months at 6%.

II.

Find the amount :

1. Of $7350 for 14 months at 6%.
2. Of $640 for 90 days at 6%.
3. Of $9365 for 1 year at $4\frac{1}{2}$%.
4. Of $980 for 60 days at 6%.
5. Of $10,600 for 4 months at 3%.
6. Of $8700 for 3 months at 4%.
7. Of $6930 for 9 months at 4%.
8. Of $1350 for 11 months at 5%.
9. Of $8756 for 6 months at $5\frac{3}{4}$%.
10. Of $11,000 from March 13, 1926, to Dec. 13, 1926.

III.

For how long a time must:

1. $3000 be at interest at 6% to produce $36 interest?

2. $7000 be at interest at 4% to produce $420.00 interest?

3. $5000 be at interest at 5% to produce $312.50 interest?

4. $9000 be at interest at $4\frac{1}{2}$% to produce $202.50 interest?

5. $400 be at interest at 6% to produce $4 interest?

6. $8000 be at interest at $5\frac{1}{2}$% to produce $330.00 interest?

7. $2500 be at interest at 6% to produce $100.00 interest?

8. $1850 be at interest at 6% to produce $74.00 interest?

9. $4900 be at interest at 6% to produce $171.50 interest?

10. $1575 be at interest at 6% to produce $1590.75 interest?

IV.

Find the rate when :

1. $9000 earns $270 interest in 6 months.

2. $11,000 earns $110 interest in 4 months.

3. $16,000 earns $160 in 2 months.

4. $1400 earns $126 interest in 2 years.

5. $2300 earns $63.25 interest in 6 months.

6. $900 earns $9 interest in 90 days.

7. $6450 earns $32.25 interest in 30 days.

8. $8000 earns $170 interest in 6 months.

9. $12,000 earns $172.50 interest in 3 months.

10. $1800 earns $99 interest in 11 months.

V.

1. Find the interest on $13,500 for 15 days at 6%.

2. What is the amount of $12,000 at 4% for $2\frac{1}{2}$ years?

3. At what rate must $700 be at interest for 8 years to amount to $721?

4. For how long is $1100 at interest at 6% when it amounts to $1133?

5. Find the sum of money which will amount to $2120 when placed at interest at 6% for 1 year.

VI.

Find the principal when it amounts to:

1. $4,360 in $1\frac{1}{2}$ years at 6%.

2. $6,180 in 9 months at 4%.

3. $5,691 in 10 months at 6%.

4. $9,856.80 in 2 years at $5\frac{1}{2}$%.

5. $3,529.20 in 8 months at 3%.

6. $8,281.20 in 30 days at 6%.

7. $6,496.00 in 90 days at 6%.

8. $8,064.85 in 60 days at 6%.

9. $17,200 in 1 year 3 months at 6%.

10. $924 in 2 years 7 months at 6%.

Complete the following:

To find the interest on any sum of money at 6% for 60 days, take —— of the principal.

To find the interest on any sum of money at any rate for 1 year take —— of the principal.

REVIEW OF PRINCIPLES AND PROCESSES

1. The product of two or more numbers is found by what operation?

2. Given a product and one factor. By what operation is the other factor found?

3. State two tests for examples in subtraction.

4. The product of three factors contains five decimal places. One of the factors has three decimal places and another two. How many decimal places has the third factor?

5. How can you tell whether or not a number is divisible by (a) 2, (b) 3, (c) 4, (d) 5, (e) 8, (f) 10, (g) 9?

6. The sum of the digits in a number is 27. What numbers will divide it?

7. The sum of the digits in a number is 18 and the figure in units' place is 6. What numbers will divide it?

8. The figure in units' place in a given number is 7. What kind of numbers will not divide the given number?

9. Name a number that has no factor but itself and one. What kind of number is it?

10. Two of the three factors of a number being given, how may the remaining factor be found?

11. Moving the decimal point two places to the right has what effect on the value of the number?

12. Moving the decimal point three places to the left has what effect on the value of the number?

13. Annexing a zero to an integer has what effect on its value? Why?

14. Annexing a zero to a decimal has what effect on its value? Why?

Promissory Notes

If a merchant should wish to enlarge his business, so that he could carry a stock of goods worth much more than he has ready money to pay for, he might borrow additional money for a specified time, giving his note in payment. Such a note is called a **promissory note**, because it is a *promise* to pay the amount of the note.

A farmer sometimes wishes to buy stock or machinery for his farm, or to use money in paying for labor and other expenses while his crops are growing. At such times he may borrow the money to use in these ways, giving his note payable at a certain time in the future, or he may give his note directly in payment for the things which he buys. When a note is so given, the maker usually agrees to pay interest on the sum named in the note.

Sometimes people are induced to borrow money from so-called brokers, pledging their future earnings, and making payments weekly or monthly. These brokers often arrange the matter so that the borrower really pays an exorbitant rate of interest, while the plan appears on the surface to be very fair.

The wisest plan in management of living expenses is to pay as you go, saving a part of your income regularly, and depositing it in a savings bank or other well-conducted savings institution, thus becoming a creditor instead of a debtor. There are, however, many circumstances under which the borrowing of money is a good business policy. Can you think of some of them? Would it ever be wise for a salaried man to borrow money with which to buy a pleasure automobile? Can you think of circumstances under which it would be wise for a building contractor to borrow money?

Promissory Notes

A written promise made by one party to pay a specified sum of money to another party at a certain time is a **promissory note**.

The party who makes the promise is the **maker** of the note.

The party to whom the money is promised to be paid is the **payee** of the note.

The party who owns a note is the **holder**.

The sum promised to be paid, not including interest, is the **face** of the note.

Note 1

$800 $\frac{no}{100}$ *Albany, N. Y., Nov. 21, 1925.*

.........*Ninety days*.........*after date,.....I.....promise to pay*

to the order of .... *C. R. Clark* ....

Eight hundred and $\frac{no}{100}$ ~~~~~~~~~~~~~~~~*Dollars*

With interest. Value received.

                                        George W. Martin

---

1. Who is the maker of this note?

2. What is the face of the note?

3. Name the payee of the note.

4. Write a note for $25, made payable thirty days after to-day to your father. Sign the note.

5. Name the payee, maker and face of this note.

A note in which the maker promises to pay interest is an **interest-bearing** note.

When the rate of interest is not stated the note bears interest at the **legal rate** of 6%.

An **indorsement** is a name or a statement written on the back of a note.

The party who indorses a note is called an **indorser**.

A person indorses a note in **blank** by merely writing his name across the back of it.

A person indorses a note in **full** by writing " Pay to the order of .... " (the name of the person to whom the note is transferred) and signing his name below.

The party to whose order a note is made payable by the indorsement is called the **indorsee**.

Note 1

Pay to the order of
Citizens National Bank.
C. R. Clark.

1. Who is the indorsee on this note?

2. Name the indorser.

3. Is this note indorsed in full or in blank?

4. Indorse in blank the note you made payable to your father.

A note is **negotiable** when it is made payable to

(*a*) the order of the payee

(*b*) the payee or bearer

(*c*) the bearer

A note is **non-negotiable** when it is drawn payable only to the payee.

A negotiable note may be transferred from one party to another.

A non-negotiable note may not be transferred.

Note 2

$1000 $\frac{no}{100}$ *Binghamton, N. Y., Nov. 19, 1925.*

........Sixty days........after date,....I....promise to pay

to the order of .... D. J. Moon ....

One thousand and $\frac{no}{100}$ ....Dollars

Value received.

Justin Matthews.

1. Is **note 1** negotiable or non-negotiable?

2. To whom was **note 1** transferred?

3. Rewrite **note 2** so that it shall be non-negotiable.

4. Is **note 2** an interest-bearing or a non-interest-bearing note?

5. What must be added to this note to make it interest-bearing?

6. Who is the holder of **note 2**?

An indorser of a negotiable note, by his act of indorsement, agrees to pay the note when due if the maker fails to pay it.

1. Suppose in the case of **note 1** George W. Martin fails to pay the note when due, who is holding for the face of the note?

2. To whom would this money be paid?

An indorser may avoid the liability for the payment of the note by writing the words " *Without recourse* " above his signature.

Note 2

Without Recourse.
D. J. Moon

When the payee of a negotiable note transfers the note he must indorse it in order to make it payable to the new holder.

3. Is **note 2** indorsed in blank or in full?

When a note is indorsed in blank it becomes payable to the holder, whoever he may be, and can be transferred again without further indorsement.

4. Write an indorsement of **note 2** which would make it payable to you.

The day on which a note becomes due, or payable, is the **day of maturity**.

A note payable on demand of the holder is a **demand note**.

Notes are usually made for thirty, sixty or ninety days.

When the maker of a note fails to pay the note on the day of maturity, it is the duty of the holder to notify the indorsers of that fact. If he is not notified within a reasonable time, he is freed from the liability for its payment.

Note 3

$3000 $\frac{no}{100}$ *Buffalo, N.Y., Dec. 1, 1925.*

......*On demand I........promise to pay....C. J. Fuller*

or order..........Three thousand and $\frac{no}{100}$..........Dollars,

for value received, with interest.

                              E. C. Wood.

---

1. What is the date of maturity for **note 1**? **Note 2?** Note 3?

2. Write an interest-bearing non-negotiable note for $500, payable to your teacher on demand.

3. Name the holder of this note. Who is the payee?

4. Write a negotiable interest-bearing note, payable thirty days after date to your mother.

5. Write the proper indorsement on the back transferring this note to your father.

Computing Interest on Notes

An interest-bearing note bears interest from the day of date to the day of payment.

The face of the note is the **principal**.

The sum of the principal and interest is the **amount**.

A non-interest-bearing note, if not paid at maturity, bears interest from the day of maturity until paid at the legal rate of interest.

Frequently the maker of a note makes payments on the note at different times. These payments are credited on the back of the note.

Note 3

```
Received on this
  within note,

Feb. 1, 1926 $30
Apr. 1, 1926 $1030.
June 1, 1926 $20.
```

1. What is the interest on the face of **note 3** for two months at 6%?

2. What is the value of **note 2** at maturity? Of **note 1**?

3. Find the amount at maturity of a thirty-day interest-bearing note.

4. A ninety-day note for $4300 with interest at 6% is paid in full at maturity. What was the value of the note?

5. Find the amount due on **note 3**, August 1, 1926.

$250　　　　　　　　　*Troy, N. Y., August 22, 1927*

　　　　Six months after date I promise to pay

----------------*James N. Day*-----------------------

Two hundred fifty~~~~~~~~~~~~~~~~~~~~~~~~~~~~~~~~~*Dollars*

Value received

　　　　　　　　　　　-------*U. G. Warren*--------

What kind of a note is the above?

The following are the date, face, time, and rate of several notes. Write the note for each, supplying the names of the maker and payee, and find the amount, due at maturity.

	Date	Face	Time	Rate
1.	Aug. 22, 1925	$450	1 yr. 6 mo.	6%
2.	May 1, 1927	$1200	3 mo.	5%
3.	Oct. 5, 1928	$526	1 yr. 4 mo.	6%
4.	Dec. 12, 1926	$4500	90 da.	4%
5.	March 9, 1925	$780	2 mo.	5%
6.	June 1, 1928	$640	30 da.	6%
7.	Jan. 4, 1927	$1000	60 da.	6%

8. Write a negotiable note of $100 for 3 months. Indorse it as payee, so that you cannot be held for the payment. Find the amount at maturity with interest at 6%.

9. Mr. Amos Coe owes you $200, payable in 90 days at 6%. He gives you his note for it, which you immediately indorse so that any holder may collect it when due. Write the note, indorse it, and compute the amount due at maturity.

Banks and Banking

There are many kinds of banking institutions, but most of them may be included in three general divisions; viz. savings banks, banks of deposit, and trust companies.

Savings banks are designed to be safe places of deposit for money where it may earn a moderate rate of interest.

In order that the money of depositors may be safeguarded, savings banks are generally forbidden by law to make loans unless secured by mortgages on real estate, or to make investments, except in government bonds, the bonds of certain states and cities, and some other kinds of property specially designated by the savings bank law.

Banks of deposit, otherwise known as commercial banks, or banks of discount, transact a much wider range of business than do savings banks.

They may loan money on notes, collect accounts and notes for customers, issue bills of exchange and letters of credit, and make many kinds of investments which savings banks are not permitted to make. As a rule they pay no interest on active checking accounts, but the services they render to customers are considered sufficient compensation for use of the money on deposit in such accounts.

Banks of deposit which are organized under Federal laws and are under the supervision of the United States government are known as **national banks**; those that are organized according to state laws and are under the supervision of state authorities are generally known as **state banks**, though each individual bank adopts its own name.

Name the kinds of banks mentioned on this page.

Which of these banks is supervised by the national government?

Can a savings bank loan money on notes?

State and national banks transact in general the same kinds of business; but national banks also perform a special function in connection with the issuance of paper money, which will be considered later.

Trust companies are similar in some respects to savings banks, and in other respects to banks of deposit.

They resemble savings banks in paying interest on deposits. They are generally not allowed to loan money on notes, except when secured by collateral, *i.e.* some specific piece of property, put into the hands of the trust company to be sold by the company if the note is not paid when due.

Otherwise they are much like banks of deposit, having in some respects even greater latitude in the kinds of business which they may transact.

Depositing and Withdrawing Money

DEPOSIT SLIP

CORN EXCHANGE NATIONAL BANK OF CLEVELAND		
Deposited to the Credit of		
Gerald W. Porter		
Cleveland, *Apr.* 28 1926		
	DOLLARS	CTS.
CURRENCY,	*125*	
GOLD,		
SILVER,	*18*	*75*
CHECKS,		
Bank of Cleveland,	*38*	*70*
,, ,, Buffalo,	*183*	*40*
AMOUNT,	*365*	*85*

A depositor in a savings bank takes his book with him whenever he deposits or withdraws money. To deposit money he merely hands it to the receiving teller, who credits in the bank book the amount of the deposit. To withdraw money, he hands his book to the paying teller, and signs a receipt for the money to be withdrawn. The teller charges in the bank book the amount withdrawn and pays it to the depositor.

In depositing money in any other bank than a savings bank, the depositor fills out a deposit slip stating in separate items the amount of paper money, of gold, of silver, and of checks which he deposits. This slip is handed in with the money and checks deposited, and is used by the teller in making up his balance at the close of the day's business.

Withdrawals from a bank of deposit are made by means of checks.

A **check** *is a written order, signed by a depositor, directing the bank to pay to a certain person, or to his order, or to the bearer, a specified sum of money.*

When the bank pays the sum directed to be paid, it charges the depositor's account with the amount.

	DOLLARS	CENTS
No. 235 $29 30/100		
June 12, 1927		
To A. L. Forbes		
For Services		
Bal. brn't for'd	279	38
Am't deposited	100	00
Total	379	38
Am't this Check	29	30
Bal. car'd for'd	350	08

No. 235

CLEVELAND, OHIO, *June 12,* 1927

THE CORN EXCHANGE NATIONAL BANK

PAY TO THE ORDER OF   *A. L. Forbes* $29 30/100

Twenty-nine and 30/100 ~~~~DOLLARS

F. M. March

STUB   CHECK

Bring to the class sample checks with stubs. In the above check which party is A. L. Forbes? Which party is F. M. March?

The amount named in a check is called the **face.**

The depositor who signs a check is called the **drawer** *of the check.*

The person to whom, or to whose order, a check is made payable is called the **payee.**

The bank on which a check is drawn is called the **drawee.**

Every depositor in a bank of deposit receives from the bank a **check book,** which consists of blank checks bound together, each check attached to a stub as shown on page 139. When a check is filled out, the stub is filled out to agree with it, and the check is then torn off, through the perforated line. When all the checks have been used, there remains a book of stubs containing a record of all the checks, the number of each check, its date, its face, the name of the payee, and the purpose for which it was used.

Checks are convenient in paying bills; for by means of them the depositor may avoid carrying or sending money. To illustrate, let us suppose that Mr. A, a merchant in Cleveland, buys a bill of goods from Mr. B, in Chicago. A fills out a check payable to B's order and mails it to B. B indorses the check, deposits it in his own bank at Chicago, and it is credited to his account. The banks attend to the rest of the business. The check is finally returned to A's bank in Cleveland, and the amount is charged to A's account, and credited to the account of B's bank in Chicago.

Most banks make a practice of returning all checks to depositors. These checks, being indorsed in each case by the payee, serve as receipts for the amounts paid.

A Comparison of Notes and Checks

1. A note is a *promise* to pay money, while a check is an *order* to pay money.

2. A check always has *three* parties, while a note may have only *two*.

3. A check, like a note, may be *negotiable* or *non-negotiable,* according to the manner in which it is drawn.

4. A negotiable check may be *transferred by indorsement* in the same manner as a note, and the indorser is liable for its payment if it is not paid by the maker or drawee.

5. The different forms of indorsement have the same force when made on a check as when made on a note.

6. A note may draw interest, but a check does not.

Name each of the parties to the check on page 139. Is the check negotiable? How must a check be worded, to be negotiable?

Savings Bank Accounts

Savings banks usually pay interest semi-annually or quarterly. The interest is computed upon the *even dollars* of the smallest balance during the interest period. The interest is usually credited as shown in the specimen account which follows. In this account the interest is at 4%, paid semi-annually. Inasmuch as each principal includes the preceding interest, savings banks are said to pay compound interest.

DATE		WITHDRAWN		DEPOSITED		BALANCE	
1925							
Jan.	1			14	00	14	00
June	11			10	00	24	00
July	1	Interest			28	24	28
Sept.	10	15	00			9	28
Oct.	1			22	55	31	83
Dec.	10	20	00			11	83
1926							
Jan.	1	Interest			18	12	01

NOTE. — In computing the interest July 1, the smallest balance of the preceding period is taken. It is that of Jan 1, 1925, or $14.00. At 4% per annum the rate for 6 mo. is 2%. 2% of $14.00 is 28 cents. The smallest balance in the period preceding Jan. 1, 1926, was that of Sept. 10, 1925, — $9.28. 2% of $9 (neglecting the cents) is 18 cents, the interest.

1. Fill in the interest item at 4% per annum, payable semi-annually, and find what the balance will be July 1.

DATE		WITHDRAWN		DEPOSITED		BALANCE	
1927							
Feb.	10			92	00	?	
April	1			64	00	?	
July	1	Interest		?		?	

Supply the entries indicated by x and find the balance at the last date given : (In each of the exercises 2 and 3 the interest is to be reckoned at 4% per annum, payable semi-annually.)

2.

Date		Withdrawn		Deposited		Balance	
1926							
Jan.	20			800	00	*x*	
April	1	75				*x*	
July	1	*Interest*		*x*		*x*	
Aug.	10	80				*x*	
Oct.	5			100	00	*x*	
1927							
Jan.	1	*Interest*		*x*		*x*	

3.

Date		Withdrawn		Deposited		Balance	
1928							
Jan.	1			93	75	*x*	
April	10	61	52			*x*	
May	5			17	00	*x*	
July	1	*Interest*			*x*	*x*	
Nov.	10			9	25	*x*	
Dec.	10	20	00			*x*	
1929							
Jan.	1	*Interest*			*x*	*x*	

4. Fred Jones started a savings bank account May 10, 1927, depositing $18. He was credited with interest July 1, deposited $12 Sept. 9, $4 Oct. 22, $13 Dec. 21, and $3 Dec. 29. How much was his balance Jan. 1, 1928, including the interest due him? Reckon interest at 4%.

5. Henry Ray's savings account began Jan. 1, 1924, with $5. He deposited $5 a month on the 10th day of each month. Interest at 4% per annum was credited to him Apr. 1, July 1, Oct. 1, and Jan. 1, 1925. What was his balance Jan. 1, 1925?

Bank Discount

A note that is payable to or at a bank is a **bank note.**

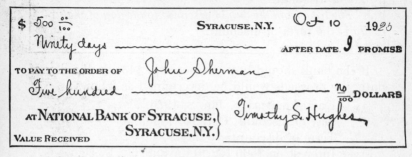

$ 500 $\frac{00}{100}$ SYRACUSE, N.Y.   Oct 10   192б

Ninety days ———————————— AFTER DATE I PROMISE

TO PAY TO THE ORDER OF   John Sherman

Five hundred ————————————— $\frac{no}{100}$ DOLLARS

AT NATIONAL BANK OF SYRACUSE,}   Timothy S. Hughes
VALUE RECEIVED   SYRACUSE, N.Y.}

A bank comes into possession of notes in two ways:

a. It may lend money directly to the maker and take his note, or,

Indorsements

Pay to the order of Charles Gibbs.

John Sherman

Charles Gibbs.

b. The note may be drawn payable to another party and be bought by the bank, or deposited in the bank for collection.

Either of these ways is equivalent to a purchase of the note by the bank. When a bank thus buys a note, it pays less than the maturity value; hence the transaction is called **discounting** the note.

> *The sum deducted from the maturity value of a note in determining the price to be paid for the note by a bank* is called the **bank discount.**
>
> *The sum paid for a note by a bank, or the difference between the maturity value and the bank discount,* is called the **proceeds** *of the note.*

The day on which a note is discounted is called the **day of discount.**

The time from the day of discount to the day of maturity is the **term of discount.**

If the bank should buy the note (p. 143) on the day of date, the proceeds would be determined as follows:

Day of maturity, Jan. 8, 1926.
Day of discount, Oct. 10, 1925.
Term of discount, 90 days.
Interest on $500 for 90 days at 6%, $7.50.
$500 − $7.50 = $492.50. *Proceeds.*

If the bank should buy the note Nov. 19, the proceeds would be determined as follows:

Day of maturity, Jan. 8, 1926.
Day of discount, Nov. 19, 1925.
Term of discount (Nov. 19, 1925, to Jan. 8, 1926), 50 days.
Interest on $500 for 50 days at 6%, $4.17.
$500 − $4.17 = $495.83. *Proceeds.*

Rule for Finding the Bank Discount and Proceeds:

1. *Find the amount due at maturity. This is the maturity value.*

2. *Find the time from the day of discount to the day of maturity. This is the term of discount.*

3. *Find the interest on the maturity value for the term of discount. This is the bank discount.*

4. *Subtract the bank discount from the maturity value to find the proceeds.*

When the time mentioned in a note is given in months, calendar months are understood. For example, a note dated July 12, payable three months after date, is due Oct. 12, or 92 days after date.

In most states, notes falling due on Sunday or a legal holiday are payable on the next business day and interest and discount are reckoned to that day.

1. How is the maturity value of an interest-bearing note found?

2. How does the maturity value of an interest-bearing note compare with the face of the note?

3. How does the maturity value of a non-interest-bearing note compare with the face of the note, if paid when due?

4. A 30-day note is dated Jan. 15. What is the day of maturity?

5. A 60-day note was dated Feb. 20, 1926. When did it mature?

6. Mr. Field, wishing to borrow from a bank, signed a 60-day bank note for $100 without interest, dated Sept. 11, 1927. What was the date of maturity? How much was due at maturity? If Mr. Field had his note discounted on the day of date, what was the term of discount? What was the discount, the legal rate being 6%?

7. A note for $400, bearing interest at 6%, dated Jan. 1, 1924, and due in 90 days, was discounted on the day of date. What was the maturity value? On what sum was the discount computed?

8. Mr. Brown bought a horse from Mr. Martin, giving in payment a bank note for $200 without interest, dated July 9, 1924, payable 90 days from date. On the 8th day of August, Mr. Martin indorsed the note and deposited it in the bank, receiving credit for the proceeds. What was the day of maturity; the day of discount; the term of discount; the bank discount at 6%? How much was credited to Mr. Martin's account?

9. A bank note for $500, without interest, due in 90 days, dated May 7, 1925, was discounted June 6, 1925. What were the proceeds, money being worth 6%?

10. A man gave his note for $720 for 90 days without interest. What was it worth the day it was made at a bank where the discount rate was 6%?

11. How much can I borrow from a bank by giving my 60-day note for $650 without interest, if the bank gives me a discount rate of 6%?

12. A merchant bought a piano for $400 cash and sold it the same day, taking in payment a 90-day bank note for $500, which he immediately indorsed and deposited in his bank, receiving credit for the proceeds at a discount rate of 6% per annum. What was his profit on the piano?

13. The following note was discounted at the rate of $4\frac{1}{2}$% per annum on the 21st day of January, 1925. What were the proceeds?

$9600   NEW YORK, December 7, 1924.

Ninety days after date I promise to pay to the order of the New York National Exchange Bank nine thousand six hundred dollars.

Value received.   CHARLES H. REDMOND.

14. What were the proceeds of a note for $300 without interest, due Jan. 7, 1926, and discounted Nov. 15, 1925, the discount rate being 6%?

15. What are the proceeds of a six-months note for $800, without interest, dated May 7, 1929, and discounted Oct. 15, 1929, at the rate of 6% per annum?

16. A man in Geneva accepted a 30-day note for $975, without interest, in payment for furniture. Nine days later he had the note discounted at the rate of 6% per annum. What did he receive for it?

17. A 90-day note for $1000 without interest was discounted at 6% on the day of date. What were the proceeds?

18. On March 1, 1925, Edward F. Jones gave John Ethridge his note for $800 for one year with interest at 6%, payable at the Corn Exchange Bank. On January 1, 1926, Mr. Ethridge had the note discounted at 6% per annum. How much did he receive for it?

Protesting Notes, Checks, and Drafts

If a bank note, check, or draft is not paid at the time specified, a notice similar to the following is sent to each of the indorsers. This is called a *notice of protest*, and sending it is called *protesting* the note, check, or draft. If the notice of protest is not sent, the indorsers are released from liability to pay.

SIR: SYRACUSE, N. Y., *Jan. 8,* 1925

PLEASED TO TAKE NOTICE THAT A *note* MADE BY *Timothy L. Hughes* DATED *Oct. 10,* 1925, FOR $*500* AND INDORSED BY YOU, WAS THIS DAY PROTESTED FOR NON-PAYMENT, AND THAT THE HOLDERS LOOK TO YOU FOR THE PAYMENT THEREOF, PAYMENT HAVING BEEN DEMANDED AND REFUSED.

YOURS RESPECTFULLY,

F. L. BARNES,

TO *Charles Gibbs*   NOTARY PUBLIC.

Sending Money by Draft

Probably the most convenient means of remitting money, or its equivalent, from one place to another is by personal bank checks. This is the method commonly employed by business men.

One who keeps no checking account at a bank must use some other method. One of the commonest of these, especially for large sums, is that of the **bank draft**, which is as follows:

Let us suppose that Henry L. Fowler, in Salt Lake City, desires to send to Charles Bryant, at Portland, Me., $100. He goes to the State Bank of Utah, in Salt Lake City, and says to the teller, "I wish to buy a New York draft for $100, payable to the order of Henry L. Fowler." The teller then fills out and hands to Mr. Fowler the draft (page 149), for which Mr. Fowler pays $100 plus a small fee to pay the bank for its services. This fee is called the **exchange**. The exchange is sometimes computed at a certain per cent of the face of the draft. It seldom exceeds $\frac{1}{4}\%$.

Banks often sell drafts to their *depositors* and *customers* with no charge for exchange.

Mr. Fowler indorses the draft as indicated on page 149, incloses it with a letter, and mails it to Mr. Bryant, who takes it to a bank in Portland, indorses it in blank, and receives $100 for it. The transaction is complete so far as Mr. Fowler and Mr. Bryant are concerned.

Let us now study the transaction between the banks. Every bank of importance has money on deposit in some bank, called its **correspondent**, in one or more of the great money centers of the country.

The National Park Bank is the correspondent of the State Bank of Utah. The bank which cashes the draft for Mr. Bryant in Portland charges $100 to its correspondent in New York and sends the draft to its correspondent. The correspondent presents the draft to the National Park Bank (through the clearing-house), which pays $100 and charges the amount to the State Bank of Utah.

Each of the banks has now received and paid out $100 in cash or credit; Mr. Fowler, in Salt Lake City, has paid out $100, and Mr. Bryant, in Portland, has received $100; and yet no money has actually been transferred from one city to the other.

A **bank draft** *is an order made by a bank in one place, directing a bank in a different place, with which the drawer has funds on deposit, to pay a specified sum of money to some person, or to his order, or to the bearer.*

The party who draws a draft is the **drawer**; *the party to whom the order is addressed is the* **drawee**; *the party to whom a draft is payable is the* **payee**; *the* **face** *of a draft is the sum ordered to be paid.*

The State Bank of Utah No. 94397

$100 ☆   *Salt Lake City*, ___ AUG 28 1927

Pay to the order of *Henry L. Fowler* $100 ⁰⁰/₁₀₀

One hundred ──ᴺᴼ/₁₀₀ ──── Dollars

to **THE NATIONAL PARK BANK,** NEW YORK CITY. N. Y. }   *Henry T. McEwan*   Ass't Cashier

A BANK DRAFT

Indorsement

Pay to the order of Charles Bryant Henry L. Fowler

In the draft given above, the drawer is the State Bank of Utah, of which Henry T. McEwan is assistant cashier; the drawee is the National Park Bank of New York, and the payee is Henry L. Fowler. The face of the draft is $100.

Observe that a bank draft is like an ordinary check, except that both the drawer and the drawee are banks, and that their places of business are in different cities or villages. A bank draft is sometimes called a *bank check*, because, like an ordinary check, it is an order drawn by one party upon another party, with whom the first party has funds deposited.

In New York, and every other large city, many checks and drafts are received by one bank, payable by other banks in the city. For the sake of convenience, all these checks and drafts are sent by the different banks to one place, called the **clearing-house**, where they are classified and sent to the banks to which they should go, and balances are settled.

Making payments by means of drafts or money orders is **exchange**. It is really an *exchange of credits*.

Exchange between places in the same country is **domestic exchange**. *Exchange between places in different countries is* **foreign exchange**.

It sometimes happens that banks in one city have large sums on deposit with banks in another city, and need currency for immediate use. They may then sell drafts at a discount from their face value in order to get the money at once. When the balance is against them, they may sell drafts at a premium, which is a certain per cent above their face value.

1. Mr. William Harris, in South Bend, Ind., desires to send $200 to his nephew Arthur Otis, who is in college in New Haven, Conn. How much will a New York draft for that sum cost, if the exchange is $\frac{1}{10}\%$?

2. The banks making the above exchange are the Farmers' Bank of South Bend and its correspondent, the Marine Bank of New York, the Exchange National Bank of New Haven and its correspondent, the Industrial Bank of New York. Describe the entire transaction.

3. Write the draft and indorse it properly.

4. Milwaukee banks have small balances in New York banks. They are selling New York exchange at $\frac{1}{4}\%$ premium. What is the exchange on a New York draft for $7500?

5. The exchange on a draft sold to Cyrus Johnson by the Northeastern Bank of Milwaukee was $20.50. What was the face of the draft, the exchange rate being $\frac{1}{4}\%$?

STATEMENT: $\frac{1}{4}\%$ of —— = $20.50.

6. Write the draft in question 5, making the Traders' Bank of New York the drawee.

7. What is the rate of exchange when a draft for $7500 costs $7505?

STATEMENT: —— % of $7500 = $5.

8. The discount on a draft for $8400 is $7. What is the rate of discount?

STATEMENT: —— % of $8400 = $7.

9. When money was scarce in San Francisco, and large balances were held in Chicago, a man in San Francisco bought a Chicago draft of $12,800, paying $12,784 for it. At what rate of discount did he buy the draft?

Sending Money by Postal Money Order

A POSTAL MONEY ORDER

These orders may be purchased at any **post office** or from any R. F. D. postman. The purchaser incloses the order in an envelope, and mails it to the payee named in the order, who may have it cashed *at any money order post office.*

The following table shows the fees that must be paid, in addition to the face, for postal money orders payable in the United States:

FACE	FEE	FACE	FEE
$ 2.50 or less	5¢	$20.01 to $ 40.00	15¢
$ 2.51 to $ 5.00	7¢	$40.01 to $ 60.00	18¢
$ 5.01 to $10.00	10¢	$60.01 to $ 80.00	20¢
$10.01 to $20.00	12¢	$80.01 to $100.00	22¢

Find the total cost of a postal money order for —

1. $3.00	**4.** $43.25	**7.** $86.31	**10.** $28.98
2. $4.28	**5.** $89.41	**8.** $72.05	**11.** $90.89
3. $1.75	**6.** $99.99	**9.** $50.10	**12.** $88.95

Express Money Orders

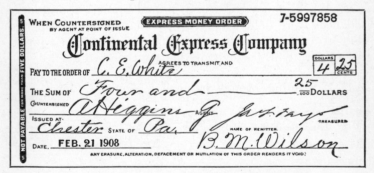

An express money order is **negotiable** *and can be transferred by indorsement, like a check or bank draft.*

An express money order, issued by any express company, will be cashed for its full face value at any of the company's offices in this country, or by any other express company, or by any bank.

The fee is the same as that for issuing a postal money order for the same amount. It is called the **exchange** for issuing the order.

Make and solve three problems about express money orders.

Telegraph Money Orders

Sending money by **telegraph money order**, being expensive, is used only in emergencies, where haste is necessary.

The person desiring to remit money goes to the telegraph office and pays the money. A message is then sent directing the telegraph office, at the place where the money is wanted, to pay the amount to the person designated. Before receiving the money, that person must satisfy the telegraph company's agent that he is the one to whom the money is directed to be paid. The present rate for telegraph money orders is the cost of a 15-word message, with these additions:

For not more than $25	25¢
Over $25 but not over $50	35¢
Over $50 but not over $75	60¢
Over $75 but not over $100	85¢
Over $100 but not over $200	$1.10 etc.

Find the cost:

1. In Syracuse, N. Y., of a telegraph money order for $75, payable in Atlanta, Ga., the cost of a 15-word message being 75¢.

2. In Scranton, Pa., of a telegraph money order for $45, payable in San Francisco, the rate for a 15-word message being $1.30.

3. In Utica of a telegraph money order for $100, payable in Harrisburg, Pa., the rate for a 15-word message being 60¢.

Find the cost of telegraph money orders, using the following data:

	AMT.	15-WORD RATE		AMT.	15-WORD RATE
4.	$21	40¢	**8.**	$39	60¢
5.	$80	30¢	**9.**	$115	70¢
6.	$96	50¢	**10.**	$90	80¢
7.	$170	60¢	**11.**	$65	70¢

Commercial Drafts

Drafts are frequently used as a means of collecting bills. For example, Horace Prang of Columbus, O., owes Loetzer & Co. of Buffalo, an account of $500, payable Aug. 26, 1919. Loetzer & Co. make out the following:

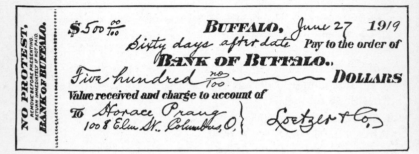

Loetzer & Co. deposit this draft in the Bank of Buffalo, which sends it to some bank in Columbus. This bank presents the draft to Horace Prang, who, if he is willing, writes in red ink across its face, "Accepted, July 1, 1919" (if that is the day on which it is presented) and signs his name. The draft is now equivalent to Mr. Prang's bank note, payable Aug. 26, indorsed by Loetzer & Co. It is returned to the Bank of Buffalo, which will discount it at once, if Loetzer & Co. are customers in good standing, and credit them with the proceeds, less a small fee for collection.

If the draft were an order to pay "sixty days after *sight*," and accepted by Mr. Prang, he would be entitled to sixty days, after its presentation and acceptance, before paying it. If not paid then, it would be protested, like a bank note.

Shippers often use commercial drafts as a means of collecting payment for goods on delivery, or of securing promise of payment at a specified time.

> *When the drawee has accepted a draft*, he is called the **acceptor** *and the draft* is called an **acceptance**.

> *A draft payable at sight* (*i.e.* at the time of presentation) is called a **sight draft**; *a draft payable at a specified time after sight* or *after date* is called a **time draft**.

A sight draft may be accepted *payable a certain time after date of acceptance*. It then has the force of a *note* and may be discounted and collected like a time draft or a promissory note payable at a bank.

The *discount* on a time draft, and the *cost of collection*, called the *exchange*, of *any* draft are computed on the *face of the draft*.

1. The Empire Elevator Co. drew on the Smith Milling Co. for $600. What was the exchange at $\frac{1}{12}$%?

2. A bill of $800 was collected by means of a sight draft. What was the cost of collection, the exchange rate being $\frac{1}{4}$%?

3. How much did a creditor receive who drew on his debtor for $1000, paying $\frac{1}{4}$% for collecting?

4. A wholesale grain merchant desires to ship a carload of corn to a customer in another city, and desires to use a commercial draft to secure payment for the corn before it is unloaded from the car. Can you find out from some merchant or banker how this may be done?

Written

5. A man drew on his debtor, through his bank, for $2100. The draft was accepted at 60 days. The bank deducted interest at 6% for 60 days, charged $2.10 for its services, and credited the balance on the man's account. How much was credited?

6. A bank charged $\frac{1}{20}$% for collecting a bill of $2640. What was the exchange?

7. A wholesale grocer collected by draft, bills of $792, $685, $1016.85, and $832.75. He paid $\frac{1}{10}$% exchange. What was the net amount received from all of the bills?

Arc and Angle Measure

An angle at the center of a circle is said to be measured by the arc, or part of a circumference, included between its sides.

A " protractor " is an instrument used in measuring angles.

NOTE. Paper protractors may be procured at small expense and profitably used at this time.

Learn the table of Arc and Angle Measure, page 157.

Oral

1. How many degrees are there in $\frac{1}{4}$ of a circumference? In $\frac{1}{2}$ a circumference? In $\frac{1}{3}$ of a circumference?

2. 180 degrees are what part of a circumference? 45 degrees? 60 degrees?

3. An angle of 90 degrees is measured by what part of a circumference? 60 degrees? 45 degrees?

4. Draw a circle. Mark off from the center an angle of 90°; an angle of 45°.

5. Show on the blackboard that a circumference is made up of 4 angles of 90°, or 4 right angles.

6. How many angles of 45° are there in an entire circumference?

Written. Reduction descending. Reduce :

7. 45° to minutes.   **11.** $46\frac{1}{2}$° to minutes.

8. 45′ to seconds.   **12.** $\frac{1}{2}$ cir. to degrees.

9. 45° to seconds.   **13.** $\frac{1}{2}$′ to seconds.

10. 180° to minutes.   **14.** $\frac{3}{4}$° to minutes.

Reduction ascending. Reduce :

15. 1200′ to degrees.   **18.** 2700′ to degrees.

16. 2700″ to degrees.   **19.** 3000″ to minutes.

17. 4800″ to degrees.   **20.** 144,000″ to degrees.

Arc and Angle Measure

TABLE

60 seconds (″) = **1** minute (′).
60 minutes = **1** degree (°).
An arc of **360°** = **1** circumference.

The difference in direction of two lines that meet is an **angle.**

The lines that meet to form an angle are the **sides** *of the angle.*

Lines are read by means of letters placed at their extremities. Angles are read by means of letters placed at the extremities of their sides.

In the angle *ABC* the lines *AB* and *BC* are the sides.

The sum of all the angles that can be formed around a point in a plane is 360°.

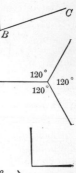

In the figure there are three angles about a point. Add the numbers of degrees.

An angle of 90° is a **right** *angle.*

An angle that is greater than a right angle is an **obtuse** *angle.*

An angle that is less than a right angle is an **acute** *angle.*

The boundary line of a circle is its **circumference;** *any part of a circumference is an* **arc.**

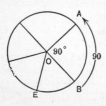

The number of degrees in an arc is always the same as the number of degrees in the angle at the center whose sides meet the extremities of the arc, thus:

The angle *AOB* is ¼ the sum of all the angles at the center, or 90°. The arc *AB* is ¼ of the circumference, or 90°. Can you tell the number of degrees in the arc *BE*? In the angle *BOE*?

Longitude and Time

A meridian is *an imaginary line extending directly north and south, on the surface of the earth, from pole to pole.* It is a semicircumference of the earth.

A prime meridian is *a meridian taken as a starting place for the measurement of distances east and west so as to determine the location of places on the earth's surface.*

By common consent, the meridian passing through the Royal Observatory at Greenwich, Eng., is generally taken as the prime meridian.

The 180° meridian, with slight modifications, has been chosen as the International Date Line. It touches no important body of land.

Whenever a ship crosses this line, going *westward*, its calendar is set forward one day; going *eastward*, its calendar is set back one day.

Distance east or west from the prime meridian, measured in degrees, minutes, and seconds, is longitude.

Degrees, minutes, and seconds west of the prime meridian are called west longitude; *east of the prime meridian* east longitude.

Longitude is measured by arc measure. Why? The number of meridians that may be represented on a globe or map is unlimited. But all places which lie on the same meridian have the same longitude. For example, Boston, Mass., and Santiago, Chile, have nearly the same longitude, though widely separated.

Lay your book on the desk, and imagine that the sun is in the ceiling directly above the middle of this drawing of a hemisphere, p. **159.** The drawing shows the half of the earth's surface that the sun shines upon. The other half is dark. If it is the 21st of March or September, it is now sunset at the prime meridian, noon at the meridian of 90° west longitude, and sunrise at the meridian of 180° west longitude.

The earth makes one rotation toward the east in 24 hours. During one rotation all the meridians will pass under the sun, on to sunset, midnight, sunrise, and noon, finally reaching the same position that they now have. Every place on the earth's surface has passed under the sun, and 360° of longitude have passed under the sun. Therefore the number of degrees of longitude passing under the sun in one hour is 360 ÷ 24, or 15°.

Imagine this drawing to be a sphere rotating toward the east. The sun remains overhead; therefore the numbers representing the hours of the day remain fixed, and the meridians pass under them.

Greenwich and all places on its meridian pass into night. In one hour the 15° meridian will be at six o'clock, the 105° meridian at noon, and so on.

In six hours the 90° meridian will be just passing the six o'clock mark, the 180° meridian will be at noon, and Greenwich will be directly opposite, at midnight.

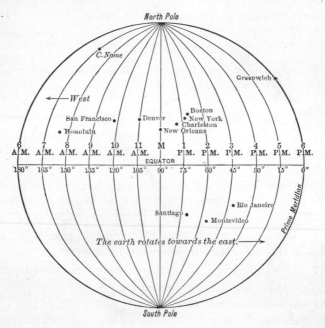

In twelve hours the 180° meridian will have passed entirely across to 6 P.M., and the meridian of Greenwich will be just coming into sight at 6 A.M. The meridians then in view will all be in east longitude and will be numbered from the prime meridian at the left, toward the right, from 0 to 180° east longitude. That is, the meridians are numbered both east and west from the prime meridian. No place can have more than 180°, either east or west longitude.

Longitude and Time

Use drawing of hemisphere on page 159 in obtaining answers.

1. When it is noon at New Orleans, what is the time at Denver? At Cape Nome? At Greenwich?

2. When it is noon at Denver, what is the time at New Orleans? At Greenwich? At Cape Nome?

3. When it is noon at Greenwich, what is the time at New Orleans? At Denver? At Cape Nome?

4. When it is noon at Santiago, what is the time at Boston? At Montevideo? At Rio Janeiro?

5. When it is noon at San Francisco, what is the time at Honolulu? At Charleston?

6. When it is 3 P.M. at New York, what is the approximate time at Santiago? At Montevideo? At Rio Janeiro?

7. When it is 5 A.M. at Charleston, what is the approximate time at San Francisco? At Honolulu? At Greenwich?

8. When it is 7 A.M. at Denver, what is the approximate time at San Francisco? At New York? At Greenwich?

9. The difference in time between two places is 2 hr. What is the difference in longitude?

10. The difference in longitude between two places is 90°. What is their difference in time?

11. When it is 9 A.M. at your home, what is the time at a place 45° farther west? At a place 20° farther east?

12.

$$\underset{A}{\overset{W.L.\ 30°}{\bullet}} \quad \underset{\text{Prime Merid.}}{\big|} \quad \underset{B}{\overset{40°\ E.L.}{\bullet}}$$

A is 30° west longitude and B is 40° east longitude. How many degrees of longitude are there between the meridian of A and that of B?

What is the difference in time between A and B?

Standard Time

The Interstate Commerce Commission has divided the country into zones as shown in the map given below. All places in each zone take the time of the meridian which passes through or near the middle of the zone. This time is called **standard time**. The zones are as follows: *Eastern, Central, Mountain,* and *Pacific.* The standard meridian for the Eastern zone is the 75th, for the Central zone the 90th, for the Mountain zone the 105th, and for the Pacific zone the 120th.

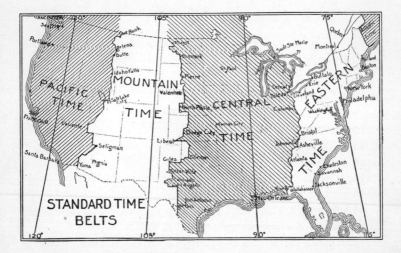

These standard meridians are 15 degrees apart: when it is noon in the Eastern zone, it is 11 A.M. in the Central zone, 10 A.M. in the Mountain zone, and 9 A.M. in the Pacific zone.

In going westward from one time zone into another, the traveler sets his watch back one hour. In traveling eastward he sets his watch ahead one hour.

Standard time is not the true solar or local time, except for places situated on the standard meridians. Yet it can vary but little more than thirty minutes from the true time, and its uniformity is a convenience.

Linear Measure

A line has but one dimension; viz. length.

The units used to measure length are the inch, foot, yard, rod and mile. These are called linear units.

The table of linear measure is given on page 445.

6 ft. 5 in. is sometimes written 6′ 5″.

Reduce:

1. 16 ft. to inches.
2. 60 ft. to yards.
3. 360 in. to feet.
4. 1280 rd. to miles.
5. 22 ft. to inches.
6. 12 yd. 1 ft. to inches.
7. 18 rd. to feet.
8. $\frac{1}{2}$ mi. to feet.
9. $\frac{1}{8}$ mi. to rods.
10. 440 yd. to feet.
11. 70 ft. to yards and feet.
12. 1350 rd. to miles and rods.
13. 282 in. to feet and inches.
14. 66 ft. to rods.
15. 27 in. is what part of a yard?
16. 8 in. is what part of a foot?
17. 9 in. is what part of a foot?
18. How many rods are there in $\frac{1}{2}$ of a mile?
19. How many feet are there in 2 rods?
20. $12\frac{1}{2}$ ft. equals how many inches?
21. A room is 12′ long and 8′ 6″ wide. What is the distance around it?
22. A rug is 12 ft. by 9 ft. How many yards of tape are required to go around it?
23. A farm is 80 rods long and 40 rods wide. What part of a mile is the distance around it?

Surface Measure

A plane or surface has but two dimensions; viz. **length** 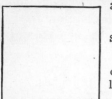 and **breadth**.

A plane figure that has four equal sides and four equal angles is a **square**.

A square that is 1 inch long and 1 inch wide is called a square inch. A square that is 1 foot long and 1 foot wide is called what?

The number of square units that a surface contains is its **area**.

The sum of all the sides of a figure is its **perimeter**.

A figure that is bounded by four straight sides and has four right angles is a **rectangle**.

This figure is divided into squares, each of which may be regarded as a square unit. Its length is that of 4 such units and its breadth is that of 3 such units. Its area is (3 × 4) square units or 12 square units. This figure is a *rectangle*.

The area of a rectangle is the product of its length and breadth expressed in the same unit.

NOTE. — It is the *number* of units which are multiplied, not the units, nor the lines measured. For example, suppose the area of a rectangle 4 ft. long and 3 ft. wide is required. The *number* of square feet in the rectangle is 3 × 4, which is 12. Its area is 12 sq. ft.

Learn the table of Square Measure, page 446.

Written.   Reduction descending.   Reduce:

1. 15 sq. ft. to square inches.

2. 340 sq. yd. to square feet.

3. 216 sq. rd. to square yards.

4. 25 A. to square rods.

5. 14 sq. yd. and 6 sq. ft. to square feet.

6. 5 A. and 50 sq. rd. to square rods.

7. 40 sq. ft. and 128 sq. in. to square inches.

8. 48 sq. rd. and 28 sq. yd. to square yards.

9. 16 A. 60 sq. rd. to square rods.

10. 19 sq. ft. 70 sq. in. to square inches.

Written. Reduction ascending. Reduce :

11. 1728 sq. in. to square feet.

12. 1800 sq. in. to square feet and square inches.

13. 120 sq. ft. to square yards and square feet.

14. 1562 sq. rd. to acres and square rods.

15. 121 sq. yd. to square rods.

16. 3200 A. to square miles.

17. 160 A. to the decimal of a square mile.

18. 36 sq. in. to the fraction of a square foot.

19. $4\frac{1}{2}$ sq. ft. to the fraction of a square yard.

20. $15\frac{1}{8}$ sq. yd. to the decimal of a square rod.

21. How many square rods and square yards are there in 254 sq. yd.?

$30\frac{1}{4}$)254   The *number* of sq. rods is the quotient of 254 divided by $30\frac{1}{4}$.

Reduce both divisor and dividend to fourths.

$$\frac{8}{121 \ fourths)\overline{1016 \ fourths}}$$
$$\frac{968}{48 \ fourths}$$

The quotient is 8 sq. rd.
The remainder is 48 *fourths* sq. yd., which equals 12 sq. yd.
8 sq. rd. and 12 sq. yd.

22. Reduce 4500 sq. ft. to square yards.

23. Reduce 2100 sq. rd. to acres and square rods.

24. Reduce 20 sq. rd. to the decimal of an acre.

25. Reduce 13,661 sq. in. to square feet and square inches.

26. Reduce 21,600 sq. in. to square feet.

Straight-line Figures

A plane figure bounded by four straight lines is a
quadrilateral; *e.g.*

QUADRILATERALS

A quadrilateral whose opposite sides are parallel is a
parallelogram.

The above figures are parallelograms.

A parallelogram that has four right angles is a **rectangle.**

Which of the above figures are rectangles?

Two lines that meet to form a right angle are **perpendicular
to each other.**

The side on which a figure is supposed to rest is its **base.**

*The perpendicular distance from the highest point of a
figure to the base, or to the base extended,* is its **altitude**; *e.g.*

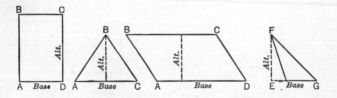

The area of a parallelogram *is the product of its base and
altitude expressed in the same denomination.*

Observe that figures *A*, *B*, and *C* are parallelograms.

The **area of a triangle** *is equal to one half the product of its
base and altitude expressed in the same denomination.*

Problems

In computing the area or volume of a figure, the given dimensions, if expressed in different denominations, should first be changed to the same denomination.

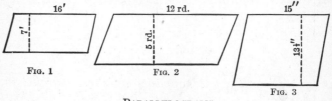

PARALLELOGRAMS

Of the following solve as many as you can mentally. Estimate the answer before every written solution.

1. Figure 1 represents how many square feet?

2. Figure 2 represents what part of an acre?

3. Figure 3 represents how many square inches?

4. The area of a parallelogram is 52 square rods. Its base is 132 feet. What is its altitude? (Change 132' to rods.)

Find the areas of triangles having dimensions as follows:

	Base	Altitude		Base	Altitude
5.	7 ft.	4 ft.	**10.**	1 mi.	100 rd.
6.	1 yd.	1 yd.	**11.**	3 ft.	20 in.
7.	5 in.	20 in.	**12.**	5 yd.	5 ft.
8.	1 yd.	1 ft.	**13.**	1 ft. 6 in.	8 ft.
9.	80 rd.	20 rd.	**14.**	640 rd.	1 mi.

15. This figure represents a triangular plot of ground that is inclosed by three streets. What part of an acre does it contain?

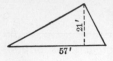

16. This figure represents a piece of cement floor at a railroad station. Find its cost at $1.08 a square yard.

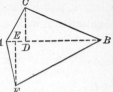

17. In this figure, $AB = 54$ in., $CD = 18$ in., $EF = 27$ in. Find the area of $ACBF$ in square yards.

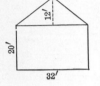

18. This cut represents the end of a barn. Find its area.

19. The diagonals of this square are each 20 ft. What is the area of the square?

20. From the dimensions given, find the area of this figure.

21.

FIG. A
RECTANGLE

FIG. B
PARALLELOGRAM

The perimeter of Fig. B compares how with the perimeter of Fig. A?

The area of Fig. B is what per cent of the area of Fig. A?

22. The altitude of a parallelogram is 37 inches; its area is 74 square feet. Find its base.

23. A city lot 33 ft. front and 132 ft. deep contains what part of an acre?

24. Measure different surfaces in your school building and on the school grounds and compute their areas.

Trapezoids

A plane figure bounded by four straight lines is a **quadrilateral**.

A quadrilateral having its opposite sides parallel is a **parallelogram**.

A quadrilateral having two opposite sides parallel and the other two not parallel is a **trapezoid**.

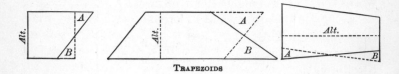

TRAPEZOIDS

In each of the above figures, how does the part *A* compare with the part *B*?

How does the area of the trapezoid compare with that of the parallelogram which is made from the trapezoid? How is the area of the parallelogram found?

Summary

The area of a trapezoid is equal to one half of the sum of the parallel sides multiplied by the altitude.

Written

1. Draw a trapezoid whose altitude is 13 inches and whose parallel sides are 17 and 19 inches. Find its area.

2. A field in the form of a trapezoid has two parallel sides of 30 rods and 34 rods; the distance between them is 20 rods. How many acres of land does the field contain?

3. A board is 1 inch thick, 12 feet long, 10 inches wide at one end and a foot wide at the other end. How many board feet does it contain?

Problems in Measurement

1. A room is 15 feet long and 12 feet wide. How much will it cost to paint the floor at $.40 a square yard?

2. Mr. Knapp has a lot 100 rods long and 70 rods wide. Find the cost of the wire for a 4-strand wire fence around it, if the wire costs $1\frac{1}{2}$ cents a foot.

3. Mr. Broderick works 8 hours a day and receives $1.32 an hour. What does he earn in four weeks if he works 6 days a week?

4. Mr. Flint's barn is 80 feet long and 36 feet wide, the average height being 22 feet. What must he pay for paint to cover the four sides with two coats of paint at $1.80 a gallon, one gallon covering 540 square feet?

5. Mr. Perry owns a lot 132 feet deep. At the rear of the lot he builds a garage 18 feet square. What will be the cost of a concrete driveway 6 feet wide, extending from the street to the garage, at $.25 a square foot?

6. A rectangular lot is 22 feet wide and twice as long. What is the perimeter?

7. Find the perimeter of a square lot 91 feet on one side.

8. Find the area and the perimeter of a plot of ground 33 feet wide and 132 feet long.

9. Mr. Jones has a field of cabbage 100 rods long and 40 rods wide. He raises 6 tons to the acre and receives $20 a ton for them. What is the crop worth?

10. A poultry man has 190 hens which average 137 eggs each a year. What is his income if he receives an average price of 37 cents a dozen?

11. Find the cost of covering a floor 20 feet long and 16 feet wide with linoleum that costs $1.20 a square yard.

12. How many acres of land in a field 167 rods long and 660 feet wide?

13. A building lot contains 5600 square feet and is 140 feet deep. How much is the lot worth at $25 a front foot?

14. A room is 16 feet long and 14 feet wide. On the floor is a rug 9 × 12. Find the cost of finishing the space not covered by the rug at $1.60 a square yard.

15. Find the cost of laying a cement sidewalk 6 feet wide on the street sides of a corner lot 35 feet wide and 120 feet long at 25 cents a square foot.

16. Oranges are bought at $8 a box. The box contains 132 oranges. What is the cost per dozen?

17. Change .125 of a ton to pounds.

18. A herd of 25 cows average 16 quarts of milk apiece per day for the month of December. The milk is sold in 40-quart cans at $2.20 a can. What is received for it?

19. An apple orchard containing 160 trees yields an average of $2\frac{1}{2}$ bushels per tree. The apples sell for 30 cents a peck. Find how much is received for them.

20. Find the cost of a farm 200 rods long and 75 rods wide at $100 an acre.

21. Mr. Smith works 8 hours a day and receives $1.40 an hour. What is his annual earning if he works 6 days a week?

22. Find in feet the perimeter of a rectangular lot 147 feet and 6 inches deep, with a frontage of $12\frac{1}{2}$ yards.

23. Make a problem on the cost of building a concrete walk.

24. Bring to the class five problems in which denominate numbers are used.

Lumber Measure

A piece of board 1 ft. long, 1 ft. wide, and 1 in. thick is a **board foot** (bd. ft.).

To the Teacher. — As material for this lesson, a real board foot — a piece of board exactly 1 ft. long, 1 ft. wide, and 1 in. thick — should be provided. Refer to it in obtaining answers to the oral questions below and whenever pupils seem to answer wide of the mark in this subject. This is very important.

1. How many inches long is a board foot? How many inches wide? How many cubic inches does a board foot contain?

2. How many board feet piled one upon another would make a cubic foot? Show with your hands how wide, long, and high this pile would be.

3. A board 1 in. thick, 1 ft. wide, and 6 ft. long contains how many board feet? Draw it full size on the blackboard, and mark off the board feet.

4. If the board in question **3** were twice as thick, how many board feet would it contain? How many inches thick would it be?

5. If it were five times as thick, how many board feet would it contain?

6. How many board feet are there in a piece of board 1 ft. wide, 16 ft. long, and 1 in. thick?

7. If this piece of lumber were 2 in. thick, how many board feet would it contain? 3 in.? 4 in.? 5 in.? 6 in.?

8. A piece of inch board 3 ft. long must be how wide to contain 1 bd. ft.?

9. A piece of board 1 in. thick, 2 in. wide, and 12 ft. long contains how many board feet?

> *To find the number of board feet in any piece of lumber, multiply together its three dimensions,* two of them expressed **in feet** *and the* other **in inches.**

Lumber less than 1″ thick is counted as 1″ thick in measuring.

10. How much lumber is used in making this box with cover? (Take outside measurements.)

11. About how many feet of lumber (board feet) are there in the top of your desk? One end of the bookcase? The cupboard door? All the shelves in the bookcase?

12. Estimate the amount of lumber in a cubical box, including the cover, made of ½-inch lumber, the length of the box being three feet.

13. The door in this hayloft is 4½′ × 4′. Two battens across the inside are 4′ × 6″. How many feet of lumber are used in the door, the lumber being 1″ thick?

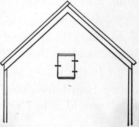

Written

14. What is the cost of 20 pieces of lumber 2″ × 4″, and 14′ long at $60 per M? "Per M" means "per 1000 feet."

SOLUTION: $\dfrac{\overset{2}{\cancel{20}}}{1} \times \dfrac{2}{1} \times \dfrac{\cancel{4}}{\underset{3}{\cancel{12}}} \times \dfrac{14}{1} \times \dfrac{1}{\underset{\underset{5}{\cancel{100}}}{\cancel{1000}}} \times \dfrac{\overset{20}{\cancel{60}}}{1} = \dfrac{56}{5} = \$11.20.$ *Ans.*

Find the cost of :

15. 18 pieces 1″ × 6″ and 16′ long at $45 per M.

16. 48 pieces 2″ × 4″ and 18′ long at $36 per M.

17. 88 pieces 3″ × 4″ and 14′ long at $40 per M.

	NUMBER OF PIECES	SIZE	LENGTH	PRICE PER M
18.	28	$2'' \times 6''$	16'	$45
19.	96	$3'' \times 10''$	24'	42
20.	29	$1'' \times 12''$	14'	60
21.	90	$2'' \times 8''$	20'	45
22.	50	$4'' \times 4''$	16'	39
23.	16	$8'' \times 8''$	18'	28
24.	128	$2\frac{1}{2}'' \times 12''$	16'	51
25.	44	$\frac{3}{4}'' \times 3''$	16'	48
26.	28	$1\frac{1}{4}'' \times 4''$	12'	63
27.	248	$\frac{3}{8}'' \times 2''$	16'	110
28.	89	$\frac{7}{8}'' \times 3''$	16'	41
29.	248	$1'' \times 6\frac{1}{2}''$	16'	40
30.	9	$6'' \times 10''$	20'	32
31.	18	$8'' \times 12''$	30'	40
32.	90	$4'' \times 10''$	30'	40
33.	150	$\frac{7}{8}'' \times 10''$	14'	62

34. In making a chest, Fred uses two pieces of lumber $\frac{1}{8}'' \times 12'' \times 2\frac{1}{2}'$, two pieces $\frac{7}{8}'' \times 12'' \times 16''$, four pieces $\frac{7}{8}'' \times 8'' \times 36''$, and one piece $\frac{1}{2}'' \times 1\frac{1}{2}'' \times 6'$. Allowing 3 bd. ft. for waste, how much lumber must Fred buy, and how much will it cost at $80 per M?

35. What must Mr. Allen pay for lumber to lay a new floor in his porch which measures 24 ft. by 10 ft.? The boards are $1\frac{1}{8}''$ thick. Mr. Allen adds an amount equal to $\frac{1}{3}$ of the entire floor, to allow for the loss in matching and for other wastes, and the lumber costs $58 per M.

36. Measure the floor of your schoolroom, and estimate the cost of lumber for a new floor $\frac{7}{8}''$ thick at $70 per M, adding $\frac{1}{4}$ of the actual surface, to allow for matching and other waste.

Building Problems

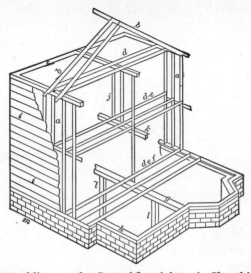

a. Outside studding	*de.* Second floor joists	*i.* Sheathing
b. Rafters	*def.* First floor joists	*j.* Partition studs
c. Plates	*g.* Girder	*k.* Partition heads
d. Ceiling joists	*h.* Sills	*l.* Piers or supports

1. Find the cost of the following bill of lumber:

NOTE. — 6″ × 10″ — 16′ means a piece 6 inches by 10 inches and 16 feet long.

4 sills	6″ × 10″ — 16′, $27 per M
2 sills	6″ × 10″ — 18′, $27 per M
1 girder	8″ × 10″ — 18′, $27 per M
26 rafters	2″ × 6″ — 14′, $27 per M
60 pieces of studding	2″ × 4″ — 16′, $27 per M

540′ of ⅞″ flooring, $38 per M
2000 feet of sheathing, $30 per M
200 feet of casings, $45 per M

2. The floor of your schoolroom is $\frac{7}{8}$ in. thick.

a. If no allowance is made for sawing and matching, how many feet of lumber are there in the floor?

b. If $\frac{1}{5}$ of the lumber was wasted in sawing and matching, the floor contains only $\frac{4}{5}$ of the lumber that was bought. How much lumber was bought?

3. A fence like this, 6 ft. high, extends around two sides and one end of a rectangular garden 40 ft. by 55 ft. Draw a diagram of the garden.

a. How many feet of boards were used?

b. How much did they cost at $27 per M?

4. A builder bought 425 half-inch boards $2\frac{1}{2}$ in. wide and 16 ft. long. How many feet of lumber did he buy?

5. How many feet of 2-inch plank will cover a barn floor 20 ft. wide and 60 ft. long?

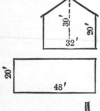

6. *a.* These figures represent one end and one side of a building covered with clapboards $\frac{5}{8}$ of an inch thick that cost $36 per M. Allowing $\frac{1}{4}$ of all the lumber purchased for waste in cutting and overlapping, how much did the clapboards for this building cost?

HINT: If there were no waste, how much lumber would be needed? This is what part of the lumber purchased, when $\frac{1}{4}$ of the lumber purchased is wasted?

b. The rafters are $2'' \times 6'' \times 20'$, and 25 rafters are used on each side of the roof. How much did they cost at $27 per M?

7. Compute the cost of the following bill of lumber:

No.	Size	Length	Kind	Board Feet	Per M	$
8	$6'' \times 8''$	16'	Hemlock	?	$48	?
7	$2'' \times 6''$	14'	Hemlock	?	45	?
8	$1\frac{1}{4}'' \times 10''$	12'	Hemlock	?	74	?
14	$1'' \times 6''$	13'	Pine	?	91	?
25	$\frac{1}{2}'' \times 4''$	12'	Pine	?	50	?
20	$1'' \times 5''$	12'	Spruce	?	56	?
280 l. f.	$1'' \times 2''$		Pine	at $1.25 per C		?
165 l. f.	4'' molding			at $4 per C		?

NOTE. — l. f. means "linear feet."

8. Shingles are put up in "bunches" of 250. Six thousand shingles are how many bunches?

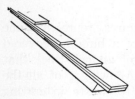

As shown in this figure, the "course" at the eaves is laid double. About $\frac{1}{4}$ of the surface of the shingle is exposed "to the weather."

9. A thousand shingles laid 4'' to the weather cover 100 square feet, or "1 square" of roof surface. How many shingles will be needed to cover a roof $30' \times 40'$?

10. If the shingles are laid $4\frac{1}{2}''$ to the weather, 800 will cover 1 square. How many bunches of 250 each, so laid, will be needed for a roof, $25' \times 50'$? What will the shingles cost at $4.80 per M?

11. What will it cost to cover a barn roof with tar roofing at $3 a square, the roof being in two parts each $30' \times 65'$?

Problems of the Shop

1. Make a drawing for a bird house using this plan.

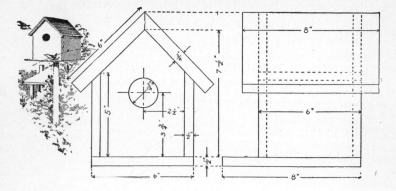

2. There are three pieces shown in this plan that are of the same dimensions. Which are they, and what are the dimensions?

3. Give the dimensions of a piece of board from which all three of these pieces could be made, allowing $\frac{1}{8}''$ on every edge of each piece for waste in cutting and dressing down.

4. Making a similar allowance for waste, what would be the dimensions of a board from which both end pieces could be cut?

5. What is the inside width of the wren-house?

6. What is the inside length of the wren-house?

7. Hubert had a $\frac{1}{2}''$ board 12 ft. long and $6\frac{1}{2}$ in. wide. He made two wren-houses like this. Allowing two inches of the length for waste in cutting and fitting, how long was the piece that was left?

8. How many board feet of lumber did Hubert use for the two bird-houses?

9. How much did it cost at 5¢ a board foot?

Circles

To construct a circle.

A circle may be easily drawn by using a compass. One point of the compass remains in one place while the other is made to move about it. The fixed point O is called the center. The curved line is the circumference. The distance from the center to the circumference OA is the radius. A line drawn through the center ending at the circumference is the diameter. The diameter is how many times the radius?

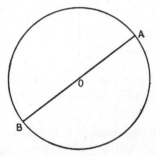

To draw a circle with a radius of $1\frac{3}{4}$ inches open the compass so that the points are $1\frac{3}{4}$ inches apart.

To draw a circle with a diameter of $1\frac{1}{2}$ inches open the compass so that the points are one half of $1\frac{1}{2}$ inches or $\frac{3}{4}$ inches apart.

Which is longer, the diameter or one half of the circumference?

Which is longer, one fourth of the circumference or the radius?

Name four parts of a circle.

If OA equals $2\frac{1}{4}$ inches, find AB.

When AB equals seven inches find BO.

What opening between the points of the compass would make a circle seven inches in diameter?

Construct the following circles.

RADIUS	DIAMETER
1. 2 inches	11. 4 inches
2. $1\frac{1}{4}$ inches	12. 3 inches
3. 1 inch	13. $3\frac{1}{2}$ inches
4. 3 inches	14. 6 inches
5. $2\frac{1}{2}$ inches	15. 5 inches
6. $3\frac{1}{4}$ inches	16. $2\frac{1}{2}$ inches
7. $1\frac{1}{2}$ inches	17. 1 inch
8. $\frac{1}{2}$ inch	18. $1\frac{1}{2}$ inches
9. $\frac{3}{4}$ inch	19. $4\frac{1}{2}$ inches
10. $2\frac{1}{4}$ inches	20. $3\frac{1}{4}$ inches

The circumference of a circle is about $3\frac{1}{7}$ or 3.1416 times the diameter. $3\frac{1}{7}$ or 3.1416 is indicated by the Greek letter π.

Give the answers in terms of π.

What is the circumference of a circle whose:

1. diameter is 6?	7. radius is 17?
2. diameter is 10?	8. radius is $7\frac{1}{2}$?
3. diameter is $2\frac{1}{2}$?	9. diameter is 13?
4. diameter is $8\frac{1}{4}$?	10. radius is 21?
5. radius is 6?	11. diameter is 25?
6. radius is 11?	12. radius is 33?

Find the radius and the diameter when the circumference is:

13. $16\,\pi$	**16.** $18\,\pi$	**19.** $3\,\pi$	**22.** $28\,\pi$
14. $7\,\pi$	**17.** $21\,\pi$	**20.** $36\,\pi$	**23.** $66\,\pi$
15. $12\frac{1}{2}\,\pi$	**18.** $48\,\pi$	**21.** $14\,\pi$	**24.** $184\,\pi$

25. How many feet of foliage border will it take to go around a flower bed that is 21 feet in diameter?

26. The circumference of a circular cistern is 66 feet. Find the diameter.

27. The top of a large pail has a radius of 7 inches. What is the circumference?

28. A merry-go-round has a diameter of 98 feet. How far does Jenny ride in going around 5 times?

29. What is the circumference of a wheel 7 feet in diameter? How many revolutions will it make in going a mile?

The area of a circle is equal to the square of the radius multiplied by 3.1416 or $\frac{22}{7}$.

The formula for the area of a circle is πR^2.

Find the area of a circle when the

1. radius is 4	**5.** diameter is 10
2. radius is 9	**6.** radius is 10
3. diameter is 6	**7.** diameter is 22
4. radius is 7	**8.** diameter is 4

9. Find the value of a circular piece of glass whose radius is 12 inches, at $2 a square foot.

10. What is the value of a circular piece of land whose diameter is 80 rods, at $800 an acre?

11. Find the cost of fencing this field at $5.25 a rod.

12. Find the cost, at 95 cents a square yard, of paving a circular court whose radius is 50 feet.

13. A cow is tied to a stake by a rope 90 feet long. Over how many square yards can she graze?

14. A circular flower bed is 35 feet in diameter. What will it cost to plant it at 20 cents a square foot?

15. A circular water tank has a circumference of 31.416 feet. Find the area of the bottom.

16. Find the circumference of a wheel 42 inches in diameter. How many revolutions does this wheel make in going a mile?

17. Which has the greater area, a square 5 yards on each side or a circle with a radius of 8.6 feet?

When two lines meet forming a right angle, they are **perpendicular** to each other. *E.g.*

Point to two sides of the window that are perpendicular to each other; two sides of the door; two sides of the blackboard; of your paper; of your book.

Find other lines in the schoolroom that are perpendicular to each other.

What lines in your street are perpendicular to each other? In your home? In your school yard?

I. Let us see how we can draw *one line perpendicular to another, through a point on the first line*. Draw line AB. Take any point O on the line. With O as center and a radius less than OA, draw an arc cutting line AB at C and D. With C and D as centers and a radius greater than OC, draw arcs cutting each other at E. Draw EO. Then EO is the line required.

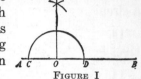

FIGURE I

II. *To draw a line perpendicular to a given line from a point outside the line.*

Draw the line AB. Take any point O outside the line. With O as a center, draw an arc cutting AB at C and D. With C and D as centers, draw arcs cutting each other at E. Draw OE. It is the line required.

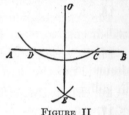

FIGURE II

Exercises

1. Draw a straight line two inches long and from the middle point of the line draw a line perpendicular to it.

2. Draw a straight line three inches long and from a point one inch from the end draw a line perpendicular to it.

3. At a point three-fourths of an inch from the end of a line erect a perpendicular.

4. From a point one and one-half inches from the end of a given line drop a perpendicular to it.

5. Is the distance OC equal to, greater than, or less than the distance OD? Fig. I.

6. How does the distance EC compare with the distance ED? Fig. II.

7. Which is greater, the distance OA or the distance OD? Fig. I.

III. *To construct a perpendicular at the end of a line.*

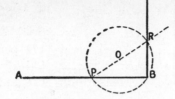

Draw the line *AB*. With any convenient radius and with any point outside line *AB* as a center draw a circle passing through point *B* and intersecting *AB* at *P*. Draw the diameter *POR*. Draw *BR*.

Then *BR* is the required perpendicular.

The angle *ABR* is a right angle.

IV. *To construct a rectangle.*

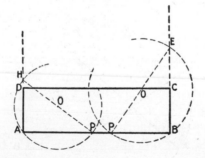

Draw the line *AB*.

At *B* erect *BE* perpendicular to *AB*.

At *A* erect *AH* perpendicular to *AB*.

Measure off *BC* a distance less than *AB* on *BE*.

Measure off on *AH* a distance *AD* equal to *BC*. Draw *DC*.

Then *ABCD* is the rectangle required.

V. *To construct a square.*

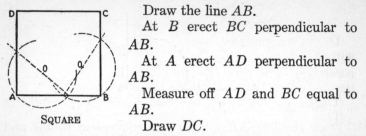

SQUARE

Draw the line AB.

At B erect BC perpendicular to AB.

At A erect AD perpendicular to AB.

Measure off AD and BC equal to AB.

Draw DC.

If the construction has been carefully done DC will equal AB.

The sides are equal and the angles are right angles; therefore $ABCD$ is the square required.

VI. *To construct an acute angle.*

An angle which is less than a right angle is called an acute angle.

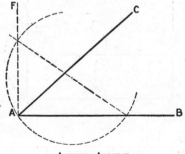

ACUTE ANGLE

Draw the line AB.

Draw the line AC so that the angle formed is less than the right angle FAB.

The angle CAB is the acute angle required.

VII. *To con-struct an obtuse angle.*

An angle greater than a right angle is called an obtuse angle.

Draw the line *AB*.

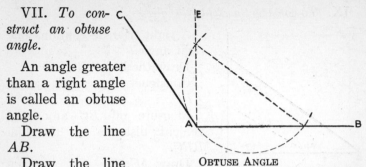

OBTUSE ANGLE

Draw the line *AC* so that the angle formed is greater than the right angle *EAB*.

The angle *CAB* is the obtuse angle required.

VIII. *To construct an acute triangle.*

An acute triangle contains neither a right nor an obtuse angle.

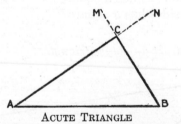

ACUTE TRIANGLE

Draw the line *AB*.

Draw the line *AN* making an acute angle with *AB*.

Draw the line *BM* making an acute angle with lines *AB* and *AN*.

Then the lines *AN* and *BM* will intersect at *C*.

The triangle *ACB* is the triangle required.

Read this triangle in two other ways.

Read the three acute angles in this triangle.

IX. *To construct a right triangle.*

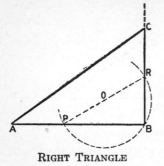

RIGHT TRIANGLE

A right triangle contains one right angle.

Draw the line *AB*.

Construct the right angle *ABC*.

Measure off *BC* any convenient distance on the line *BRC*.

Draw *AC*.

Then *ABC* is the right triangle required.

Read the acute angles of this triangle each in two ways.
What is the difference between a triangle and an angle?
How many angles has a triangle?
How many sides has a triangle?
How many angles has a square?
How many sides has a square?

X. *To construct an obtuse triangle.*

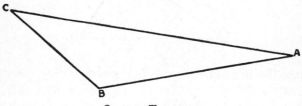

OBTUSE TRIANGLE

Draw the line *BA*.
Draw the line *BC* making an obtuse angle *CBA* with *BA*.
Draw *CA*.
Then *CBA* is the obtuse triangle required.

Read this triangle in two other ways.
Read the acute angles in this triangle.
Read the obtuse angle.

Draw a straight line from one corner of a sheet of paper
to the corner diagonally opposite.
How many triangles are formed?
What kind of triangles are these?
Make a similar line on a sheet of paper that is square.
How many triangles are found?
What kind of triangles are these?

XI. *To construct an angle equal to a given angle.*

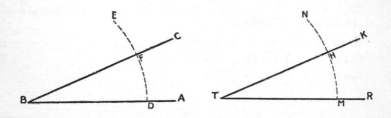

Given the angle *ABC*.
Draw the line *RT*.
With *B* as a center and any convenient radius draw the
arc *DE*.
With *T* as a center and the same radius draw the
arc *NM*.
With *M* as a center and *DF* as a radius draw an arc
intersecting arc *NM* at *H*.
Draw **THK.**
Then *RTK* is the required angle.
How many equal angles are there in a square? How
many are there in a rectangle?

XII. *To construct a parallelogram.*

A parallelogram is a four-sided figure whose opposite sides are equal and parallel.

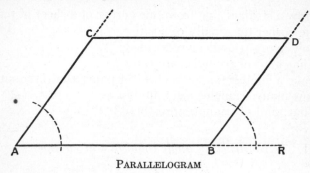

PARALLELOGRAM

Draw the line *AR*.

Measure off on this line a distance *AB*.

At *B* draw the acute angle *DBR*.

At *A* construct the acute angle *BAC* equal to angle *DBR*.

Make the distance *AC* equal to *BD*.

Draw *CD*.

Then *ABDC* is the parallelogram required.

Draw the diagonal *CB*.

This divides the parallelogram into two acute triangles which contain neither an obtuse nor a right angle. The diagonal *AD* in the parallelogram forms two obtuse triangles, the diagonal *BC* forms two acute triangles, while the diagonal of either a square or a rectangle forms two right triangles.

A polygon is any figure containing three or more sides. A three-sided polygon is a triangle, a four-sided polygon may be either a square, a rectangle, or a parallelogram.

1. Draw the right triangle ABC having base $BC = 3''$ and altitude $AB = 2''$.

2. Draw CD perpendicular to BC at C, making CD 2'' long. Draw BD.

3. Construct a parallelogram having sides 4'' and 5''.

4. Construct a rectangle having sides 4'' and 5''.

5. Draw a square with 5'' sides.

6. Construct a rectangle 10'' by 2''.

7. Construct an obtuse triangle.

8. Construct an acute triangle.

9. Find the area of a rectangle 10'' by 4''.

10. Find the area of a right triangle with base 5'' and altitude 6''.

11. Construct a square having an area of 36 square inches.

12. Construct a rectangle having a base of 3 inches and an area of 6 square inches.

13. Construct a right triangle having a base of 4 inches and an area of 8 square inches.

For exercises on drawing to scale see page 375.

Tests of Accomplishment

I

1. A field is 80 rd. square. Find its perimeter in feet.

2. A mirror $2\frac{3}{4}' \times 1\frac{1}{2}'$ contains how many square inches?

3. Find the cost of 8 gross of copybooks at 12 cents each.

4. What per cent of 10 bushels is 2 pecks?

5. Estimate the circumference when the diameter is 12 ft.   Test it.

6. A triangular park has the following dimensions; alt. 108 yd., base 60 yd.   What is the area in square feet?

7. If a bushel of pears costs $2.40, what will a half peck cost at the same rate?

8. How many square yards of asphalt will pave a roadbed 400 ft. by 30 ft.?

II

1. Goods that were bought for $750 were sold for $1000.   What was the per cent of profit?

2. What is the net price of goods listed at $240 and bought at $\frac{1}{8}$ off?

3. A floor contains 270 sq. ft. of surface.   What is the length when the width is 15 ft.?

4. Find the exact number of days between Dec. 15, 1923 and March 5, 1925.

5. What is the list price of shoes that sell for $3.60 after a reduction of 10%?

6. An agent collected $2500 at $5\frac{1}{2}$% commission. What amount of money did he remit to his employer?

7. A merchant sold goods for $1800, which was 10% less than they cost.   What did they cost?

8. What is the interest on $2500 for 1 yr., 4 mo., 24 da., at 6%?

9. A park in the form of a circle has a radius of 10 ft. What is the circumference?   What is the area?

10. How many feet of lumber are there in 10 boards 16 ft. long, 10 in. wide and 1 in. thick?

III

1. Cloth costing $2.40 must be marked at what price to make a profit of 20% on the cost?

2. Write a negotiable interest-bearing note for $550 at 6% for 90 days.   Compute the interest.

3. What is the cost of 8 beams, each 8″ × 12″ × 25′, at $80 per M?

4. How many times can a 50-lb. basket be filled from 3 tons of coal?

5. What is the amount of $300 for 6 months at $4\frac{1}{2}$%?

6. If you study $4\frac{1}{2}$ hr. each school day, and $1\frac{1}{4}$ hr. each school evening, how many hours will you study in 2 weeks?

7. Write a 60-day note without interest.   Find the proceeds if discounted at 6% on the day of date.

8. What is the weight in pounds of hay as follows: $8\frac{3}{4}$ cwt., $5\frac{7}{10}$ cwt., $7\frac{4}{5}$ cwt., $5\frac{1}{2}$ cwt., and $6\frac{19}{20}$ cwt.?

9. Find the net price of goods listed at $1440, and discounted at 20% and 10%.

10. If goods costing $6250 are damaged so that they sell for $3750, what is the per cent of loss?

IV

1. On June 1, a retailer bought goods listed at $1600. On July 1 he paid the bill.   Terms, 15%, 30 days.   What did he pay?

2. What is the cost of a piece of land 60 rd. wide, 80 rd. long at $80 per acre?

3. At what rate of loss are knives sold, when they cost $6 a dozen and are sold for 30¢ each?

4. What are the proceeds of a 60-day note for $250 with interest at 6%, discounted on the day of date at 6%?

5. If a merchant sells damaged goods for $3684 at a reduction of 33⅓%, what did the goods cost?

6. A triangular park has an altitude of 660 rd. and a base of 495 rd. What is the area in acres?

7. List price $720, trade discount 25%, 10%. Find net price.

8. Compute a 12½% loss on goods costing $1808.16.

V

1. How must a merchant mark goods costing $275 so that he may make a 20% profit on the cost?

2. My income this year is $4028. This is 24% less than it was last year. How much was it last year?

3. Compute the proceeds of a 90-day note for $3000 discounted at a bank at 6%, 30 days after its date.

4. Find the net price of goods listed at $1660 with successive discounts of 10% and 5%.

5. What part of a ton is 7½ cwt.?

6. A close fence is 100′ long and 9′ high. What is the cost of painting both sides at 10¢ a square yard?

7. Ten bushels of chestnuts cost $3.20 per bushel, and were sold at 8¢ a pint. What was the profit?

8. The rate of circumference to diameter is approximately 3⅐. Find circumference when diameter is 21 ft.

Problems with Numbers Omitted

1. What is the interest on —— dollars for —— years at —— %?

2. Find the cost of —— miles of railroad fare at —— cents a mile.

3. What must be paid for paving a street —— feet wide and —— rods long at —— dollars per square foot?

4. How many hours at —— cents an hour must a boy work to earn enough to buy a pair of shoes costing —— dollars?

5. How many pint bottles can be filled from —— cans each containing —— quarts of milk?

6. What is the gain on —— bushels of potatoes bought at —— dollars a bushel and sold at —— dollars a bushel?

7. How long will it take to travel —— miles when —— miles is the average number of miles given for —— minutes?

8. What must be paid for —— carloads of brick each containing —— thousand at —— dollars per M.?

9. Find out what amount of money an agent receives for selling —— dollars' worth of rugs at —— per cent commission.

10. The list price of an article is —— dollars. On sale a reduction offered is —— per cent. How many dollars will the article cost if bought at a reduction sale?

11. A sum of money on interest for —— days at —— per cent yields how much interest?

12. A sum on interest for a number of years at a certain rate produces how much interest?

13. A sum of money on interest for 1 year produces $—— interest. What is the rate?

14. What is the bank discount on a note for $——, without interest, due in —— days and discounted the day it was given?

15. A school district must raise $—— in taxes on property assessed at $——. What is the tax rate?

16. Mr. Daly pays $—— in city taxes when the rate is ——. What is the assessed valuation of his property?

17. When my property is assessed at $—— and my taxes amount to $——, what is the rate?

18. The base of a rectangle is —— ft. Its altitude is —— ft. What is its area?

19. A commission merchant sold $—— worth of goods. The rate of his commission was ——%. What was the commission?

20. An agent received $—— for selling $—— worth of goods on commission. What was the rate of his commission?

21. What per cent discount is allowed when goods marked $—— are sold for $——?

22. When goods bought for $—— are sold for $——, what is the rate of gain or loss?

23. In the schools of a city —— teachers receive $—— salary each; —— teachers each receive $—— and —— teachers each receive $——. What is the average salary?

Percentage not Involving Money

1. Water expands 10 per cent of its volume when it freezes. What per cent of its volume does ice contract when it melts?

2. Five per cent of pea coal is slate. How many tons of slate are there in 60 tons of pea coal?

3. Fifteen per cent of the brick in certain building are number two brick. If there are 30 M number two brick used, find the total number of brick required for the building.

4. Greenland is $\frac{1}{9}$ as large as South America. Greenland is, therefore, what per cent of the area of South America?

5. Ninety per cent of the one billion seven hundred fifteen million people living on the earth reside at an altitude less than 1500 feet above sea level. How many people live at an altitude greater than 1500 ft.?

6. Twenty per cent of the known iron ore of the world is located in Newfoundland; 25% is found in Brazil near Rio de Janeiro. What per cent of the world's supply is found elsewhere?

7. Eighty-five per cent of the possible water power of the Genesee River is undeveloped. If 45,000 horsepower is now used, what horsepower is wasted?

8. The careful oiling of a certain machine was found to save $12\frac{1}{2}\%$ on the power required for its operation. If the power used after oiling was 35 horsepower, how many horsepower was saved by proper oiling?

9. The proper adjustment of the carburetor of an auto enabled the car to be driven 20 miles on a gallon of gas as compared with 16 miles before adjustment. Find the percentage increase in mileage due to this adjustment.

10. The membership of the Chamber of Commerce was increased from 200 members to 300 members. What was the increase in per cent?

11. The number of different pupils taking part in the assembly programs during a certain year was 445. The school population was 657. What per cent of the students participated in the assembly programs?

12. At an Honor Assembly 96 honor pupils received the scholarship block letter. The enrollment of the school was 839. What per cent of the pupils received the block letter?

Home Problem I

Go to the store and find the cost of 2 yards of percale and of 2 yards of gingham suitable for this apron. Estimate the number of yards of trimming required. Find the cost of this trimming per yard.

1. What would be the total cost of the material for this apron if made of percale?

2. What would be the total cost of the material for this apron if made of gingham?

3. Which is the cheaper and how much?

4. If the material for an apron cost 45 cents and the labor 60 cents, at what price must the apron be sold so that a profit of 20% may be realized?

Home Problem II

This school bag requires ½ yard black oilcloth, ½ yard sateen, ½ ball of red yarn and ¼ ball of green yarn. The oilcloth cost 59 cents per yard,

the sateen 50 cents per yard, and the yarn 10 cents per ball.

1. Find the cost of making one bag.

2. What is gained when one of these bags is sold for 75 cents?

3. If a crippled girl can make three per day, how much money would she earn in thirty days?

4. At a sale she bought 40 yards of oilcloth at $20. How many bags can be made from it? What would be her total profit on these?

Home Problem III

Dairy

Doris Hallows raised a Holstein calf. She kept the following account:

Cash Outlay

Date	Article		Value
March 1	Calf-weight 90 lb.		$5.00
March	120 lb. milk at 2½ cents per lb.		
March 5	Straw		1.60
April 1	Dairy Rations and Middlings		3.50
April	180 lb. milk		
May	180 lb. milk		
June	180 lb. milk		
July	180 lb. milk		
July	Pasture		.50
August	120 lb. milk		
August	Pasture		.75
Sept.	100 lb. milk		
Sept.	Pasture		.75
Oct.	Silage		3.00
	Shelter		3.00
	Weight 320 lbs.	Total	

Summary of Returns

Value of manure		8.00
Calf sold for		35.00
	Total	
	Total Cost	
	Return for work done $	

1. How many pounds of milk did this calf drink? What was its value at 2½ cents a pound?

2. Fill out the above outline and determine the amount realized for the work done.

Home Problem IV

Roland Davis purchased a 17 weeks' old Duroc Jersey pig weighing 100 pounds for $8. On November 13 he sold the pig for $36.

He purchased on July 7th 100 lb. of middlings for $2.60;

on September 20th 100 lb. of corn for $2.10; on September 25th 50 lb. of middlings for $1.30.

Roland estimated that the pasture for the pig was worth $2, the milk he drank $1, and the bedding 10 cents. Make out an itemized statement of the costs and the returns showing the amount Roland had left for his work.

Home Problem V

Garden

George Baker planted a plot of ground 120 ft. long and 15 ft. wide to vegetables. On May 1 he paid his father one dollar for plowing the plot. On May 5 he purchased tomato plants for 25 cents and on May 10 he bought 25 cents worth of pepper plants. The seeds which he purchased on May 25 cost a dollar.

The sales from his garden were as follows: July 5, 14 quarts string beans at 10 cents a quart; July 10, 2 heads lettuce at 8 cents each; July 15, 2 heads lettuce at 8 cents each; August 1, 1 quart dry beans at 12 cents; August 5, 20 heads lettuce at 6 cents each; September 10, 1 bushel tomatoes at $1.00; September 20, ½ bushel tomatoes at 50 cents; October, 6 dozen peppers at 20 cents a dozen; October 15, 4 bushel carrots at $.75 a bushel; 15 cabbages at 10 cents each; ½ bushel beets at $1.00 per bushel.

Make out an account showing George's total expenditures, total income and profit from his garden.

At the same rate what would be the profit on a garden containing one acre?

George's labor charged against his garden is as follows: May 24 hours, June 30 hours, July 10 hours, August 10 hours, September 5 hours, and October 15 hours. How many hours did he work in his garden? How much did he earn per hour?

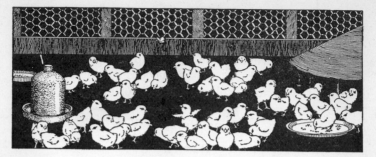

Home Problem VI
Poultry

Joseph Worden bought 50 day-old chicks at 22 cents each on May 26. His cash outlay thereafter was as follows:

May	26	brooder house	$5.00
May	27	25 lb. chick starter	1.00
May	27	kerosene oil	1.57
June	15	50 lb. mash	1.62
July	10	80 lb. mash	2.60
August	5	155 lb. mash	4.87
September	10	75 lb. corn	2.35
October	1	50 lb. corn	1.50

His returns were as follows:

August	29	2 broilers at 60 cents each
September	19	7 broilers at 70 cents each
October	15	25 pullets at $1 each

Make out a statement of Joseph's account showing how much he received for his labors. How many of his chickens did he fail to market? If these had been sold for 40 cents each, how much would have been added to his returns?

Mental Tests

1

1. A man makes a profit of $20 on goods costing $200. What is his gain per cent?

2. What is the interest on $500 for 2 months at 6%?

3. I borrow $700 for 1 year at 6%. How much must I pay back at the end of the year to settle the debt?

4. A lawyer collected 75% of a debt of $360. How much did he collect?

5. What will 1000 pounds of feed cost at $50 per ton?

6. If 4 pounds of butter cost $2.20 what will 10 pounds cost?

7. Find the interest on $4000 for 3 mo. at 6%.

8. 20% profit is made on an article costing $10. What was the gain?

9. 8 is what per cent of 64?

10. 10 is what decimal part of 20?

2

1. Find the interest on $1200 for 1 yr. 3 mo. at 4%.

2. How many quarts are there in $1\frac{1}{3}$ pk.?

3. What is 50% of half a dollar?

4. What is the interest on $1600 for 8 mo. at 6%?

5. What rate of interest must be charged in order that $1000 shall amount to $1060 in one year?

6. 50 is 20% of what number?

7. For how many years must $100 be at interest at 5% to amount to $120?

8. Find the interest of $150 for 3 yr. at 6%.

9. Find the amount of $300 for 4 years at 5%.

10. $5 \div .5 = ?$

3

1. Three acres of land cost $240. Find the cost of 4 acres.

2. A merchant reduced the price of goods from $1.60 to $1.20 a yard. What was the per cent of reduction?

3. Find the cost of 2 tons of coal at $7.50 per 1000.

4. A man sold a horse for $80, losing 20%. What was the cost of the horse?

5. Two dozen oranges cost $1.20. Find the cost of 8 oranges.

6. A note, due August 6, was discounted July 17. Find the term of discount.

7. A family uses 2 quarts of milk a day. At 12¢ a quart, what is their milk bill for the month of July?

8. In a room of 48 children, 32 are girls. What per cent are boys?

9. A house rents for $540 a year. What is the rent per month?

10. At 11¢ a pint, find the cost of 1 gallon of vinegar.

4

1. An agent sold $2000 worth of goods at 10% commission allowing $70 for other expenses. What was remitted to the owner?

2. What is the interest on $600 at 6% for 90 days?

3. An automobile averages 18 miles on a gallon of gasoline. At 16¢ a gallon, how much will it cost to go 144 miles?

4. Change 8969 pounds to tons.

5. Find the area of a square field that is 60 rods long.

6. A man paid $400 rent. This was $12\frac{1}{2}$% of the value of the house. What was its value?

7. 3 oranges cost 16¢. Find the cost of 1 dozen oranges.

8. $\frac{1}{2}$ acre of land costs $40. How many acres can I buy for $240?

9. Julia spent 50% of her salary for living expenses and 30% for advancement. What amount was left for savings from a salary of $2000?

10. A lady bought a $900 car at a discount of 15%. What did the car cost?

5

1. Find the area in acres of a field that is 60 rods long and 40 rods wide.

2. A boy saved $2 when he bought a pair of skiis for $6. What per cent did he save?

3. A newsboy paid $1.20 for papers and received $1.80. How many papers did he have when he sold them at 3¢ apiece and what per cent did he gain?

4. John had $10. He bought a pair of skiis for $4.50, a pair of skates for $4 and a hockey stick for 75¢. How much change had he left?

5. A girl paid $12 for a dress that was marked down 20%. What was the list price?

6. A man who earns $4000 saves $1000. What per cent does he spend?

7. A boy can walk 5 miles in 1 hour. How far can he walk in 48 minutes?

8. 2 yards of cloth cost $8½. Find the cost of 3 yards.

9. A 60-day note for $600 with interest at 6% is discounted the day it is made. Find the proceeds.

10. How many baskets will I need for 5 dozen lemons with 20 in a basket?

6

1. Divide 8 by ¼.   **2.** Add 2½ yards and 1¾ yards.

3. Of 60 pupils who took an examination 10% failed. How many passed?

4. Find the cost of 1200 copper rings at $3 per 100.

5. What will 12 bars of castile soap cost when 25 cents is paid for one box containing three cakes?

6. After spending $66\frac{2}{3}\%$ of his weekly income for a book, a pupil had 30 cents left. What is the amount of his weekly income?

7. Sales = $5000. Rate of commission = 7%. Proceeds = ?

8. A magazine having 200 pages devoted 80 pages to advertisements. What per cent of the magazine is filled with other material?

9. Find 200% of $200.   **10.** What is ½% of $200?

7

1. Multiply 8 by ¼.   **2.** Subtract $66\frac{2}{3}\%$ from 2.

3. One tablespoonful of coffee weighs ¼ ounce. How many tablespoonfuls are there in a pound?

4. One yard of ribbon costs 60 cents. How much will 21 inches cost?

5. What is ¼% of $2400?

6. If 7 is 25% of a number, what is the number?

7. At 32 cents a pound, find the cost of 24 ounces of cheese.

8. Face of Policy = $5000.   Rate of Insurance = $23 on $1000. Premium = ?

    9. Cost $500.   Loss 10%.   Find selling price.

    10. Cost $500.   Gain 10%.   Find selling price.

8

    1. Divide 2400 by 400.   **2.** $25 is what per cent of $30?

3. Four yards of ribbon cost $1.   How much will 9 yards cost?

4. The rate of taxation is $25 on $1000.   The assessed valuation is $6000.   Find the annual amount of money paid for taxes.

5. A grocer buys eggs at 60 cents a dozen and sells them at 72 cents a dozen.   What per cent of the cost is gained?

6. Find 125% of 240.   **7.** What per cent is 6 of 72?

8. An agent collected $2500 on a ten per cent commission.   What amount of money is due the agent for his services?

9. Twenty cents is paid for $\frac{1}{2}$ pint of ice cream.   At that price, what will be the cost of one quart of ice cream?

10. A house listed at $8000 is offered for $7000.   What rate of reduction is given?

9

    1. Subtract $\frac{2}{3}$ from $1\frac{1}{3}$.   **2.** Find the product of $\frac{3}{4}$ and $\frac{2}{3}$.

3. At 25 cents each, how many handkerchiefs can be bought for $3?

4. A real estate agent had a tract of land divided into 120 lots. At an auction 30 lots were sold.   What per cent of the lots were not sold?

5. How many badges 4 inches long can be made from 10 yards of ribbon?

6. At a food sale a profit of 60 cents is made on four cakes.   At that rate how much money will be realized on the sale of 24 cakes?

7. What part of $\frac{1}{2}$ is $\frac{1}{4}$?   **8.** Divide $2\frac{1}{2}$ by $\frac{1}{4}$.

9. A merchant lost $37\frac{1}{2}$% on goods costing him $800.   How much money did he lose?

10. The list price of a set of books was $65.   How much money will be saved by paying cash when a cash discount of 20% is offered?

10

1. Divide 2.4 by .04.   **2.** Subtract 10% of 90 from 90.

3. Oranges were quoted at 45 cents per dozen.   What will be the cost of 54 oranges?

4. The assessed valuation of a home is $4500, for which the rate of taxation is $32 on $1000.   What is the amount of tax to be paid by the owner of this home?

5. Sales = $5000.   Commission = $300.   Rate of commission = ?

6. How many hours must a boy work at 30 cents an hour to earn $5?

7. Find $\frac{1}{3}$% of 300.   **8.** Find $33\frac{1}{3}$% of 300.

9. Marked price $28; selling price $21; find the per cent of discount.

10. For a salary of $2400 a year, a budget system plans 15% for savings.   How many dollars are left for other items?

11

1. Divide 5 by $\frac{1}{5}$.   **2.** Multiply $2\frac{1}{3}$ by $3\frac{1}{2}$.

3. Find the cost of 5 quarts of maple sirup at $2.25 a gallon.

4. 40 square rods is what per cent of an acre?

5. Lemons bought at 20 cents a dozen are sold at the rate of 6 for 15 cents.   What is the gain per cent?

6. Find 1% of $26.50.   **7.** Subtract $1\frac{1}{2}$ from 5.

8. At $20 a ton, what will 75 per cent of a ton of hay cost?

9. Three cents is the price paid for $\frac{1}{2}$ pint of milk.   What will 10 quarts delivered in $\frac{1}{2}$ pint bottles cost?

10. What is the premium on a policy for $7000 when the rate of insurance is $32 on $1000?

12

1. What change should I receive from $5 when I buy 10 two-cent stamps, 4 three-cent stamps, and 25 one-cent stamps?

2. A merchant gained 25% when he sold a coat for $75.   What was the cost?

3. How many square yards of roofing are required for a roof 24 ft. by 30 ft.?

4. Find the area of a parallelogram whose base is 12 ft. and altitude 8 ft.

5. Find $\frac{1}{3}\%$ of $1500. **6.** Multiply 36 by $2\frac{2}{3}$.

7. How many board feet are there in a plank 12 ft. long, 6 inches wide, and 2 inches thick?

8. The expense of selling a piece of property was 5% of the selling price. The owner received $950. What was the selling price?

9. What will 2500 feet of lumber cost at $30 per thousand?

10. Gain $10; rate of gain 5%. Find cost.

13

1. The area of a floor is 180 square feet. Its width is 9 feet. What is its length?

2. 30% of a ton equals how many hundredweight?

3. Find the number of board feet in 10 sticks of timber each 12 ft. long, 4 inches wide, and 2 inches thick.

4. How many tons of hay at $16 per ton can be bought for $67\frac{1}{2}$?

5. The area of a parallelogram is 160 square rods and its base is 16 rods. What is its altitude?

6. A man bought a car for $840 and sold it for $770. What per cent of the cost did he lose?

7. A 90-day note for $1200 is discounted at 6% on the day it is made. Find the proceeds.

8. Find $\frac{1}{4}\%$ of $1200. **9.** Divide 4.2 by .2.

10. What is the area of a circle whose radius is 10, when $\pi = 3.1416$?

14

1. What is the circumference of a circle whose radius is 5?

2. How many acres are there in a field 20 rods by 16 rods?

3. Find the interest on $2400 for 60 days at 6%.

4. Find the cost of 6 tons of feed at $2.50 per hundred.

5. A merchant lost 20% on an article, selling it for $40. Find the cost.

6. How many days are there from June 6 to July 6?

7. What per cent of the perimeter of a square is one side of the square?

8. If 4 yards of cloth cost $1, what will 7 yards cost?

9. The circumference of a circle is 36 π. What is its radius?

10. What will 1500 board feet of flooring cost at $90 per M?

15

1. A pint is what per cent of a gallon?

2. Find the amount of $1500 for 1 year at 6%.

3. What will 40 square rods of land cost at $400 an acre?

4. Goods bought at $400 are sold at a loss of 10%. What is the selling price?

5. Find the cost of a rug 9 ft. by 12 ft. at $3 per square yard.

6. What is the interest on $1500 for 1 month at 6%?

7. Find the area of a triangle whose base is 12 ft. and whose altitude is 30 ft.

8. Add $\frac{3}{4}$ and $\frac{3}{8}$.   **9.** What is $\frac{2}{3}$ of $72?

10. Find the diameter of a circle whose circumference is 49 π in.

16

1. The radius of a circle is 18. What is the circumference in terms of R?

2. Find the cost of 500 brick at $38 per M.

3. What part of a ton is 1500 pounds?

4. Change 10 gallons to pints.

5. A house costing $8,000 was sold for $10,000. What was the gain in per cent?

6. Add $\frac{2}{3}$ and $\frac{5}{6}$.   **7.** Find $33\frac{1}{3}$% of 60.

8. $60 is what per cent of $1000?

9. 25% of what number equals 100?

10. Change 3 yards to inches.

STANDARDIZED TEST — ADDITION

Pupils completing the seventh grade should be able to do correctly 8 of the examples given below in five minutes. Eighth grade pupils should be able to do 9 examples.

8276	8906	9184	9751	7267
3051	6372	9170	8441	8062
7116	2959	8594	7009	5563
8257	6106	5282	9567	4320
7933	4639	6041	2712	3921
7885	4226	2714	3941	7469
3250	8996	5337	3825	4250
1739	5247	8011	7559	5470
3823	4620	8507	3441	2088
9751	7267	8496	2914	7885
7862	6809	8941	5917	6772
5013	7623	7910	4814	6028
1761	5299	9845	9007	6535
5872	6601	8522	6975	2340
3739	3496	1046	1227	2319

STANDARDIZED TEST — SUBTRACTION

Pupils completing the seventh grade should be able to do correctly 8 of the examples given below in one minute. Eighth grade pupils should be able to do 10 examples.

752	1839	987	1075	562
347	968	926	801	229

571	1308	1230	784	1897
443	847	968	506	152

1935	710	1077	856	1119
371	468	511	698	759

854	931	1028	1377	916
380	463	774	802	624

954	1077	1328	939	1316
483	704	872	654	827

STANDARDIZED TEST — MULTIPLICATION

Pupils completing the seventh grade should be able to do correctly 9 of the examples given below in six minutes. Eighth grade pupils should be able to do 10 examples.

8745	7851	9264
92	36	47

6054	6592	1362
58	64	23

4678	7029	2315
89	75	76

3657	7638	4259
38	53	49

1253	5376	3786
38	76	49

5492	6187	4395
53	28	73

STANDARDIZED TEST — DIVISION

Pupils completing the seventh grade should be able to do correctly 5 of the examples given below in ten minutes. Eighth grade pupils should be able to do 7 examples.

Copy these examples as you do them.

$47)\overline{27589}$ $79)\overline{36893}$ $36)\overline{28296}$

$68)\overline{31824}$ $96)\overline{56064}$ $28)\overline{21980}$

$57)\overline{22572}$ $89)\overline{25365}$ $48)\overline{32304}$

$76)\overline{36708}$ $67)\overline{39932}$ $98)\overline{46844}$

STANDARDIZED TEST — ADDITION OF FRACTIONS

Pupils completing the seventh grade should be able to do correctly 5 of the examples given below in four minutes. Eighth grade pupils should be able to do 7 examples.

Reduce your answers to lowest terms.

$$\frac{1}{6} + \frac{3}{5} = \qquad\qquad \frac{3}{12} + \frac{5}{8} =$$

$$\frac{3}{5} + \frac{1}{2} = \qquad\qquad \frac{4}{9} + \frac{1}{6} =$$

$$\frac{1}{3} + \frac{4}{7} = \qquad\qquad \frac{4}{15} + \frac{5}{9} =$$

$$\frac{1}{2} + \frac{2}{3} = \qquad\qquad \frac{7}{10} + \frac{3}{8} =$$

$$\frac{1}{3} + \frac{3}{4} = \qquad\qquad \frac{3}{8} + \frac{5}{6} =$$

$$\frac{1}{7} + \frac{2}{5} = \qquad\qquad \frac{1}{10} + \frac{1}{15} =$$

$$\frac{2}{5} + \frac{2}{3} = \qquad\qquad \frac{3}{10} + \frac{1}{4} =$$

$$\frac{4}{7} + \frac{3}{5} = \qquad\qquad \frac{3}{8} + \frac{2}{3} =$$

STANDARDIZED TEST — SUBTRACTION OF FRACTIONS

Pupils completing the seventh grade should be able to do correctly 6 of the examples given below in five minutes. Eighth grade pupils should be able to do 8.

Reduce your answers to lowest terms.

$$\frac{3}{4} - \frac{2}{5} = \qquad\qquad \frac{5}{6} - \frac{3}{4} =$$

$$\frac{1}{2} - \frac{2}{7} = \qquad\qquad \frac{7}{10} - \frac{1}{6} =$$

$$\frac{2}{3} - \frac{1}{2} = \qquad\qquad \frac{5}{6} - \frac{2}{15} =$$

$$\frac{3}{4} - \frac{1}{3} = \qquad\qquad \frac{7}{9} - \frac{1}{6} =$$

$$\frac{2}{3} - \frac{3}{5} = \qquad\qquad \frac{5}{6} - \frac{3}{8} =$$

$$\frac{3}{4} - \frac{2}{7} = \qquad\qquad \frac{7}{12} - \frac{3}{8} =$$

$$\frac{5}{6} - \frac{3}{5} = \qquad\qquad \frac{8}{15} - \frac{4}{9} =$$

$$\frac{4}{5} - \frac{1}{3} = \qquad\qquad \frac{7}{10} - \frac{1}{8} =$$

STANDARDIZED TEST — MULTIPLICATION
OF FRACTIONS

Pupils completing the seventh grade should be able to do correctly 7 of the examples given below in one minute. Eighth grade pupils should be able to do 8 examples.

Reduce your answers to lowest terms.

$$\frac{2}{3} \times \frac{3}{4} = \qquad \frac{2}{5} \times \frac{3}{7} =$$

$$\frac{5}{12} \times \frac{3}{5} = \qquad \frac{4}{9} \times \frac{2}{5} =$$

$$\frac{1}{3} \times \frac{3}{8} = \qquad \frac{1}{2} \times \frac{1}{3} =$$

$$\frac{2}{5} \times \frac{3}{4} = \qquad \frac{4}{5} \times \frac{1}{3} =$$

$$\frac{7}{12} \times \frac{4}{7} = \qquad \frac{3}{8} \times \frac{1}{4} =$$

$$\frac{2}{7} \times \frac{1}{6} = \qquad \frac{1}{3} \times \frac{1}{2} =$$

$$\frac{4}{15} \times \frac{5}{8} = \qquad \frac{4}{5} \times \frac{7}{9} =$$

$$\frac{1}{6} \times \frac{3}{10} = \qquad \frac{5}{12} \times \frac{2}{5} =$$

STANDARDIZED TEST — DIVISION OF FRACTIONS

Pupils completing the seventh grade should be able to do correctly 5 of the examples given below in two minutes. Eighth grade pupils should be able to do 6 examples.

Reduce your answers to lowest terms.

$$\frac{2}{5} \div \frac{1}{3} = \qquad \frac{4}{7} \div \frac{2}{3} =$$

$$\frac{3}{8} \div \frac{2}{3} = \qquad \frac{5}{6} \div \frac{5}{8} =$$

$$\frac{3}{7} \div \frac{4}{5} = \qquad \frac{7}{12} \div \frac{4}{9} =$$

$$\frac{1}{2} \div \frac{1}{3} = \qquad \frac{2}{3} \div \frac{8}{9} =$$

$$\frac{2}{3} \div \frac{3}{4} = \qquad \frac{4}{7} \div \frac{8}{11} =$$

$$\frac{3}{5} \div \frac{3}{4} = \qquad \frac{1}{4} \div \frac{1}{6} =$$

$$\frac{4}{5} \div \frac{1}{2} = \qquad \frac{2}{5} \div \frac{3}{7} =$$

$$\frac{5}{12} \div \frac{4}{9} = \qquad \frac{3}{4} \div \frac{2}{9} =$$

STANDARDIZED TEST — ARITHMETIC PROBLEMS

See suggestions in the introduction for using standardized tests and the directions for scoring a pupil's work upon these problems. A score is given for a correct principle (P) and correct answer (C). Sixth grade pupils should make a score of 14 on correct principle (P) and a score of 10 on correct answer (C). Seventh grade pupils should make scores of 20 and 13.

Solve these problems in the way that you have been taught. Arrange your work so that it can be easily understood in marking your papers but you are not expected to copy. Number the work for each problem. Be sure to put down all of the work. Solve the problems in the order in which they are given. Work rapidly but remember that a problem must be done correctly to count on your score. You will be allowed twenty-five minutes to do as many of these problems as you can.

1. A girl having $\frac{3}{4}$ yd. of ribbon bought $\frac{1}{8}$ yd. more. What part of a yard had she then?

2. A piece of ribbon $4\frac{3}{8}$ yd. long is cut from a bolt containing 10 yd. How many yards are left?

3. There are 31.5 gallons in a barrel. How many gallons are there in 63 barrels?

4. If a horse eats $\frac{3}{8}$ bu. of oats a day, how long will 6 bu. last?

5. When a 20-pound cheese is worth $1.90, how much will a 10-pound cheese cost?

6. Four loads of hay are to be put into a barn. The first load weighs 1.125 tons; the second, 1.75 tons; the third, 1.8 tons; the fourth 1.9 tons. Find the weight of the four loads.

7. A baker used $\frac{3}{5}$ lb. of flour to a loaf of bread. How many loaves could he make from a barrel (196 lb.) of flour?

8. My telephone bill is $12.85 a month. At that rate how much should I pay in $2\frac{3}{4}$ years?

9. A man spent $6.50 for board, $12.25 for clothing, $5.20 for books, and had $12 left. How many dollars and cents had he at first?

10. A boy saves $1\frac{3}{4}$ cents on a picture by doing his own developing and printing. This makes a saving of how much on each dozen pictures?

11. Make out the following account for a day. Cash on hand, $174.30; Receipts, mdse. $12.50, $6.75, $0.42, $17.30, $9.50, $42.75; Expenses, Perry and Co., bill, $75.82.

12. Muslin is to be bought for 12 new curtains each requiring $2\frac{7}{8}$ yd. How much will the muslin cost at $12\frac{1}{2}$ cents a yard?

13. A market man has 7850 pounds of ice put into his refrigerator at one time. How much does it cost at $3.90 a ton?

14. A man bought two suits of clothes, one costing $35.75 and the other $28.50. How much more did the one cost than the other?

15. A farmer raised 500 bushels of wheat on a field of 40 acres. What was the average yield per acre?

STANDARDIZED TEST — ARITHMETIC PROBLEMS

See suggestions in the introduction for using standardized tests and the directions for scoring a pupil's work upon these problems. A score is given for a correct principle (P) and correct answer (C). Sixth grade pupils should make a score of 14 on correct principle (P) and a score of 10 on correct answer (C). Seventh grade pupils should make scores of 20 and 13.

Solve these problems in the way that you have been taught. Arrange your work so that it can be easily understood in marking your papers. Do not copy the problem. Number the work of each problem. Be sure to put down all of the work. Solve the problems in the order in which they are given. Work rapidly but remember that a problem must be done correctly to count on your score. You will be allowed twenty-five minutes to do as many of these problems as you can.

1. From Chicago to Wheaton is 24.9 miles; from Wheaton to Geneva is 10.6 miles; from Geneva to Clinton, Ia., is 102.6 miles; and from Clinton to Cedar Rapids is 81.3 miles. How far is it from Chicago to Cedar Rapids?

2. A kerosene can holds 5 gallons. How much is left after $1\frac{3}{4}$ gallons have been drawn?

3. At 26 bushels to the acre, how many bushels of wheat will 8.75 acres yield?

4. How long will it take to earn $28 at $1.75 a day?

5. At the rate of $4 for an 8-hour day, how much is due a man for $6\frac{1}{2}$ hours' work?

6. Five tubs of butter contain, respectively, $27\frac{1}{3}$ lb., $30\frac{3}{4}$ lb., $24\frac{1}{4}$ lb., $32\frac{1}{2}$ lb., and $34\frac{1}{4}$ lb. How many pounds are there in the five tubs?

7. How many lengths ¾ yard long can be cut from 15 yards of goods?

8. A boy's wages in a certain store were 12½¢ an hour. How much is that a week (6 days) if he works 8 hours a day?

9. A fowl weighing 4½ lb. sells for $1. What is the price per pound?

10. A tailor uses 9¾ yd. of cloth for a suit. How many yards will it take for 32 suits?

11. A housekeeper receives $60 a month, out of which she pays the housekeeping expenses of her family. For groceries, she spends one month, $28.75; for meats, $9.20; for laundry, $4.80; for fuel, lighting, and incidentals, $10.98. What was the balance left from the $60 at the end of the month?

12. What is the gain on 36 bunches of bananas bought at $1.37 each and sold at $1.95 each?

13. A miller uses 18 bushels of wheat for 4 barrels of flour. How many barrels can he make from 207 bushels?

14. A jacket which cost a merchant $5.67 was sold for $7.25. How much did the merchant gain?

15. A man's wages amounted to 46 dollars for 9⅕ days' work. How much did he receive per day?

SHORT TESTS

1.

To be dictated.   Write answers only.

1. Find the cost of forty planks 2″ by 6″ by 12′ at $60 per M.

2. Find the tax on a house assessed at 80% of its value if the value of the house is $8000 and the tax rate is $17 per thousand.

3. What is the circumference of a circle whose diameter is 10 ft.?

4. 7 is what decimal part of 42?

5. 100 pounds is what per cent of a ton?

6. Mr. Johnson paid a premium of $57 for three years insurance on his house.   The rate of insurance was $\frac{1}{5}$% per year.   For what amount was Mr. Johnson's house insured?

7. Find the amount of $4600 at interest for 90 days at 6%.

8. What is 6% of $3000?

9. The base and altitude of a right triangle are 6 ft. and 8 ft.   What is its area?

10. What is net price of goods listed at $80 and sold at a 10% discount?

2.

1. $32.04
5.68
7.92
48.37
5.60
8.75
3.84
99.89
4.68
.39

2. Subtract 3,059,603 from 82,059,600.

3. Multiply $7830.65 by .028.

4. Divide 32.876 by 1.25.

5. $\frac{2}{3} + 3\frac{1}{8} + 8\frac{5}{12} + 17\frac{11}{18} - 29\frac{3}{5}$.

(Count every answer 0, if it is not exactly correct.)

EIGHTH GRADE — FIRST HALF

Add:

1.	62,545	2.	86,721	3.	49,658	4.	$18.76
	90,739		45,483		76,439		4.95
	17,492		27,918		27,862		23.64
	53,127		38,675		51,374		45.31
	79,364		91,586		96,941		.75
	86,886		59,867		30,286		6.78
	45,603		78,231		64,125		89.54
	38,558		87,654		98,507		68.73
	22,395		93,142		83,786		9.78
	71,972		64,379		49,103		14.24

5. Add the following:

43.125; 673.24; 87.9; 538.375; 79.63; 2691.425; 9843.667; 10.875; 382.333; 77.25.

6. Find the sum of $1\frac{5}{8}$, $5\frac{1}{2}$, $\frac{4}{9}$, and $\frac{5}{22}$.

7. Add $3\frac{1}{2}$, $\frac{2}{3}$, $\frac{2}{5}$, and $7\frac{1}{2}$.

8. The frame of a hat cost $\frac{3}{4}$; it was covered with $1\frac{1}{2}$ yards of velvet at $1.50 a yard and the trimmings cost $4.50. If the making cost $1.50, what was the total cost of the hat?

9. A sheet of postage stamps contains 100 stamps. Find the total value of 75 sheets of 1-cent stamps, 60 sheets of 2-cent stamps, 45 sheets of 3-cent stamps, 25 sheets of 5-cent stamps and 10 sheets of $1\frac{1}{2}$-cent stamps.

10. A manufacturer employs 57 men at $3.25 per day each and 19 men at $3.75 per day each; what is the amount of his pay roll for a month of 26 working days?

11. Add $8.5 + \frac{3}{4} + 2\frac{1}{8} + .25$.

12. Add 17.282; 674.8; 3.275; 18.027; 278.649; 10.7; 2497.728; 82.975; 2.466; 9826.425.

Subtract:

1. 306,791
   206,949

2. 79,864
   15,298

3. 742,868
   19,829

4. From $18\frac{7}{16}$ subtract $6\frac{17}{24}$.

5. From $7\frac{1}{4}$ subtract the sum of $\frac{5}{6}$, $\frac{7}{8}$, and $\frac{2}{3}$.

6. From 3727.66 subtract 469.77.

7. From 986.756 subtract 462.12.

Subtract:

8. $19\frac{2}{3}$
   $7\frac{7}{10}$

9. $28\frac{4}{15}$
   $19\frac{1}{5}$

10. $81\frac{5}{8}$
    $16\frac{1}{20}$

11. $24\frac{7}{8}$
    $20\frac{2}{3}$

12. From 30 yd. of canvas three pieces are cut; the first piece is $8\frac{3}{4}$ yd. long, the second $5\frac{1}{3}$ yd. long, and the third $12\frac{7}{8}$ yd. long. Find the length of the canvas left.

13. A warship makes the following record in 4 hours: first hour, 19.5 miles; second hour, 21.75 miles; third hour, 22.2 miles; fourth hour, 22.9 miles. What is the average rate of speed per hour?

14. From a farm of $124\frac{1}{2}$ acres, Mr. Brown sold $18\frac{1}{2}$ acres, $24\frac{3}{4}$ acres, and $7\frac{7}{8}$ acres. How many acres were there remaining?

15. From 897.249 subtract the sum of 219.28 and 162.496.

16. Subtract the sum of 86.748 and 279.816 from 528.177.

17. From a car containing 48,300 pounds of corn, ten tons are sold. How many tons remain?

18. What must be added to 8.004 to make 11.031?

19. $4000 − $1384.90 = ?

Multiply :

  1. 496 by 37$\frac{7}{8}$.   **2.** 129 by 21$\frac{2}{3}$.   **3.** 864 by 19$\frac{7}{8}$.

  4. Multiply the sum of $\frac{2}{3}$, $\frac{1}{2}$, $\frac{3}{4}$, $\frac{5}{6}$, $\frac{7}{12}$ by $\frac{3}{10}$.

  5. From 3727.66 subtract 469.77 and multiply the remainder by 5.8.

  6. From 9305.21 subtract 8046.39 and multiply the remainder by 6.7.

Multiply :

7.	79,864	**8.**	16,249	**9.**	28,216	**10.**	84,726
	7,906		2,816		4,709		9,277

  11. Subtract 6793 from the product of 4853 and 796.

  12. Multiply 6$\frac{2}{3}$ × 8$\frac{7}{8}$ × 20$\frac{3}{4}$.

  13. Find the cost of 60 bats at 1.33\frac{1}{3}$ each.

  14. A carpenter took a job of repairing a barn for $385; he hired 8 men at $5.50 a day and 3 men at $5.75 a day; all the men worked 9 days. Did the carpenter gain or lose and how much?

  15. A celery grower had 3 acres of celery to which he applied 700 pounds of salt per acre; find the cost of the salt at $2.10 per barrel of 280 pounds.

  16. A boy sold 94 papers every day except Sunday; his profit was $\frac{1}{2}$ of a cent on each paper. What was his profit for the month of August? (Assume that there were 31 days in the month, including four Sundays.)

  17. Subtract 2986 from the product of 862 and 1928.

  18. Find the cost of 144 pencils at $.035 each.

  19. Multiply 3.1416 by 49.

  20. Multiply 1.73 by 64.

  21. What must be paid for 81 posts at $.165 each?

Divide :

1. 1322.4 by 4.56. **2.** 186.375 by 497.

3. 18305.1 by 38.7. **4.** 555.808 by 789.

5. 860.89 by 43.7. **6.** 22.464 by 1.44.

7. The product of two numbers is 38,412 and the multiplicand is 792; what is the multiplier?

Divide:

8. $18\frac{2}{3}$ by $2\frac{1}{2}$. **9.** $144\frac{1}{8}$ by $10\frac{3}{4}$. **10.** $\frac{8}{20}$ by $1\frac{4}{5}$.

11. An automobile was driven 64.4 miles in $3\frac{1}{2}$ hours; what was the average rate of speed per hour?

12. A boy bought an overcoat for $13.75, a suit of clothes for $21, and a pair of shoes for $4; he paid for them in work at $1.25 a day. How many days did he work?

13. An entertainment for the benefit of The Athletic Association was held in a high school auditorium containing 900 seats; $\frac{1}{3}$ of the seats were sold for $1 each, $\frac{1}{3}$ for 75 cents each, and $\frac{1}{3}$ for 50 cents each. How many gymnasium suits at $5 each could be purchased with the proceeds?

14. Five horses weigh respectively 1246 lb., 1384 lb., 1428 lb., 1503 lb., and 1629 lb. What is their average weight?

15. A crate holds 32 quarts; how much will a merchant receive for a crate of strawberries if he sells them at the rate of 2 quarts for 25 cents?

16. What fractional part of 3 yards is $\frac{3}{4}$ of a yard?

17. A newsboy paid $1.50 for 100 papers and sold them at 2 cents each; how much did he make?

18. From the sum of $18\frac{3}{4}$ and 12.5 subtract the sum of $7\frac{3}{8}$ and $3.87\frac{1}{2}$.

19. Subtract 279.6 from the sum of 121.47 and 167.216.

20. Multiply $21\frac{1}{3}$ by $8\frac{3}{4}$ and subtract the product from the product of $18\frac{1}{2}$ multiplied by $10\frac{2}{3}$.

21. Divide 3823.556 by 142.67 and multiply the quotient by $19\frac{1}{2}$.

22. $7.5 + \frac{1}{4} - 3\frac{1}{8} + .75 = ?$

23. To the quotient of 175.562 divided by 21.41 add the quotient of 348.678 divided by 19.8.

24. Helen's report card shows the following standing:

Arithmetic	85	Spelling	100
Geography	80	English	75
Physiology	70	History	95

Find her average standing correct to one decimal place.

25. A class in cooking gave a luncheon for which the following materials were used: 2 cans salmon at 14 cents a can; 4 eggs at 36 cents a dozen; $\frac{1}{3}$ peck of potatoes at 30 cents a peck; 2 cans peas at 13 cents a can; 2 quarts peaches at 15 cents a quart; flour 10 cents; 1 pound butter at 47 cents; 1 pound sugar 8 cents; other items 15 cents. Sixteen persons were served. Find the cost per person.

26. If a family uses $1\frac{1}{2}$ pounds of meat a day, how much more will be spent in a month of 30 days by buying steak that costs 36 cents a pound rather than steak that costs 32 cents a pound?

27. How much change should you receive from a five-dollar bill, after paying for $2\frac{1}{4}$ pounds butter at 54 cents a pound and $1\frac{1}{2}$ dozen eggs at 60 cents a dozen?

Accounts and Bills

Merchants and others transacting any considerable amount of business have sets of books in which accounts are kept.

There are various methods of recording transactions as they occur, and arranging them in the different forms to suit the needs of the business; but it is the general custom to copy all accounts, finally, in a ledger, which shows in clear, concise form the complete account of each person, firm, or company with whom business is transacted.

In the ledger, each person's account is headed by his name. Money paid, services rendered, and goods *sold to* him are entered in the *left-hand* or **debit** side of the account.

Money, services, and goods *received from* him are entered in the *right-hand* or **credit** side of the account.

Accounts are balanced at regular intervals by footing the debit side and the credit side, and subtracting the smaller amount from the greater. The difference, called the **balance**, is then entered on the side having the smaller amount. This makes the two sides equal, or balance, each other.

Horizontal lines are then drawn below the footings, and the balance is brought forward to begin the account for a new period.

The use of computing and billing machines of various kinds is causing great changes in the method of keeping accounts and rendering statements. Even ledger accounts are often kept on loose sheets, in files made for the purpose, rather than in books.

Individuals or groups of individuals transacting business with one another are called **parties** *to the transactions.*

A record of the business transactions between two parties is an **account**.

The party who sells the goods is the **creditor**; *the party who purchases the goods* is the **debtor**.

In common usage, the term *debtor* means *anyone who owes a debt,* and the term *creditor* means *anyone to whom a debt is owed.*

Members of the class should visit business houses and ask to be shown the books and have their uses explained. Most merchants will welcome such a call.

The following form represents the ledger account of Andrew Pine, for October and November, at a hardware store. The number in the column at the left of dollars refers to the page of the day book (the book in which each day's transactions are recorded as they occur) in which the item was first entered.

Which column (left or right) shows articles that Mr. Pine has bought? What does the other column show?

Dr.			ANDREW PINE						Cr.		
1928						1928					
Oct.	7	Nails	6	$ 5	75	Oct.	20	Locks	49	$ 1	75
	13	Doors	32	18	50		28	Cash	54	50	
	19	Door trimmings	48	7	48		31	Balance		41	48
	26	Windows	51	61	50						
				93	23					93	23
Nov.	2	Bal. brought for'd		41	48	Nov.	9	Cash	58	20	
	10	White lead	60	7	40		16	Labor	63	2	50
	17	Shovel	65		75						

NOTE. — Many bookkeepers omit from the ledger the words describing the articles bought and sold, as *nails*, *locks*, etc., leaving those columns blank. This practice is increasing.

Copy Mr. Pine's account for November; balance it, and make the proper entry to begin the account for December.

At the time of balancing an account, it is customary to send to the debtor a copy of the account for the period for which the balance is made. This is called a **bill** or **statement**. Many business houses send monthly statements to their customers. Some business houses send a bill, **or invoice**, as it is called, with each list of goods sold.

1. Mention five things that a bill should contain.

2. Why should the date of each transaction be given?

3. Why should a bill be receipted?

4. What should the debtor do with his receipted bill? Why?

5. When an employee receipts a bill, instead of the creditor himself, how should he do it?

6. When one receives a bill how soon should he pay it?

7. In Form 1, below, what does $6.19 show?

8. Who is the debtor?

9. Who is the creditor?

10. Has the bill been paid?

11. By whom should this be receipted when paid?

12. Are there any credit items in this bill?

13. In Form 2, page **229**, how is $301.79 obtained? How is $826.79 obtained? How is $258.02 obtained?

The following forms illustrate some of the ways in which bills are made out:

(FORM 1)

THE FAIR

STATE, ADAMS AND DEARBORN STREETS

CHICAGO Oct. 1, 1926

SOLD TO

S. F. CHAMPION,
3122 DIVISION ST.
BERWYN, ILL.

FOLIO 1366

Bills Payable 1st of Month following Purchase.   Make Checks Payable to The Fair

	Sept							
16003	1	GROCERIES			96			
1626		BACON		2	10			
		HAM		3	13		6	19
1675	9	GROCERIES					2	62
1620	12	GROCERIES					2	84
105	14	2 PKG. CLOTHES PINS	12					24
							11	89

(FORM 2)

STATEMENT

Philadelphia, Pa., *Jan. 1,* 1928

A. J. Reach Company

Makers of " *The Very Best* " Sporting Goods

TULIP AND PALMER STREETS

M _Simmons Hardware Co.,_

St. Louis, Mo.

Terms : — NET CASH 30 DAYS

1927						
Dec.	1	Balance			525	00
	4		25	67		
	5		24	31		
	18		10	15		
	22		163	25		
	29		78	41		
					301	79
					826	79
		Cr.				
	6	By mdse	23	10		
	12	" freight	4	67		
	13	" cash	465	00		
	24	" mdse	76	00		
					568	77
		RECEIVED PAYMENT			258	02
		1 mo. 19 day 1928				
		A. J. REACH CO.				
		per *J. W. M.*				

Make out and foot bills of the following items, supplying dates and addresses; receipt them, either as creditor, or as the creditor's agent:

1. Bought by W. J. McCarthy from Bentley and Settle, 20 bbl. patent flour, $8 per barrel; 2000 lb. granulated sugar, $7.15 per hundredweight; 300 lb. Java coffee, 38¢ per pound; 250 lb. maple sugar, 18¢ per pound.

Mr. McCarthy has paid $125 in money.

2. A. Walrath sold to Donald Anderson,

> 5 lb. rice at 9¢.
> 4 dozen eggs at 41¢.
> 2 brooms at 50¢.
> 18 lb. chicken at 45¢.
> 8 lb. tomatoes at 13¢.

3. Debtor, Miss Margaret Maddox;
Creditor, H. G. Stone & Son.

> Account rendered, $12.35.
> 24 yd. lace at 25¢.
> 2 spools twist at 10¢.
> 6¾ yd. net at $.62.
> 6¾ yd. linen at $1.25.
> *Credit*
> Cash, $10.

4. Find out your mother's last order at the grocery and at the market, and make out bills for them.

5. Make out a bill from a clothing or department store. Secure the prices for this bill from an advertisement in the daily paper.

6. Make out a bill to the man who lives across the street from your house, or to the lady next door. What kind of service could you perform that might be put into such a bill? What could you raise, or make to sell?

Salesmanship

The selling of goods has an important place in the commercial world. Practically everyone has the experience of buying or selling. It is well to know something about salesmanship.

The people who make a business of selling goods may be divided into two classes; the retail salesman and the traveling salesman. The retail salesman sells goods from the counter to the customer. The traveling salesman who goes from town to town sells his merchandise usually at wholesale. The salesman, either retail or traveling, performs a very necessary service in the distribution of goods from the manufacturer to the final consumer.

For both classes the salary varies widely. The ordinary retail clerk, engaged in selling necessities for which there is a steady demand, is usually paid a comparatively small salary. Why? More highly trained salesmen who are engaged in selling furs, stocks, insurance, imported rugs, bonds, and like items receive much higher salaries. Often they are paid a commission ranging from 5% to 20% on all sales made in addition to a fixed salary.

The majority of traveling salesmen work on a "straight commission basis." They have a "drawing account" which entitles them to draw each week or each month an amount sufficient to cover their expenses. The amount so drawn is subtracted from the amount of commissions due and this difference is paid at regular intervals. It is not unusual however to find traveling salesmen working on a "salary and commission" basis. Some receive a fixed salary. When sales reach an especially large volume a business house may pay an additional compensation in the form of bonuses. In salesmanship as in many other lines of business, the salary is based on the salesman's success.

The successful salesman must know the goods he is trying to sell. He must have confidence in the value and desirability of his merchandise. He must be neat in appearance and courteous in manner. He must know the selling process.

A good salesman develops a sale in four definite steps. First he *attracts the attention* of the customer to the article on sale. Second he proceeds to *arouse interest* in the merchandise by giving definite information. Third he *creates a desire* for the goods. Fourth *he closes the sale.* Another asset in salesmanship is the ability to compute with accuracy.

Every good salesman is courteous. He strives to produce the impression that he is really trying to render a friendly service to his customer which will benefit both and be the basis of future pleasant business relations. He refrains from selling his customer goods which he knows will prove unsatisfactory for the same reason.

He does not debate with his customer and is careful to do as little talking as possible. He talks just enough to display the advantages of his wares.

Finally he is very careful in giving prices and in computing the amount of the bill. Accuracy in multiplication and in the use of fractions is very essential. It is in these two arithmetical processes that a salesman is likely to be most deficient. If he receives the pay for his goods in money, he is very careful to be accurate in counting out the change the customer should receive.

Fill out this form to show the proper prices.

Remember that the final price cannot show a fraction of a cent.   A merchant would charge 32 cents for $2\frac{1}{2}$ yards of cloth at $12\frac{1}{2}$ cents a yard.

	YD.	A	B	C	D	E
1.	1	$12\frac{1}{2}$¢	75¢	$1.10	$1.80	$3.00
2.	$\frac{1}{2}$					
3.	$\frac{1}{3}$					
4.	$\frac{1}{6}$					
5.	$\frac{3}{8}$					
6.	$\frac{3}{4}$					
7.	$\frac{7}{8}$					

Using the above table, find the cost of:

8. $8\frac{1}{2}$ yd. @ 75¢

9. $12\frac{1}{2}$ yd. @ $12\frac{1}{2}$¢

10. $2\frac{1}{4}$ yd. @ 75¢

11. $6\frac{1}{3}$ yd. @ $1.10

12. $5\frac{3}{8}$ yd. @ $3.00

13. $4\frac{1}{8}$ yd. @ $1.80

14. $9\frac{3}{4}$ @ $12\frac{1}{2}$¢

15. $1\frac{1}{8}$ yd. @ 75¢

16. $3\frac{1}{2}$ yd. @ 75¢

17. $10\frac{7}{8}$ yd. @ $12\frac{1}{2}$¢

18. Suppose a customer purchases goods amounting to $4.30 and offers you a twenty-dollar bill in payment. How would you count out the change to him?

19. If the customer bought $8\frac{3}{8}$ yards of cloth at $1.10 a yard and offered a twenty-dollar bill in payment, how would you count out the change?

A Commission Merchant's Transaction

Mr. E. R. Jones, Syracuse, dealer in farm produce, consigns the following to William A. Higgins Co., commission merchants in New York, to be sold by them on a commission of 5%:

40 bbl. potatoes, 10 tons hay, 100 crates beans, 100 bbl. apples. Shipped Aug. 11, 1927, D. L. & W. R. R. from Syracuse.

It is customary for the consignee (the commission merchant) to pay certain charges, and deduct them from the proceeds of the sales. A check for the difference between the proceeds of sales and the expenses was mailed, with the **Account-Sales,** to Mr. Jones.

Account-Sales

Sept. 25, 1927.

MR. E. R. JONES IN ACCOUNT WITH

WILLIAM A. HIGGINS CO., COMMISSION MERCHANTS

392 Washington St., New York

Date of Arrival, Aug. 16, 1927.

	Sales				
20	Bbl. Potatoes	@ 5.50	110 00		
20	Bbl. Potatoes	@ 5.00	100 00	210 00	
10	Tons Hay	@ 20.00		200 00	
100	Crates Beans	@ 4.00		400 00	
40	Bbl. Apples	@ 4.00	160 00		
60	Bbl. Apples	@ 4.50	270 00	430 00	
	PROCEEDS OF SALES				$1240 00
	Expenses				
	Cartage			32 00	
	Storage			12 40	
	Insurance			9 10	
	Re-packing			4 60	
	Commission, 5% of $1240			62 00	120 10
	CHECK HEREWITH				$1119 90

The goods were sold between Aug. 16 and Sept. 25. The potatoes and apples were sold at different times at different prices.

NOTE. — The following problems will be of much greater value if the pupils are required to rule and fill out an "Account Sales" for each of them, following the model given on page 234.

1. Mr. E. G. Sage shipped the following to be sold at a commission house in New York, at 8% commission:

400 lb. butter, 1000 lb. cheese.

The consignees sold the butter at 38¢, and the cheese at 22¢.

The cartage was $4.50, storage $1.96, and insurance $4.15. What were the proceeds of sales? Make an account-sales of the above.

2. A commission house sold for a dealer a shipment of 1480 lb. dried peaches, 1760 lb. dried prunes, and 1200 lb. dried currants.

The prices were as follows: dried peaches 1000 lb. at 15¢, 480 lb. at 17¢; dried prunes at 18¢; and currants at 16¢. The commission was 10%, and the other expenses $35.84. What were the proceeds of sales?

3. Mr. Jones shipped the following consignment of grain to a commission merchant in Chicago: 1000 bu. corn, 2000 bu. wheat, and 1500 bu. rye.

The grain was sold as follows: corn $1.96, wheat $2.10, and rye $1.56. The expenses were cartage $46, storage and elevator $28, insurance $5.20. The commission was 5%. What were the proceeds of sales?

4. A commission merchant received a consignment of goods on which he paid $15.60 for cartage, and $6 for storage. He sold the goods, deducted his commission of 8%, and his disbursements for cartage and storage, and then had $7338.40 net proceeds of the sale, which he remitted to his principal. For how much did he sell the goods?

In the following examples the agent is buying for his principal. Find the missing numbers.

	Price Paid by Agent	Agent's Commission in Per Cent	Agent's Commission in Dollars	Cost to the Principal
1.	$14,742	3%	?	?
2.	?	5%	$110.40	?
3.	$13,958	?	?	$14,655.90
4.	?	6%	?	$21,624.
5.	$8,128	?	$243.84	?
6.	$15,729	5%	?	?
7.	?	?	$1913.10	$7379.10
8.	$5,325	?	?	$5751.
9.	?	3%	$1572.	?
10.	?	?	$503.70	$17,293.70
11.	$16,812	2½%	?	?
12.	$6,152	?	$246.08	?
13.	$16,550	?	?	$16,715.50
14.	?	9%	?	$1,364.68
15.	?	?	$1934.	$9,670.
16.	?	2%	$35.38	?
17.	?	7%	?	$9,545.47
18.	$15,905	?	$318.10	?
19.	?	2½%	?	$701.10
20.	$13,626	?	?	$15,669.90
21.	?	?	$149.79	$15,128.79
22.	$14,961	?	$748.05	?
23.	?	7%	$386.40	?
24.	$6,034	4%	?	?

25. What must be paid for 10,000 tons of raw sugar at $2\frac{3}{4}$¢ a pound?

26. How many quarts of milk at $.035 a quart can be bought for $700?

27. Find 125% of $4000.

28. $600 is what per cent of $66,000?

29. Find $33\frac{1}{3}$% of $9,630.

Discount

1. A man bought a dining room suite for $630 after a deduction of 10% had been made from the marked price. What was the marked price?

2. An article is marked at $360, which is 20% above the cost. Find the cost.

3. A book, listed at $1.60, is sold at $1.20. What is the rate of discount?

4. A box of soap is sold for $6.80, which is 15% below the marked price. Find the marked price.

5. A monument is marked so as to gain 40%. If the marked price is $70, what was the cost?

6. An automobile tire, costing $18, is marked to gain 45%. What is the marked price?

7. A bookcase, listed at $14, is sold for $11.90. Find the per cent of discount.

8. The list price of a lawn mower is $8.80. It is sold at a discount of 25%. What is the net price?

9. The discount on a cart was 10% or $.55. What was the price of the cart?

10. By paying cash for a plow, a farmer was allowed a discount of 5%. If his discount was $3, what was the price of the plow?

11. A picture was bought at a discount of 6% from the list price. If the picture cost the purchaser $26.32, what was the list price?

12. A farm wagon is listed at $150, with a discount of 18%. What is the net price?

13. A mowing machine, selling for $48, was marked $50. What was the rate of discount?

1. Find the rate of discount from the regular price on each article in the following advertisement:

	Regular Price	Sale Price		Regular Price	Sale Price
Girls' Cloth Dresses .	$2.50	$1.50	Inlaid Linoleum (sq. yd.)	$1.25	$ .82
Women's Sweaters . .	6.00	3.75	Cluny Sash Curtains (pr.)	2.25	1.79
Women's Handkerchiefs	.25	3 for 25¢	Axminster Rugs . . .	6.25	4.00
Men's Handkerchiefs .	.15	3 for 25¢	Dinner Knives (doz.) .	5.00	.25 each
Wide Ribbons (yd.) .	.98	.55	Window Shades . . .	.75	.50
Boys' Corduroy Suits .	6.75	5.75	Umbrellas	2.10	1.65

2. The following advertisement is taken from a daily paper. Find the rate of discount offered on each article.

The marked prices stand at the left. Carry the rate to the nearest hundredth of 1 per cent when the division is not exact.

$18.50 Suits and Overcoats
$20.00 Suits and Overcoats } Choice at $14.00
$23.50 Suits and Overcoats

$25.00 Suits and Overcoats
$27.00 Suits and Overcoats } Choice at $17.50
$30.00 Suits and Overcoats

3. A speculator bought a quantity of peaches for $280, and marked them 40% above cost. They began to spoil and he was obliged to sell them at a discount of 40% from the marked price. Did he gain or lose, and how much?

4. Mr. Parker marked silk that cost him $1.20 a yard so that he could allow a discount of 20% and still make a profit of 10%. At what price did he mark it?

5. Mr. Burton listed shoes at $12 a pair and sold them at a discount for $9. What was the rate of discount?

6. What rate of discount is equal to a $4 reduction on a $10 purchase?

Successive Discounts

1. The list price of a bill of goods is $240. Find the net cost when the successive discounts are 20%, 10%, and 5%.

SOLUTION

20% of $240 = $48	*First discount*
$240 − $48 = $192	*First net price*
10% of $192 = $19.20	*Second discount*
$192 − $19.20 = $172.80	*Second net price*
5% of $172.80 = $8.64	*Third discount*
$172.80 − $8.64 = $164.16	*Net price*

2. Find the net cost of a piano marked $600 with trade discounts of 3, 8, and 10%.

3. Find the net amount of a bill of $940 with trade discounts of 20% and 5%.

4. Find the cost of a bill of goods amounting to $7000 from which the following discounts were allowed; 37%, 4%.

5. A merchant bought goods listed at $8000, from which the following discounts were allowed; 10%, 5%, and 6%. What did the goods cost him?

6. On a bill of goods amounting to $14,000, I receive commercial discounts of 15%, 10%, and 5%. Find the net cost of the goods.

7. A machine, listed at $1260, is sold at discounts of 15% and 5%. What is the net price?

8. A bill of goods amounting to $3850 is given discounts of 14%, 10%, and 5%. Find the net amount.

Profit and Loss

Test 1

1. Cost $100; gain 20%; what is the selling price?
2. Cost $200; loss 10%; what is the selling price?
3. Gain 10%; gain $10; what is the cost?
4. Loss 20%; loss $40; what is the cost?
5. Gain 10%; selling price $110. Find the gain.
6. Loss 10%; selling price $180. Find the cost.
7. Cost $100; gain $25. Find the gain per cent.
8. Cost $200; loss $40. Find the loss per cent.
9. Cost $50; selling price $100. Find the gain per cent.
10. Cost $100; selling price $50. Find the loss per cent.

Test 2

1. Cost $2; gain 50%. Find the selling price.
2. Cost $2; loss 50%. Find the selling price.
3. Selling price $2; gain 100%. Find the cost.
4. Selling price $2; loss $33\frac{1}{3}$%. Find the cost.
5. Gain $2; gain $33\frac{1}{3}$%. Find the cost.
6. Gain $3; gain $33\frac{1}{3}$%. Find the selling price.
7. Loss $5; loss 25%. Find the cost.
8. Loss $6; loss 25%. Find the selling price.
9. Cost $12; selling price $15. Find the gain in per cent.
10. Cost $12; selling price $8. Find the loss in per cent.

Problems

1. When the selling price of an article is twice the cost, what is the gain per cent?

2. Find the loss per cent when an article is sold at one half its cost.

3. If the selling price is 150% of the cost, what is the gain per cent?

4. What is the loss per cent when an article is sold at seven eighths of the cost?

5. When an article costs three fourths of its selling price, what is the gain per cent on the cost?

6. An article is sold at a gain of one half the cost. Find the gain per cent.

7. The selling price of a damaged coat is one third the cost. What is the loss per cent?

8. An article costs 80% of the selling price. What is the gain per cent?

9. What fractional part of the selling price is the cost, when the gain is 25% of the cost?

10. What fractional part of the cost is the selling price, when the loss is 25% of the cost?

11. When the cost is one third the selling price, what is the gain per cent?

12. When the gain is equal to the cost, what is the gain per cent?

13. If the loss is three eighths the cost, what is the loss per cent?

14. A merchant neither gains nor loses on a sale. What is the relation of the cost to the selling price?

15. An automobile costing $1250 is stolen. What is the loss per cent if no insurance is carried?

16. If the cost is 50% of the selling price, what is the gain per cent of the cost?

17. An article costing $100 is sold at a gain of 20% on the selling price. How much more does the dealer gain than he would by selling it at a gain of 20% on the cost?

18. If strawberries are bought at $6.40 a bushel, at what price per quart must they be sold in order to gain 20%?

19. I sold an auto for $800, which was $\frac{4}{5}$ of the cost. What was the per cent of gain?

20. A house was sold for $7990 at a loss of 6%. For what price should it have been sold in order to gain 15%?

21. If tea sold at 44¢ a pound gives a profit of 10%, what per cent profit would there be if it were sold at $.48 a pound?

22. Hats, bought at $30 a dozen, are sold at $3.50 each. Find the gain per cent.

23. A merchant bought 450 bushels of wheat at $1.50 a bushel. He sold one half of it so as to gain 40%, and the remainder at cost. Find the average gain on a bushel.

24. A dealer buys 400 yards of cloth at 87½¢ a yard. At what price per yard must he sell the cloth to make a profit of ⅟₇ of the cost?

25. A grocer buys 80 bushels of potatoes at $.80 a bushel, and sells them at 30¢ a peck. Find the whole gain and the gain per cent.

26. Gasoline, bought at $7 a barrel, is sold at 26¢ a gallon. What is the gain in per cent?

27. Twenty acres of land are divided into building lots each containing 16 square rods. These lots are sold at $200, thereby making a gain of 300%. What was the cost of the land per acre?

28. A square mile of land was bought at $15 an acre and sold at a gain of 66⅔%. What was the total gain?

29. Thirty per cent was lost by selling a farm for $2800. For what should it have been sold to gain 30%?

30. A cow was sold for $138, which was a loss of 8%. Find the cost.

31. Milk is bought at $3.60 per 40-quart can and is sold at 12¢ a quart. What is the gain per cent?

In the following find the missing numbers:
Compute all rates on the cost.

	Cost	Gain	Gain %	Loss	Loss %	Selling Price
1.	?	?	$37\frac{1}{2}\%$			$1210
2.	?	?	24%			$10.56
3.	?			?	13.5%	$1487.50
4.	?				3.875%	$7690
5.	?	$9.45	?			$85.05
6.	?	?	$33\frac{1}{3}\%$			$17.64
7.	?			?	9.5%	$357.52
8.	?	$89.50	?			$268.50
9.	?			$1000	?	$9000
10.	$3762	$564.30	?			?
11.	?	?	$14\frac{1}{2}\%$			$52.67
12.	?			?	4.75%	$8382
13.	?	$.89				$4.45
14.	$13,145	$1840.30	?			?
15.	$21,955			$3951.90	?	?
16.	?	?	8.25%			$95.26
17.	?			?	7.25%	$6102.95
18.	?	$270	?			$720
19.	?			$2500	?	$9500
20.	$.85	$.238	?			?
21.	?	$373.80				$1263.80
22.	?			$511	?	$3139
23.	$586			$111.34	?	?
24.	$397	?	16.5%			?
25.	$89.50			?	18%	?
26.	?			$12.81	?	$72.59
27.	$.64	?	12.5%			?
28.	?			$197.26	?	$789.04
29.	$1865			?	24%	?
30.	$85	?	250%			?

1. A farmer sells chickens to a butcher at 30 cents per pound; the butcher sells them at a 60% advance on the cost. How much would a customer save in purchasing a three-pound chicken if he could purchase direct from the farmer?

2. How much more does a table marked $16.50 with a discount of 20% cost than one selling at $11.75?

3. The total cost of a shipment of sugar, including a commission of 2%, was $1224; compute the commission.

4. A merchant bought goods listed at $1472 and was allowed successive discounts of 12½% and 10%; how much did he pay for the goods?

5. A dealer offers a piano at $450, with discounts of 10% and 5% or a single discount of 14%; which is the better offer and how much better?

6. Find the cost of 15 dozen hammers listed at $9 a dozen, with discounts of 40, 20, and 10.

7. By selling woolen blankets for $2.56 above cost a merchant gained 32%; what did they cost?

8. An errand boy earns $4 a week; he can have a 25% increase or he can secure an office position at $25 a month. Which position would pay the more annually and how much more?

9. Arnold and Hatch bought a carload of 800 bushels of potatoes at $.90 a bushel. They paid $40 for freight charges and sold the potatoes at a gain of 20% on the total cost. What was the selling price per bushel?

10. A builder paid $1200 for a lot, $860 for labor, $1120 for plumbing and heating fixtures, $1650 for lumber, $89 for plaster and cement, and $81 for paint. He sold the house for $6600. Find his gain per cent.

Marking Goods

A merchant adopted the word *blacksmith* as his key word, by means of which the cost of his goods might be known only to himself and his salesmen.

The figures corresponding to the letters of the key word were as follows:

b	l	a	c	k	s	m	i	t	h
1	2	3	4	5	6	7	8	9	0

He sometimes used *x* as a repeater, to prevent repeating the same letter. $1.33 could be marked *bax*, or *baa*.

It is the custom to write the cost above and the selling price below, and the selling price may be written in letters or figures. Thus, $\frac{lki}{abh}$ is sometimes written $\frac{lki}{\$3.10}$, the mark above the line being the cost.

Write these price marks in figures:

1. *lcs*   **3.** *cmx*   **5.** *sbk*

2. *mih*   **4.** *bhk*   **6.** *acl*

7. If a hand mirror bearing the mark $\frac{lch}{lmh}$ is sold, the profit is what per cent of the cost?

lch = $2.40 = Cost.   The profit is $.30.
$\overline{lmh}$ = 2.70 = Sale Price.   ? per cent of $2.40 is $.30.

Find the rate of profit or loss based on cost:

8. $\frac{ksk}{smi}$ **10.** $\frac{tch}{\$11.75}$ **12.** $\frac{bhkh}{bchx}$

9. $\frac{blc}{\$1.86}$ **11.** $\frac{ash}{ahs}$ **13.** $\frac{iih}{mtl}$

Find the selling price, at the rates of profit or loss indicated:

14. *ic*, profit $12\frac{1}{2}\%$ ($112\frac{1}{2}\%$ of *ic*)   **17.** *cmh*, loss 20%

15. *cth*, loss 10% (90% of *cth*)   **18.** *blsc*, profit 25%

16. *mks*, profit $33\frac{1}{3}\%$ **19.** *kxh*, loss 18%

Find the profit or loss and selling price as indicated:

20. *cxh* (5% loss)   **23.** *kamk* (20% loss)

21. *sch* ($12\frac{1}{2}\%$ gain)   **24.** *khic* (25% gain)

22. *blsx* (15% profit)   **25.** *cmlh* (10% loss)

26. The sale price marked on a pair of shoes was *ixh*. If, at that price, the dealer made a profit of 10%, what was the cost? 110% of ? $= ixh$.

Find the cost marks for the following sale prices, at the per cents of profit or loss indicated.

The selling price stands below the line.

27. $\overline{sa}$ (10% loss)   **29.** $\overline{skh}$ (30% gain)

28. $\overline{abl}$ (30% profit)   **30.** $\overline{ai}$ (5% loss)

31. A piano costing \$500 was marked to sell at a 40% profit and was sold at 80% of the marked price. For how much was it sold?

140% of \$500 = marked price.
80% of marked price = sale price.

32. A hatter wishes to mark hats costing him \$3.00 so that he can make a reduction of 10% from the marked price and still make 30%. Find the marked price.

130% of \$3.00 = \$3.90, actual sale price.
\$3.90 is 90% of the marked price. $3.90 \div .90 = \$4.33$. *Ans.*

33. I want to mark gloves so that I can reduce the price 20% and still make 20%. The cost is $3.20. What is the selling price? What is the marked price?

34. A jobber bought 2000 wheelbarrows at $2.25 apiece, marked them at 115% of their cost, and sold them for 95% of the marked price. What did he receive for them?

35. A hardware merchant bought a bill of goods for $560 and marked them to be sold at a price which was 140% of the cost. At what price did he mark the goods? He sold the goods for 90% of the marked price. What did he receive for them?

36. A machine costing $120 marked to be sold at 40% profit is sold at $\frac{1}{8}$ off from the marked price. What is the gain? $\frac{1}{8}$ off is $12\frac{1}{2}$% reduction.

37. How much do I gain or lose when I mark goods costing $48 to be sold at 50% advance, and sell them at 40% below the marked price?

38. A bill of goods that cost $500 was marked to be sold at a profit of 50%, but was sold at 25% off the marked price. What was the gain?

39. A merchant bought a carpet at 60 cents a yard. He marked it so that he might take off 10% and still make 20% on the cost. At what price did he sell the carpet? At what price did he mark it?

40. At what price must goods costing $285 be marked so that the dealer may give a reduction of 5% and still make a profit of 18% on the cost?

41. A merchant sold his stock of goods at a reduction of 10% from the marked price and still made a profit of 14% on the cost. He received $4560. Find the marked price and the cost.

Insurance

Insurance is a plan of sharing losses. The payment of comparatively small sums of money for a certain period of time by many parties can make certain or *insure* the payment of losses in the relatively few cases that occur. The important kinds of insurance are fire, life, accident, health, burglary, and liability. Insurance is carried on by organizations called *insurance companies*.

The *insurance policy* is a written agreement between an individual or company and the insurance company by which, in return for the payment of certain sums, the individual or company is repaid in case of loss. The *face of the policy* is the sum of money the insurance company agrees to pay the insured when the loss occurs. The *premium* is the sum of money the insured pays the insurance company for this protection.

1. A man owned a house worth $6000; he insured it for three years for 75% of its value, the insurance rate being $4.50 per $1000 for the three years. How much premium did he pay?

2. Mr. Jenkins insured each of two houses for $5000. On one he took out a 5-year policy at the rate of $15 per $1000; on the other he took out an annual policy at the rate of 50 cents per $100. Which was the cheaper policy for the 5-year period and how much cheaper?

3. Mr. Smythe insured his house on a 3-year policy for $2800. If the rate is 75 cents for $100, find the premium.

4. Mr. Coon carries an endowment policy which will pay him, after 20 years, the amount for which his life is insured. If the policy is for $8000 and the annual premium is $43.10 per $1000, how much of the $8000 will Mr. Coon have paid in during the 20 years?

5. Mr. Battle insures his automobile for $1950 at the rate of 70 cents per $100 against fire and 80 cents per $100 against theft. Find the total premium.

6. Mr. Francis takes out an annual health policy which will pay him $25 weekly in case of total disability. The premium is $64 yearly. If Mr. Francis is ill in bed for 10 weeks, how much has the policy profited him?

7. Mr. Maycumber's estate received at his death $5000, on which Mr. Maycumber had paid an annual premium of $127.19 for 16 years. How much more did the estate receive than Mr. Maycumber had paid?

8. The Superior Goods Manufacturing Co. carries burglary insurance at the annual rate of $2\frac{1}{2}\%$ on its $50,000 valuation. Find the cost of the insurance for 5 years.

9. A Workman's Compensation Law requires companies to insure their employees for 30% of their weekly wage. Find the amount received by a man earning $45 a week, if he is disabled for 8 weeks.

10. Mr. Nichols insures his store and its contents for 75% of their value at the rate of 40 cents per $100. If the building is valued at $3500 and the contents at $5500, find the yearly premium.

11. A high school building is insured for $13,000 with the Hanover Fire Insurance Co., $35,000 with The Home Insurance Co., $30,000 with the Niagara Insurance Co., $15,000 with the Providence Washington Insurance Co. The total premium paid is $702.81. Find the rate of insurance and the amount of premium on each policy. If the building is insured for 80% of its value, what is the value of the building?

12. A house worth \$5600 was insured for $\frac{2}{3}$ of its value, and the contents, worth \$3800, were insured for $\frac{1}{2}$ of their value. The rate of insurance was 70 cents on \$100. The house and contents were entirely destroyed by fire within a year.

(*a*) How much did the company lose on the insurance?

(*b*) How much did the owner lose by the fire?

13. Mr. Drake paid \$19 a year to insure his car against fire and theft. He paid \$30.25 a year public liability insurance and \$8.15 a year for insurance against property damage. What was the cost of the entire insurance on his car?

14. A man took out a \$7000 ten-year endowment life insurance policy, on which the semi-annual premium was \$55.70 per \$1000. If he lived ten years after taking the policy, and paid all the premiums when due, how much did he pay to the company?

15. Miss Blake had an accident insurance policy which cost her \$35 a year. After she had paid three years' premiums, she was injured by an accident and received \$20 a week for 6 weeks. She received how much more than she paid?

16. A schoolhouse in a village is insured for \$85,000 at $\frac{3}{4}\%$. The agent's commission is 20% of the premium. Find the agent's commission.

17. A manufacturing company insured its plant worth \$250,000 for 75% of its value. At a rate of \$4.50 per \$100 find the annual premium.

18. A house valued at \$16,000 is insured for 80% of its value at the rate of \$6.30 per thousand. What is the premium?

Taxes

> A **tax** *is money required for public use, and is levied upon real property and incomes.*

1. The money to be raised by tax in a town is $12,000. The property of the town is assessed at $600,000. What is the tax rate? Find the tax on $2500 worth of land.

2. The assessed valuation of a school district is $564,-000; the amount to be raised by tax is $5000. What is the amount of school taxes on property valued at $1200?

3. The assessed valuation of the property of a town is $1,875,000; if the total tax to be raised is $7500, how much will a property owner whose assessment is $1300 be required to pay?

4. In 1925 the tax rate was $43 on every $1000 worth of property owned in the city of Cortland. Find the amount of tax paid on property assessed for $5000.

5. Find the tax rate for your village or city. Make a problem, using this tax rate.

6. In 1924 the assessed valuation of a piece of property was $3600; in 1925 the assessed valuation was increased 25%. If the tax rate in 1925 was $2.89 on every $100, what was the amount of tax paid on the property?

7. The tax rate of a county is $.0025 per dollar. The tax budget is $125,000. Find the assessed valuation of the property in the county.

8. Mr. Hall's property is assessed at $5000. The city tax rate is .015, the county rate is .004, and the state rate is .0018. What is Mr. Hall's entire tax?

9. The tax raised in Lincoln County is $12,000 on an assessed valuation of $3,000,000. If Mr. Rutherford's tax is $160, what is the value of his property?

Interest

Interest is the product of 3 factors, *principal*, *rate*, and *time*. When any three of the four terms are given, the other may be found.

Find the interest on $1200 for $2\frac{1}{2}$ years at 4%.

SOLUTION: $1200 × $\frac{4}{100}$ × $\frac{5}{2}$ = $120.

1. $650, 4 yr., 6%
2. $428, $1\frac{1}{4}$ yr., $4\frac{1}{2}$%
3. $280, 2 yr., $4\frac{1}{4}$%
4. $372, $4\frac{1}{2}$ yr., 5%

5. $600, $2\frac{5}{12}$ yr., $5\frac{1}{2}$%
6. $460, $1\frac{1}{3}$ yr., 6%
7. $65.50, $\frac{2}{3}$ yr., 6%
8. $750, 8 mo., $4\frac{1}{2}$%

Find the principal which will yield $86.40 in 2 yr. at 6%.

$86.40 ÷ ($\frac{6}{100}$ × 2) = $86.40 × $\frac{1}{2}$ × $\frac{100}{6}$ = $770.

9. $81.00, $1\frac{1}{2}$ yr., $4\frac{1}{2}$%
10. $43.00, 4 yr., 5%
11. $29.61, $2\frac{1}{3}$ yr., $4\frac{1}{2}$%
12. $135.00, 3 yr., 5%

13. $16.52, $2\frac{1}{3}$ yr., 4%
14. $36.00, 6 yr., 6%
15. $38.50, $2\frac{1}{2}$ yr., $5\frac{1}{2}$%
16. $20.46, $2\frac{3}{4}$ yr., 4%

Find the time in which $190 will yield $22.80 at 4%.

22.80 ÷ ($\frac{4}{100}$ × 190) = $22.80 × $\frac{100}{4}$ × $\frac{1}{190}$ = 3. Therefore 3 yr.

17. $1820, $245.70, $4\frac{1}{2}$%
18. $125, $18.75, 3%
19. $267, $37.38, 6%
20. $1500, $123.75, $5\frac{1}{2}$%

21. $423, $59.22, 4%
22. $218, $11.99, $5\frac{1}{2}$%
23. $1200, $54.00, 6%
24. $750, $168.75, $4\frac{1}{2}$%

Find the rate at which $265 will yield $39.75 in 3 years.

SOLUTION: $39.75 ÷ (265 × 3) = 39.75 × $\frac{1}{265}$ × $\frac{1}{3}$ = .05 or 5%.

25. $185, $29.60, 4 yr.
26. $390, $52.65, 3 yr.
27. $1250, $156.25, $2\frac{1}{2}$ yr.
28. $1600, $176.00, $2\frac{3}{4}$ yr.

29. $1240, $111.60, $1\frac{1}{2}$ yr.
30. $938, $56.28, $1\frac{1}{3}$ yr.
31. $62, $12.40, 5 yr.
32. $127, $30.48, 4 yr.

Find the terms indicated by x:

	PRINCIPAL	RATE	TIME	INTEREST	AMOUNT
33.	$1275	4%	x	$76.50	x
34.	$3500	4½%	3 yr.	x	x
35.	$850	x	1½ yr.	x	$913.75
36.	x	6%	2 yr. 3 mo.	$262.80	x
37.	x	4½%	1 yr.	$339.75	x
38.	$426	x	2⅓ yr.	x	$480.67
39.	x	5%	x	$343.75	3093.75
40.	$1460	x	4 yr.	$262.80	x
41.	$2700	5½%	2½ yr.	x	x
42.	$1500	4½%	x	$405.00	x

43. At what rate of interest will $2350 gain $141.00 in 1 year 6 months?

44. What sum of money placed at interest for 2 years at 5% will gain $120?

45. At what rate will $1600 gain $200 in 2½ years?

46. In what time will $850 gain $127.50 at 4½%?

47. What is the interest on $5000 for 2½ years at 4%?

48. What sum of money will gain $450 in 4 years at 4½%?

49. The property of a town is assessed at $1,250,000. The tax to be raised is $15,325. What is Mr. Reynolds' tax if his property is assessed at $8350?

50. Find the amount of the taxes of Mr. James Snyder, if he owns property worth $12,500, assessed at 60% of its value. The rate is $2.20 per $100.

51. The tax rate of a county is .003. The valuation is $2,175,000. Find the tax budget for the county.

Compound Interest

Compound interest *is interest computed by adding the unpaid interest to the principal at regular interest periods, and taking the sum for a new principal for each succeeding interest period.*

Written

1. Find the compound interest on $350 for 2 yr. and 6 mo. at 6%.

SOLUTION

$350.00	Principal
21.00	Interest for 1st year
$371.00	Amount taken as new principal
22.26	Interest for 2d year
$393.26	Amount used as new principal
11.80	Interest for 6 mo.
$405.06	Amount for 2 yr. 6 mo.
350.00	1st principal
$55.06	Compound interest for 2 yr. 6 mo. *Ans.*

When interest is compounded semi-annually, the rate for each period is one half the annual rate; when quarterly, one fourth.

When no interest period is mentioned, use one year.

2. What is the amount of $600 for 1 year at 6%, compounded semi-annually?

3. Find the compound interest on $2500 at 5% for 1 yr. 6 mo., compounded semi-annually.

4. What is the amount of $4000 at 6% for 1 yr. 9 mo., interest compounded semi-annually?

For the 4th period the time is 3 months.

5. Find the compound interest on $360 for 4 years at 5%, compounded annually.

Compound Interest Table

In actual practice, compound interest is computed by means of compound interest tables. The following table gives the amounts of one dollar for from one to ten periods, at various rates for each period. The required amount is obtained by multiplying the amount of one dollar, for the required number of interest periods, at a given rate, by the given principal. If the compound interest is desired, omit the 1 at the left of the decimal point in the multiplicand.

NUMBER OF PERIODS	1%	1½%	2%	2½%	3%	3½%	4%
1	1.010000	1.015000	1.020000	1.025000	1.030000	1.035000	1.040000
2	1.020100	1.030225	1.040400	1.050625	1.060900	1.071225	1.081600
3	1.030301	1.045678	1.061208	1.076891	1.092727	1.108718	1.124864
4	1.040604	1.061364	1.082432	1.103813	1.125509	1.147523	1.169859
5	1.051010	1.077284	1.104081	1.131408	1.159274	1.187686	1.216653
6	1.061520	1.093443	1.126162	1.159693	1.194052	1.229255	1.265319
7	1.072135	1.109845	1.148686	1.188686	1.229874	1.272279	1.315932
8	1.082857	1.126493	1.171659	1.218403	1.266770	1.316809	1.368569
9	1.093685	1.143390	1.195093	1.248863	1.304773	1.362897	1.423312
10	1.104622	1.160541	1.218994	1.280085	1.343916	1.410599	1.480244

6. What is the compound interest on $830 for 3 years at 2½%?

7. What is the amount of $650 for 4 years at 4% interest, compounded semi-annually?

Interest for 4 years at 4%, compounded semi-annually, is computed for 8 interest periods at 2% each.

8. What is the compound interest on $365 for 2 yr. 6 mo. at 5%, compounded semi-annually?

9. What is the compound interest on $640 for 4 years at 5%, compounded semi-annually?

Find the amounts of the following sums of money, compounded annually, for the time indicated:

1. $4000 for 2 yr. at 6%
2. $6000 for 2 yr. at 5%
3. $8000 for 2 yr. at 4%
4. $10,000 for 2 yr. at 6%

5. $5000 for 2 yr. at 5%
6. $7000 for 2 yr. at 4%
7. $10,000 for 4 yr. at 6%
8. $2000 for 5 yr. at 5%

9. Find the compound interest on $12,000, compounded annually, from March 1, 1925, to March 1, 1928, at 6%.

10. Find the amount of $6000, compounded annually at 6% for 5 years.

Many banks add the interest to the principal twice a year, on January 1 and July 1.

11. On Jan. 1, 1923, Mr. Harper deposited $1600 in a trust fund paying 4%, compounded semi-annually. What sum did he have to his credit on July 1, 1925?

12. Mr. Thorpe placed $3600 in a bank paying 4% interest, compounded semi-annually. Find the amount of interest earned by this sum in $3\frac{1}{2}$ years.

13. Which is better, and how much, $1000 at simple interest for 5 years at 6%, or to place it in a bank which pays 4% compounded semi-annually for the same period?

14. From the following data determine the sum of money to Mr. Sweet's credit on July 1, 1925, if the bank pays 4% compounded semi-annually:

> July 1, 1923, deposited $2000.
> Jan. 1, 1924, deposited $1000.
> July 1, 1924, deposited $2000.
> Jan. 1, 1925, deposited $3000.

Exact Interest

Exact interest *is computed by taking as many 365ths of the interest on a given principal for one year as there are days in the interest period.*

When a day is called $\frac{1}{360}$ of a year, in computing interest, the interest obtained is a trifle greater than it would be if each day were taken as $\frac{1}{365}$ of a year — its exact value. Interest computed by the usual method is therefore slightly inexact; yet business men seem to consider that its greater convenience compensates for its lack of accuracy.

The exact method of computing interest is employed by the United States government and, to a limited extent, elsewhere.

1. What is the exact interest on \$731.46, at 6%, for 175 da.?

SOLUTION: $\frac{6}{100} \times \frac{731.46}{1} \times \frac{175}{365} = 21.042$, or \$21.04. *Ans.*

Find the exact interest on:

 2. \$5000 at 5% for 180 da.

 3. \$584 at 4% for 120 da.

 4. \$109.50 at 3% for 125 da.

 5. \$2190 at 6% for 73 da.

 6. \$75.50 at $3\frac{1}{2}$% for 90 da.

 7. \$8000 at 6% for 110 da.

 8. \$250 at 6% for 240 da.

 9. \$3000 at 4% for 35 da.

 10. \$3500 at 5% for 177 da.

Partial Payments

When payments are made in sums less than the entire amount of a note, the holder indorses them on the back of the note, and they are known as **indorsements**, or **partial payments**.

The rule given below is the one adopted by the Supreme Court of the United States for determining the amount due on a debt on which partial payments have been made.

United States Rule for Partial Payments

Find the amount of the debt to the time when a payment, or the sum of the payments, equals or exceeds the interest due, and from that amount subtract such payment or sum of payments. With this remainder for a new principal, proceed as before to the time of settlement.

This rule means that neither the whole interest nor any part of it shall be used to increase the principal on which interest is paid; but whenever more than enough to cover the interest has been paid, the excess shall be used to diminish the principal.

$1820~   *Watertown, N. Y., Jan. 1, 1925*

On demand, for value received, I promise to pay to the order of _____ *A. D. Parsons* _____ ~~One thousand eight hundred twenty~~dollars *with interest.*   *Robert S. White*

Three payments were made on this note and were indorsed on the back of it as shown on the following page.

Received on the within note:

May 25, 1925	*$250*
Jan. 25, 1926	*$45*
April 7, 1926	*$375*
Settled July 13, 1926	

The diagram at the left shows a part of the back of the note on the preceding page, on which indorsements were made as given. The amount due at date of settlement is computed by the United States rule.

The legal rate of interest in New York State is 6 per cent.

Subtract each date from the one above to find interest periods:

	Yr.	Mo.	Da.			
a.	1926	7	13			
b.	1926	4	7	3 mo. 6 da. = 96 da.,	*4th Int. per.*
c.	1926	1	25	2 mo. 12 da. = 72 da.,	*3d Int. per.*
d.	1925	5	25	8 mo. 0 da. = 240 da.,	*2d Int. per.*
e.	1925	1	1	4 mo. 24 da. = 144 da.,	*1st Int. per.*
	1	6	12 =	552 da.,	552 da., *Proof of Int. periods*

Subtracting *e* from *a*, we obtain 1 yr. 6 mo. 12 da., which is equal to 552 da., the sum of the interest periods. This proves that the interest periods are correct.

$$\frac{6}{100} \times \frac{\$1820}{1} \times \frac{144}{360} =$$

$1820.00	*First principal*
43.68	*Interest for 1st period*
$1863.68	*Amount*
250.00	*First payment*
$1613.68	*New principal*

$$\frac{6}{100} \times \frac{\$1613.68}{1} \times \frac{240}{360} = 64.55 \quad \text{\textit{Interest for 2d period exceeds payment}}$$

$$\frac{6}{100} \times \frac{\$1613.68}{1} \times \frac{72}{360} =$$

19.36	*Interest for 3d period*
$1697.59	*Amount*
420.00	*Sum of 2d and 3d payments*
$1277.59	*New principal*

$$\frac{6}{100} \times \frac{\$1277.59}{1} \times \frac{96}{360} =$$

20.44	*Interest for 4th period*
$1298.03	*Amount due at settlement. Ans.*

1. Write an interest-bearing note, dated Warsaw, N. Y., Aug. 15, 1927, promising to pay $1200 eight months from date, with $200 indorsed Nov. 17, 1927. How much was due April 15, 1928, the legal rate being 6%?

2. What was due March 1, 1925, on a note for $1000 with interest at 6%, dated March 1, 1924, with indorsements as follows: Aug. 10, 1924, $300; Sept. 1, 1924, $100?

3. What amount was necessary to settle Oct. 20, 1927, a note for $2000, with interest at 6%, dated July 20, 1926, bearing an indorsement of $700, Oct. 20, 1926?

4. A note for $700 with interest at 7% was given Dec. 12, 1924. Payments of $200, Dec. 12, 1925, and $159, April 5, 1926, were made. What was due Oct. 30, 1926?

5. How much was due Aug. 1, 1928, on a note for $380, with interest at 5%, dated Aug. 1, 1926, on which were indorsed payments of $15, May 1, 1927, and $90, Jan. 1, 1928?

6.

$300   TROY, N. Y., *Oct. 12*, 1925
　　On demand, I promise to pay 〜〜〜 *S. D. Cleveland* 〜〜〜
or order, *Three hundred* 〜〜〜〜〜〜〜〜〜〜〜dollars,
with interest. Value received.

　　　　　　　　　　　　　　　J. H. Van Alstyne.

A payment of $150 was made on this note June 27, 1927. What was due Oct. 9, 1927?

7. On a note for $500, with interest at 6%, dated June 10, 1924, were the following indorsements: April 5, 1925, $14.30; July 14, 1926, $250. How much was due Sept. 20, 1927?

Banks and Banking

There are three kinds of banks.

(a) Savings Banks
(b) National Banks } Commercial Banks
(c) State Banks

Savings banks are designed to be safe places for the deposit of money. They were originally designed for wage earners who were not acquainted with the best methods of investing money. Savings banks are now extensively used by all classes of investors.

Commercial banks accept deposits, loan money, and discount evidences of indebtedness. These banks have two departments, one for interest-bearing accounts and the other for checking accounts.

Commercial banks organized under Federal laws are called Federal or National banks.

Commercial banks organized under state laws are called state banks.

Some state banks are granted the right by law to act as administrators of estates, guardians of minor children, and trustees of bond issues. These banks are called Trust Companies.

Banks derive their income from the use of non-interest-bearing deposits. Many banks require of each depositor a free balance of at least $200.

Notes

A promissory note is an agreement on the part of the first party to pay the second party a definite sum of money at a stipulated time.

$ _____ *Fulton, N. Y.* _____192_ _____*months after date*___*promise to* *pay to the order of*_____ _____*Dollars* *For value received.* _____ _____ *No.*_____ *Address*_____	*Due*_____ *No.*_____ *Amount,* $____ *Maker* _____ *Endorser* _____ _____
NOTE	STUB

A bank note is a promissory note made payable to the bank.

$ _____ *Fulton, N. Y.* _____192_ _____*months after date*___*promise to* *pay to the* CITIZENS' FIRST NATIONAL BANK, *or order*_____*Dollars* *For value received at the* _____ **Citizens' First National Bank** Fulton, New York *No.*_____ *Address*_____	*Due*_____ *No.*_____ *Amount,* $____ *Maker* *Endorser* _____ _____
NOTE	STUB

Secure a blank form of a promissory note from a local bank. What is the purpose of the stub?

Stocks

A stock company consists of a number of persons, organized under a general law or by special charter, and empowered to transact business as a single individual.

The capital stock of a company is the amount named in· its charter.

A share is one of the equal parts into which the capital stock of a company is divided.

In this book, a share will be considered as $100 of stock unless otherwise indicated.

A stockholder is a person who owns one or more shares of capital stock.

The par value of a share of stock is its face value. The market value of a share of stock is the price for which the share will sell in the market.

The market values of leading stocks fluctuate from day to day, and are quoted in the daily papers. " N. Y. C., 131 " means that the stock of the New York Central R.R. Co. is selling to-day at $131 a share.

When the market price is the same as the par value, the stock is at par; when the market value is greater than the par value, it is above par, or at a premium; when the market value is less than the par value, it is below par or at a discount.

The par value never changes. A share that was originally $100 is always $100, though its market value may be more or less than $100. The par value of stock, therefore, represents a certain quantity or part of the entire capital stock of a company. If a company had capital stock to the amount of $100,000, then one share with a par value of $100 would represent $\frac{100}{100000}$ of the stock of the company.

Dividends are the net profits of a stock company divided among the stockholders according to the amount of stock they own.

Assessments are the losses apportioned among, and required to be paid by, the stockholders according to the amount of stock they own.

Both dividends and assessments are computed at a certain per cent of the par value. If a company is capitilized at $100,000, and makes a net profit of $2000 during one year, the profit is 2% of the par value of the stock.

Stock companies often issue two kinds of stock.

Preferred stock consists of a certain number of shares on which dividends are paid at a fixed rate, and

Common stock consists of the remaining shares, among which are apportioned whatever profits are left after the required dividends on preferred stock are paid.

Stocks are bought and sold by brokers, who act as agents for the owners.

Brokers receive as their compensation a certain sum per share of the stock bought or sold. This is called brokerage.

Most stock exchanges follow the practice of the New York stock exchange, which allows the broker 15¢ per share for buying or selling any stock that brings from $10 to $125 per share, and 20¢ per share for stocks bringing more than $125 per share. There is a minimun brokerage charge of $1 per sale.

The daily market quotations of stock sales show a rise or fall in the selling price according to the demand for stocks of a particular kind or according to the condition of the organization back of the stock.

1. How many dollars of stock are represented by fifty $100 shares?

2. Explain the meaning of each of the following quotations: Pacific Transportation Co., $57\frac{1}{4}$; Great Northern, preferred, $117\frac{7}{8}$; American Sugar, $101\frac{3}{8}$; Mexican Central, $14\frac{1}{2}$; Lighting Co., 188; U. S. Rubber, common, 20, preferred, 77.

3. When stock is quoted at 85, what is the market value of 100 shares? What is the par value? Is it at a premium or at a discount? What per cent?

4. When stock is quoted at $132\frac{1}{2}$, what is the rate of premium? What is the market value of two shares?

5. When stock is quoted at 90, what is the rate of discount? What is the market value of one share? How many shares will $450 buy? What will 1000 shares cost?

6. When stock sells at a discount of $21\frac{3}{8}\%$, what is the quotation?

7. What is the market value of one share of stock which is quoted at 120? Of 8 shares? Not including brokerage, how many shares can be bought for $480? For $1080? For $360?

8. When stock is quoted at 75, what is the market value of 1 share? Of 4 shares? Of 3 shares? Of 20 shares? Not including brokerage, how many shares can be bought for $150? For $375? For $7500? For $1500?

9. What must be paid for 100 shares of Rapid Transit R.R. stock at $49\frac{1}{4}$?

$$\$49.25 + \$.15 = \$49.40$$
$$100 \times \$49.40 = \$4940.00. \quad \text{Cost.}$$

10. Find the cost, including brokerage, of 100 shares of Pennsylvania R.R. at 44.

The following quotations were copied from a daily paper. Use them in solving problems **11–20**.

Allied Chemical	$90\frac{1}{4}$	N. Y. Central	$117\frac{5}{8}$
American Woolen	$68\frac{3}{4}$	National Biscuit	$66\frac{3}{4}$
American Sugar	$63\frac{1}{2}$	Northern Pacific	$63\frac{1}{4}$
Baltimore and Ohio	$76\frac{3}{4}$	Pullman Co.	$143\frac{1}{2}$
Brooklyn Manhattan Transit	$42\frac{1}{2}$	Radio Corp.	$58\frac{1}{4}$
Chicago, Mil., and St. Paul	$9\frac{3}{4}$	Pacific Oil	39
Chicago, Northwestern	$55\frac{3}{4}$	Southern Pacific, preferred	103
Del. & Hudson	$150\frac{3}{4}$	Western Union	$133\frac{1}{4}$

Remember that brokerage for buying stock is added to the market value to determine the cost; it is subtracted from the market value to determine amount received.

Find the cost, including brokerage, of

11. 150 shares of American Woolen Co.

12. 250 shares of Western Union Telegraph.

13. 300 shares of Del. and Hudson.

14. 200 shares of Radio Corp.

What will the seller realize from the sale of

15. 175 shares of American Sugar Comapny?

$$\$63.50 - \$.15 = \$63.35$$
$$175 \times \$63.35 = ?$$

16. 95 shares of Brooklyn Manhattan Transit R.R.?

17. 200 shares of Chicago and Northwestern R.R.?

18. 400 shares of Chicago, Milwaukee, and St. Paul R.R.?

19. 350 shares of Pacific Oil stock are worth how much less than the same quantity of Southern Pacific, preferred?

20. How many shares of the Pullman Company can be bought for $7472.40, which includes brokerage?

Bonds

We have learned how individuals borrow money by giving their notes, and paying interest on them.

Cities, towns, school districts, counties, states, and countries borrow money for public use, by selling their bonds to any one who will buy them. These bonds are promises to pay the amounts named in them, at some specified future time, with interest payable annually or semi-annually, at a fixed rate. When one buys a government bond, he merely lends to the government the amount paid for the bond.

Stock companies and other corporations, such as churches, clubs, railroad companies, express companies and manufacturing companies, also borrow money by selling their bonds. But such bonds are secured by a mortgage or other instrument specifically pledging the property of the corporation for the payment of the bonds when due.

Bonds are generally issued in denominations of $100, $500, or $1000, just as paper money is issued in denominations of $1, $5, $20.

Registered bonds are bonds that are recorded by number in the name of the owner, on the books of the government or corporation that issued them.

A coupon is an interest certificate attached to a bond.

Shares of stock represent the property of a corporation, while bonds represent debts of the corporation. Stockholders are, therefore, the owners of the property of the corporation, while bondholders are its creditors.

The income on shares of stock is in the form of dividends, and its amount fluctuates (except on preferred stock), depending on the prosperity of the corporation's business;

whereas the income on bonds is in the form of interest at a fixed rate, and must be paid, regardless of the condition of the business.

The market value of bonds, like that of stocks, fluctuates from day to day; they may be at par, at a premium, or at a discount.

Bonds are bought and sold through brokers in the same manner as shares of stock, and at the same rates of brokerage.

The market values of bonds are quoted in the same way as the market values of shares of stock; *e.g.* " U. S. 5's, 110," means that one dollar of United States bonds bearing 5% interest is worth $1.10.

The premium, discount, and brokerage on bonds are computed on the par value. In this respect, do bonds resemble or differ from capital stock?

1. What is the par value of ten 500-dollar bonds?

2. When selling at 110, what is their market value?

3. What must be paid for five 100-dollar bonds when they are quoted at 120?

4. When bonds are quoted at 80, how many dollars of bonds can be bought for $400?

5. What is the annual interest on ten 100-dollar $3\frac{1}{2}\%$ Liberty Bonds of 1917?

6. How many dollars of 4% Liberty Bonds of 1917 must I own in order to receive an annual income of $1200 from them? A semi-annual income of $1200?

7. How many 5% 100-dollar bonds must I own in order to receive from them an annual income of $750? To receive an annual income of $1000?

8. What is the market value of $40,000 of U. S. 2% registered bonds due in 1930, when quoted at 104?

9. What is the annual interest?

10. How many dollars of these bonds will $20,800 buy?

11. At one time, U. S. 4% coupon bonds were quoted at 120. What was the cost of $21,500 of those bonds?

12. What interest did the government pay annually on them?

Anglo-French	5's	. . .	$93.10	Detroit Tunnel 4½'s	. . .	$90.50
Argentine Govt.	5's	. . .	91.55	N. Y. Central 3½'s	. . .	85.55
City of Paris	6's	. . .	95.85	West Shore 4's	. . .	92.35
Chile Copper	7's	. . .	135.50	U. S. Rubber 6's	. . .	102.50

Using the above quotations from a daily paper and allowing brokerage at $1.50 per 1000 par value, find:

13. The cost of $100,000 of Anglo-French 5's.

14. The interest on them.

15. The quantity of West Shore 4's that $1850 will buy.

16. The annual interest received from $27,195 invested in Detroit Tunnel 4½'s.

17. The net receipts from the sale of $50,000 of N. Y. Central 3½'s.

18. The annual interest earned by them.

19. The cost of $33,000 of U. S. Rubber 6's.

20. The annual interest received from $27,130 invested in Chile Copper 7's.

21. The cost of a sufficient quantity of Argentine Government 5's to yield an annual interest of $280.

22. The cost of 200 City of Paris 6's.

23. The income on $19,943 invested in Detroit Tunnel 4½'s.

Investments

Many stocks and bonds are unsafe for investment. Bonds of the United States government, of your own state, of certain cities and of certain corporations are generally safe.

If a company's stock is not good, its bonds are not good. The only advantage of bond investments over stock investments is that the income rate does not fluctuate and the market price is likely to be more stable.

Securities that promise a high rate of income on the investment are generally attended by a high degree of risk. People investing savings should not consider such securities. A low rate of income with perfect security is always more profitable in the end.

Persons inexperienced in investing funds should buy only such securities as are legal for the investment of trust funds; and even then with great caution and after securing trustworthy advice.

Always consult experienced investors, whom you know well, before buying stocks or bonds. Consult others than those who have the securities to sell.

Bankers are usually able to obtain reliable information about securities for investment.

Ask your father to select from the stocks listed in the Wall Street Report on the next page five stocks that he considers safe. Imagine that you purchase 10 shares of each of these at the price listed in the Report.

The Wall Street Report shows the highest and the lowest price paid for these stocks during the year. Suppose you sell these shares at the highest prices quoted. What would be the gain? Suppose you are forced to sell them at the lowest price quoted for the year. What would be the loss?

NEW YORK STOCK EXCHANGE REPORT

Saturday, Feb. 7, 19——

No.	1925		Sales		Feb. 7, 1925	
	High	Low			High	Low
1.	$89\frac{7}{8}$	$85\frac{1}{2}$	1,500	American Tobacco	$89\frac{7}{8}$	$88\frac{7}{8}$
2.	$53\frac{1}{2}$	$50\frac{1}{8}$	1,100	Bethlehem Steel	51	$50\frac{1}{2}$
3.	$152\frac{3}{8}$	$147\frac{3}{4}$	200	Canadian Pacific	151	151
4.	$37\frac{5}{8}$	$35\frac{1}{8}$	4,100	Chile Copper	$37\frac{1}{8}$	$36\frac{3}{4}$
5.	$78\frac{3}{8}$	$75\frac{7}{8}$	6,900	Consolidated Gas	$78\frac{3}{8}$	78
6.	$71\frac{3}{8}$	$68\frac{1}{8}$	600	Great Northern	$70\frac{3}{4}$	$70\frac{1}{4}$
7.	$110\frac{7}{8}$	$105\frac{1}{8}$	300	International Harvester . .	$107\frac{1}{2}$	107
8.	$106\frac{7}{8}$	104	100	Mack Trucks 1st pf. . . .	$105\frac{7}{8}$	$105\frac{7}{8}$
9.	$25\frac{1}{2}$	23	100	Moon Motors	$24\frac{3}{8}$	$24\frac{3}{8}$
10.	$124\frac{3}{4}$	$117\frac{1}{2}$	2,700	New York Central	$123\frac{1}{4}$	$122\frac{5}{8}$
11.	48	$43\frac{1}{2}$	2,900	Anaconda Copper	46	$45\frac{3}{4}$
12.	$42\frac{1}{2}$	31	1,200	Atlantic Gulf and West Indies	$41\frac{1}{8}$	$39\frac{1}{4}$
13.	$74\frac{1}{2}$	66	300	Beech-Nut Packing	$69\frac{3}{4}$	$69\frac{3}{4}$
14.	18	$13\frac{1}{8}$	11,300	Chicago and Alton	18	$16\frac{1}{8}$
15.	$91\frac{3}{4}$	80	2,400	Coca-Cola	91	$90\frac{1}{4}$
16.	140	$114\frac{1}{2}$	500	Federal Light and Traction .	138	137
17.	$52\frac{3}{8}$	42	11,600	General Petroleum	$51\frac{3}{4}$	$50\frac{3}{4}$
18.	510	461	100	Kresge Co.	499	499
19.	142	$110\frac{1}{4}$	700	Laclede Gas	141	$140\frac{1}{4}$
20.	290	$193\frac{1}{2}$	300	Nash Motors	273	270

A. Use this list for problems.

B. Select one good investment. State why it is a good investment.

C. Bring to the class a report from the New York Stock Exchange.

21. When Arthur Smith graduated from high school he went to work. He earned an average income of $2400 a year from the time he was 18 until he was 60. His chum, Henry Small, went to college. His course cost him $6000. His average salary from the time he was 22 until he was 60 was $4200. If the difference was due to the extra education, what was the money value of the college course?

1. What sum of money must a man invest at $5\frac{1}{4}\%$ to secure an annual income of $2100?

2. Mr. Ferguson bought a house for $4000. He rented it for $40 a month. His average annual expenses for a term of years were: insurance $10, taxes $78.50, repairs and incidentals $98.10. He sold the house at cost. What rate of income did he receive on his investment during the period he owned the house?

3. Mr. Perkins bought three Liberty Bonds for $965 each. Three years later he sold them for $3010. During the time he collected $4\frac{1}{2}\%$ interest on their par value of $1000 each. What was his profit?

4. Mr. Slocum owns a house which cost him $3600. He estimates that his taxes are $52, insurance $8, and repairs $24 annually. How much rent per month must he charge to realize 6% on his investment?

5. Which is the more profitable and how much more per year, — to rent a house at $40 a month or to buy a house for $4000, if money is borrowed at 6% and $175 is allowed for taxes, insurance, repairs, and depreciation?

6. How much must be invested at $5\frac{1}{2}\%$ to secure an annual income of $6000?

7. How much must be invested at $4\frac{1}{2}\%$ to secure an annual income of $6000?

8. Bobby Jones bought a paper route. He had 60 customers. He made a profit of 9¢ a week on each customer. After delivering eight weeks he sold his route for $2 more than it cost him. What was his total income?

9. Mr. Seymour bought an old house in a good location for $2400. He spent $1250 in repairs and sold it at a profit of 15% on his total investment. What did he gain?

Measurements

1. What unit of measure is usually used to express the length of a road? To express the length of a foot-race? To express the thickness of a board? To express the length of a strip of cloth? To express the dimensions of a house?

2. What unit of square measure is used in measuring farm land? In measuring pavements? In measuring the area of a state? In measuring steam pressure?

3. Given the length and breadth of a surface expressed in the same units, how is the area found?

4. Given the area in square feet and the length in feet, how is the width in feet found?

5. Change 4 feet 6 inches to inches.

6. Change 2 acres to square rods.

7. Change 27 square feet to square yards.

8. Change 2 rods to feet.

9. A house has a frontage of 50 feet on the street. The lot is 8 rods deep. How many square feet are there in the lot?

10. What will it cost to cement the floor of a cellar 36 feet long and 24 feet wide at $1.60 a square yard?

11. A room has a hardwood floor 12 feet by 15 feet. The rug on it is 9 feet by 12 feet. Find the cost at $3\frac{1}{2}$ cents a square foot of varnishing the part of the floor not covered by the rug.

12. What will 16,675 pounds of coal cost at $13.50 per ton?

13. A school buys 160 half-pint bottles of milk daily for a week. What does it cost at 12 cents a quart?

14. How many feet of barbed wire will be required to build a 5-strand fence around a field 60 rods long and 36 rods wide, allowing 400 ft. for joints and guys?

15. How many 4-ounce packages can be made from 25 pounds of tacks?

16. How many pieces, each $\frac{3}{4}$ of an inch long, can be made from a bar of iron 1 foot long?

17. If an automobile travels at the rate of 20 miles an hour, how far will it travel in one minute?

18. What is the cost of 1000 yards of wire at 1 cent a foot?

19. How many inches are there in $\frac{3}{8}$ of a yard?

20. Find the cost of $7\frac{1}{2}$ gallons of milk at 9 cents a quart.

21. A rectangular plot containing an acre of land has a frontage of 132 feet on the street; how deep is it?

22. A telephone connects two farmhouses $\frac{5}{8}$ of a mile apart; at 3 cents a foot, what is the cost of a single line of wire?

23. How many bandages 3 inches wide and 6 feet long can be made from 14 yards of linen $\frac{3}{4}$ of a yard wide?

24. A swimming tank is 40 feet long and 18 feet wide; how much will it cost to cement the bottom at $1.12 per square yard?

25. What is the cost of 14,640 pounds of coal at $13.75 a ton?

26. Find the annual returns on an investment of $6000 in a business which earns 8%.

27. Mrs. Johnson owns property worth $6400. She is taxed for 75% of its value at $2.15 per $100. Find the amount of her taxes.

28. The school budget in a district is $3000. The property is assessed at $750,000. Find the school tax paid on a farm worth $15,000.

Cubic Measure

A solid bounded by six rectangles is a **rectangular prism**.

A solid bounded by six squares is a **cube**.

This rectangular prism is divided into cubes. It is as long as 4 cubes, as wide as 2 cubes, and as high as 3 cubes. In the top layer there are 2 × 4 or 8 cubes. There are 3 such layers, so in all there are 2 × 4 × 3 or 24 cubes.

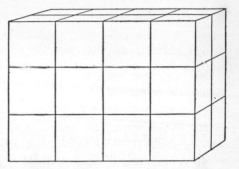

If each of these cubes has an edge of 1 inch, it is a cubic inch, and the volume of the above prism is 24 cubic inches.

The volume of a rectangular prism is the product of its length, width, and height, all being expressed in the same linear unit.

Find the volume of a rectangular prism:

1. 4 ft. by 8 ft. by 6 ft.
2. 9 in. by 4 in. by 5 in.
3. 3 ft. by 5 ft. by 7 ft.
4. 8 ft. by 2 ft. by 3 ft.
5. 9 in. by 3 in. by 3 in.
6. 7 in. by 7 in. by 2 in.
7. 3 in. by 7 in. by 11 in.
8. 8 in. by 12 in. by 12 in.
9. 5 ft. by 2 ft. by 2 ft.
10. 6 ft. by 7 ft. by 9 ft.
11. 9 yd. by 5 yd. by 4 yd.
12. 20 yd. by 4 yd. by 3 yd.

> 1728 cubic inches (cu. in.) = 1 cubic foot (cu. ft.)
> 27 cubic feet   = 1 cubic yard (cu. yd.)

1. A room is 15 ft. long, 12 ft. wide, and 8 ft. high. How many cubic feet of air does it contain?

15
12
180
8
1440

"The *number* of cubic feet is the product of 15 × 12 × 8, which is 1440."

15 ft., 12 ft., and 8 ft. are the dimensions of the room. 1440 cu. ft. is the volume or cubic contents of the room.

Find the volume of:

2. A box 2 ft. by 3 ft. by 3 ft.

3. A cistern 4 ft. by 4 ft. by 5 ft.

4. A reservoir 60 ft. by 50 ft. by 9 ft.

5. A trunk 35 in. by 22 in. by 20 in.

6. How many cubic inches are there in a bar of soap 4 in. by 3 in. by $1\frac{1}{2}$ in.?

7. If a cubic foot of ice weighs 60 lb., what is the weight of a cake of ice 2 ft. by 2 ft. by 1 ft.?

8. Will's lunch box is 8 in. long, 4 in. wide, and 3 in. thick. What is its volume?

9. Find the contents of a box 3 in. by 4 in. by $2\frac{1}{2}$ in.

10. How many cubic feet are there in a rectangular bin 8 ft. by 4 ft. by 4 ft.?

Volume and Capacity

---

1 gallon contains 231 cu. in.
1 bushel contains 2150.42 cu. in.

---

1. In what denominations are measures of volume expressed? Measures of capacity?

2. If the volume in cubic inches of a tank is known, how may its capacity in gallons be found?

3. When the volume in cubic inches of a box, bin, or barrel is known, how may we find its capacity in bushels?

4. When we know the capacity of a bin in bushels, how may we find its volume in cubic inches? In cubic feet?

5. How many liquid quarts will a rectangular tin can 7 in. by 3 in. by 11 in. hold?

6. The volume of a bin is 215,042 cubic inches. How many bushels will it hold?

7. What is the volume of a cask that holds 100 gallons?

8. Find in gallons the capacity of a rectangular cistern 11 ft. long, 7 ft. wide, and 6 ft. deep.

SOLUTION

$$\frac{\overset{2}{11} \times 7 \times \overset{}{6} \times 1728}{\underset{\underset{3}{21}}{231}} = 3456 \text{ gal.} \quad Ans.$$

The expression above the line indicates the volume in cubic inches.

9. A box car is 33 ft. long and 8 ft. 8 in. wide, inside measure. It is filled with oats to a height of 6 ft. How many bushels of oats are there?

Find the capacity in gallons of a cistern:

1. $5' \times 4' \times 6'$.   4. $6' \times 4' \times 6'$.   7. $5' \times 7' \times 9'$.

2. $7' \times 5' \times 4'$.   5. $8' \times 8' \times 4'$.   8. $4' \times 4' \times 6'$.

3. $4' \times 8' \times 6'$.   6. $5' \times 5' \times 7'$.   9. $7' \times 7' \times 6'$.

10. Find the capacity in cubic feet of a vat holding: 270 gal.; 276 gal.; 900 gal.; 1000 gal.; 1800 gal.

11. A barrel contains $31\frac{1}{2}$ gal. This is how many cubic feet?

12. A rectangular cistern is $8' \times 6' \times 6'$. How many gallons does it contain?

13. A cistern contains 1386 gallons. What is its capacity in cubic feet?

14. A cistern $6' \times 6' \times 5'$ is half full of water. About how many gallons does it contain?

15. How many barrels of $31\frac{1}{2}$ gallons will be contained in a cistern $5' \times 5' \times 6'$?

16. Find the number of barrels that a cistern 4 ft. by 4 ft. by $5\frac{1}{2}$ ft. will hold.

17. What must be the volume of a cistern to hold 1365 gallons?

18. A cistern containing 462 cu. ft. will contain how many gallons?

19. A tank is $7' \times 5' \times 3'$. How many gallons will it contain?

20. A large vat holds 5768 gallons of water. How many cubic feet are there in the volume of the vat?

21. How many gallons of water will fill a cistern $7' \times 11' \times 6'$?

22. How many gallons of water will be required to two thirds fill a reservoir $21' \times 30' \times 44'$?

Find the capacity in bushels of a bin:

1. 4 ft. by 5 ft. by 4 ft.   5. 10 ft. by 6 ft. by 6 ft.

2. 3 ft. by 3 ft. by 4 ft.   6. $17' \times 12' \times 10'$.

3. 7 ft. by 4 ft. by 3 ft.   7. 6′ 4″ by 9′ by 4′.

4. 8 ft. by 4 ft. by 5 ft.   8. 5′ 6″ by 4′ 6″ by 8′.

9. How many bushels of grain will just fill a wagon box 3 ft. 6 in. wide, 12 ft. long, and 16 in. deep?

10. How many tons of coal, estimating a ton to be 34 cu. ft., will be contained in a bin 8 ft. by 8 ft. 6 in. by 5 ft.?

11. An ice house is filled with a pile of ice 100 ft. long, 48 ft. wide, and 30 ft. high. If 33 cu. ft. of ice weigh a ton, how many tons of ice are stored in this house?

12. How many bushels will be contained in a bin 6 ft. by 8 ft. by 12 ft.?

13. How many bushels of grain will be contained in a freight car 35 ft. by 8 ft. by 8 ft.?

14. How many bushels will fill a box $4' \times 4' \times 3' 6''$?

15. How many bushels will fill a bin of 15,000 cu. ft.?

16. A bin having a cubic capacity of 24,000 cu. ft. will hold how many bushels?

17. A grain bin is 10 feet square and 7 feet deep. Find its capacity in bushels.

18. Ice weighs approximately $62\frac{1}{2}$ pounds to the cubic foot. How many pounds in a piece of ice 3 feet long, $2\frac{1}{2}$ feet wide, and 16 inches thick?

19. It requires approximately 34 cubic feet of coal to weigh a ton. Mr. Williams' bin is 9 feet long and 8 feet wide. If it holds $9\frac{1}{2}$ tons, how deep is it?

Ratio

1. A rectangular field is 40 rd. long and 20 rd. wide. The length is how many times the width?

2. When 5% interest is paid on borrowed money, the annual interest is what part of the principal?

3. A pupil who attends school 15 days out of 20 attends what part of the time?

4. 50 is how many times 10? $85 \div 5 = ?$ $39 = ? \times 3$

When one number is divided by another, the quotient is called the **ratio** *of the dividend to the divisor.*

E.g. $6 \div 2 = 3$, 3 is the ratio of 6 to 2; $5 \div 15 = \frac{1}{3}$, $\frac{1}{3}$ is the ratio of 5 to 15; the ratio of 5 to 3 is $1\frac{2}{3}$; the ratio of 3 to 5 is $\frac{3}{5}$.

---

5. What is the ratio of 99 to 33?   Of 18 to 57?

6. The ratio of 323 to what number is 19?

$$(323 \div ? = 19)$$

7. Take a tape measure and find the circumference of a pail.   Find its diameter.   Divide the circumference by the diameter.

8. Do the same with other round objects (a paste jar, a tumbler, a vase, a silver dollar, a tin can, etc.).   How do the results compare?   What is the ratio of the circumference to the diameter of a circle?

9. You have found the ratio of the circumference of a circle to its diameter to be very nearly 3.1416, or $3\frac{1}{7}$. Supposing the circumference of the earth at the equator to be 24,882 miles, and the ratio of the circumference to the diameter to be $3\frac{1}{7}$, what is the diameter of the earth at the equator? $(24,882 \div ? = 3\frac{1}{7}.)$

1. The length of the United States is 2700 miles. Its width is 1500 miles. (*a*) What is the ratio of its length to its width? (*b*) What is the ratio of its width to its length?

2. The water surface of the earth is 143,517,000 sq. mi. The land surface is 55,641,000 sq. mi. What is the ratio of the water surface to the land surface?

3. The length of a field is 40 rd. and the ratio of the length to the width is $1\frac{1}{3}$. What is the width? $(40 \div ? = 1\frac{1}{3}.)$

4. In a cement mixture, Mr. Delaney uses 3 bu. of cement to 7 bu. of sand. What is the ratio of sand to cement in the mixture?

5. The ratio of the length to the breadth of a city lot is 2. If the breadth is 4 rods, what is the length? Illustrate by a drawing.

6. The ratio of the height of a boy to the height of a tree is $\frac{1}{7}$. If the tree is 35 feet high, how tall is the boy? Illustrate by a drawing.

7. What is the ratio of the length of a rod measure to the length of a yardstick?

What is the ratio of

8. One gallon to one quart?

9. Two gallons to 16 quarts?

10. One bushel to one pint?

11. Five dollars to 25 cents?

12. Eighty cents to one dollar?

13. Five pounds to five ounces?

14. One square foot to one square yard?

15. One cubic inch to one gallon?

16. Give two numbers whose ratio is 5.

17. Give two numbers whose ratio is 16.

Simple Proportion

We have learned that ratio is the relation of two numbers, expressed by their quotient. The numbers compared are the **terms** of the ratio; the first term is the **antecedent,** the second term is the **consequent.**

The relation of the terms and quotient in a ratio is easily understood if we think of the ratio sign (:) merely as the sign of division, which it really is, though the line is omitted.

Find the missing numbers in the following :

1. $38 : 19 = ?$ **2.** $35 : ? = 5$ **3.** $? : 4 = 3$

4. $\frac{3}{4} : \frac{1}{2} = ?$ **5.** $? : \frac{2}{3} = \frac{3}{7}$ **6.** $2\frac{1}{2} : ? = 1\frac{1}{4}$

7. The ratio of the length to the breadth of a city lot is 2. If the breadth is 3 rods, what is the length? Illustrate by a drawing.

Compare the following ratios :

15 : 3 compares how with 10 : 2?

$48 : $8 compares how with 12 da. : 2 da.?

15 apples : 30 apples compares how with 8 lb. : 16 lb.?

The answers to the above questions may be expressed:

$$15 : 3 = 10 : 2$$
$$\$48 : \$8 = 12 \text{ da.} : 2 \text{ da.}$$
$$15 \text{ apples} : 30 \text{ apples} = 8 \text{ lb.} : 16 \text{ lb.}$$

Of what is each of the above statements composed?

An equality of ratios is **a proportion.**

The first of the above proportions is read, "15 *is to* 3 *as* 10 *is to* 2." Read the others. Let each pupil in the class write three proportions. What must be true of two ratios that they may form a proportion?

Complete the following proportions:

1. $45:9 = 10:?$ 3. $\$12:\$6 = 6$ da.$:?$ da.
2. $33:3 = ?:2$ 4. 12 mi.$:24$ mi. $= 2$ hr.$:?$ hr.

The first and fourth terms of a proportion are the **extremes**; *the second and third terms are the* **means**.

The sign $(::)$, called the sign of proportion, is sometimes used instead of the sign of equality, and means the same.

In the following proportions, verify the principle that *the product of the means is equal to the product of the extremes.*

Thus, in the proportion $15:5 = 12:4$,

The product of the means is 5×12, or 60.

The product of the extremes is 15×4, or 60.

5. $9:3 = 6:2$ 7. $3:60 = 6:120$ 9. $7:2 = 28:8$
6. $63:21 = 3:1$ 8. $14:28 = 2:4$ 10. $3:9 = 9:27$

11. Complete the proportion, $88:24 = 264:x$, by finding the value of x.

SOLUTION

$$88 \times x = 24 \times 264. \quad \text{Why?}$$

$$x = \frac{\overset{3}{24} \times \overset{24}{264}}{\underset{11}{88}} = 72. \quad \text{Therefore, } 88:24 = 264:72. \quad \textit{Ans.}$$

12. Complete the proportion, $92:x = 69:12$.

SOLUTION

$$69 \times x = 92 \times 12. \quad \text{Why?}$$

$$x = \frac{\overset{4}{92} \times \overset{4}{12}}{\underset{23}{69}} = 16. \quad \text{Therefore, } 92:16 = 69:12. \quad \textit{Ans.}$$

13. If 12 yards of cloth cost \$14, what will 132 yards cost at the same rate?

Since the ratio of 12 yards to 132 yards is the same as the ratio of \$14 to the required number of dollars, the numbers in this problem may form a proportion.

Let x represent the required number of dollars and let it be the fourth term, thus,
$$? : ? = \$14 : \$x.$$

Then, since 132 yards will cost *more* than 12 yards, the fourth term will be *greater* than the third term; therefore the second term must be greater than the first term, and the proportion is

$$12 \text{ yd.} : 132 \text{ yd.} = \$14 : \$x.$$

Solving, $\qquad 12\,x = 132 \times 14.$ Why?

$$x = \frac{\overset{11}{\cancel{132}} \times 14}{\cancel{12}} = 154.$$

Therefore, 132 yards will cost \$154. *Ans.*

There are many ways of stating a proportion for the solution of a problem, but it is well to adopt some one of them, and use it whenever a problem is to be solved by proportion.

The following outline has been found helpful:

1. *Let the fourth term be x, the required number.*

2. *Let the third term be the given number that denotes the same kind of quantity as the required answer.*

3. *Determine, by reading the problem, whether the answer will be greater or less than the third term, and arrange the other two given numbers accordingly, as the first and second terms of the proportion.*

4. *Solve the proportion.*

Solve the following problems by proportion:

14. At the rate of 9 tons for \$117, how many tons of coal can be bought for \$468?

15. If a man can earn \$217 in 43 days, how much can he earn in 301 days working at the same rate?

Find the missing term:

1. $48 : 16 = 12 : ?$ 5. $\$12 : \$6 = 6$ da. : ? da.

2. $7 : ? = 2 : 6$ 6. 24 mi. : 12 mi. = ? hr. : 2 hr.

3. $45 : 9 = 10 : ?$ 7. $? : 16 = 6 : 2$

4. $33 : 3 = ? : 2$ 8. 4 ft. : 12 ft. = 5 in. : ? in.

9. A 10-pound sack of sugar cost 85 cents. How much would 25 pounds cost at the same rate?

10. If 5 tons of hay cost $90, what would 2 tons cost at the same rate?

11. Traveling at the rate of 49 miles in 196 minutes, in how many minutes will a trolley car run 7 miles?

12. What must be paid for 5700 cubic feet of gas when 3800 cubic feet cost $3.61?

13. What will 8 tons of coal cost, when $17\frac{1}{2}$ tons cost $78.75?

14. How far will a train run in 7 hours at the rate of 380 mi. in 8 hours?

15. What will it cost to buy a new arithmetic for each pupil in a class of 19 pupils, when 24 arithmetics cost $13.20?

16. A messenger boy rode his bicycle 126 miles in 7 days. How far would he ride in 29 days at the same average rate per day?

17. Write the numbers 27, 18, 26, 39, so as to form a proportion.

18. A farmer sowed 6 bushels of grain on $4\frac{4}{5}$ acres of land. At the same rate, what quantity of seed is required for $13\frac{1}{2}$ acres?

19. A crate of eggs holding 30 dozen sold for $16.50. At that rate, find the amount received from a sale of 81 dozen.

20. The taxes on property assessed at $5000 were $87.50. At the same rate, what will be the taxes on property assessed at $12,000?

21. John swam 90 yards in 46 seconds. At the same rate, how long will it take him to swim a mile?

22. What number has the same ratio to 80 as 1 has to 8?

23. If seven tons of coal cost $87.50, what will fifteen tons cost at the same rate?

24. A blue-print is made so that one inch represents 16 feet. What distance is represented by a line on this blue-print $2\frac{1}{4}$ inches long?

25. At the rate of 33 miles per hour, how long will it take an auto to go $181\frac{1}{2}$ miles?

26. If the circumference of a circle whose diameter is 10 is 31.416, what is the circumference of a circle whose diameter is 35?

27. William saves $1.30 during the first two weeks of January. If he continues at this rate, how much will he save in 52 weeks?

28. What will it cost to build 40 rods of fence if 3 rods cost $8?

29. If nine men earn $31.50, what will thirty-five men earn at the same rate?

30. If you know the number of tons of hay required to winter five cows, how can you determine the number of tons required for thirty-eight cows?

Partitive Proportion

In the business of life, it is often necessary to divide a sum of money or a quantity of material into unequal parts that shall be in a certain ratio to one another, or, as we commonly say, "in a certain proportion." The following problems are of that class:

1. Find the quantity of each ingredient in a concrete mixture of 910 cu. ft. composed of Portland cement, sand, and crushed rock in the proportion of 1, 2, and 4.

SOLUTION

$\dfrac{1}{2}$
$\dfrac{4}{7}$

In every 7 cu. ft. of mixture, $\frac{1}{7}$ is cement, $\frac{2}{7}$ sand, and $\frac{4}{7}$ crushed rock. Then in 910 cu. ft. of mixture,

$\frac{1}{7}$ of 910 cu. ft. = 130 cu. ft. Portland cement ⎫
$\frac{2}{7}$ of 910 cu. ft. = 260 cu. ft. sand ⎬ *Ans.*
$\frac{4}{7}$ of 910 cu. ft. = 520 cu. ft. crushed rock ⎭

2. A plum relish is made from these ingredients: 3 lb. plums, $\frac{1}{2}$ lb. raisins, $\frac{1}{2}$ lb. walnuts, $\frac{1}{4}$ lb. oranges, 3 lb. sugar. How much of each ingredient should be used in $72\frac{1}{2}$ lb. of the relish?

12 lb.
2 lb.
2 lb.
1 lb.
12 lb.

29 lb

SOLUTION

To dispose of the fractions, multiply the quantity of each ingredient by 4. This will not alter their ratio to one another. Then,

$\frac{12}{29}$ of 72.5 lb. = 30 lb.

etc.

> *Separating a number into two or more parts that have a given ratio* is called **partitive proportion.**

3. Divide 91 into two parts having the ratio of 3 to 4.

Divide as indicated:

NUMBER DIVIDED	NUMBER OF PARTS	RATIO OF PARTS
4. 1200	2	11, 13
5. 3690	3	2, 7, 1
6. $923	4	4, 5, 1, 3

Number Divided	Number of Parts	Ratio of Parts
7. 3179	4	1, 2, 3, 5
8. 418 bu.	4	4, 5, 7, 3
9. 624 miles	5	2, 7, 1, 2, 1
10. $2640	5	9, 8, 7, 6, 3
11. 430	5	1, 2, 6, $\frac{2}{5}$, $\frac{3}{5}$
12. 18,000	2	97, 83

13. Joe and Harry earn $25 a month. Harry earns $3 while Joe is earning $2. How much per month does each earn?

14. Mr. Olsen and his two sons together received $192 on pay day, Mr. Olsen receiving $4 as often as each of his sons received $2. How much did each receive?

15. A kind of medicine is composed of licorice, ipecac, and muriate of ammonia in the ratio of 10, 3, and 2. In three pounds (Avoirdupois) of this medicine there are how many grains of each of the three ingredients? (1 lb. = 7000 gr.)

16. A cargo of wheat valued at $45,000 was entirely destroyed. One third of it belonged to A, two fifths to B, and the remainder to C. What was each one's share of the insurance and of the loss, there being an insurance of $36,000?

17. Three boys received 5\frac{1}{2}$ for clearing up vacant lots. The money was divided among them in proportion to the time they worked. If the first worked 9 hr., the second 7$\frac{1}{2}$ hr., and the third 5$\frac{1}{2}$ hr., how much did each receive?

18. A 12-foot board was sawed in two so that the two pieces were in the ratio of 1$\frac{1}{3}$ to 2$\frac{2}{3}$. Find the lengths of the pieces.

19. A rich concrete mixture is 2 parts cement to 3 of sand and 6 of gravel. How much is there of each in 990 cu. ft. of concrete?

Powers of Numbers

> *The product of equal factors* is a **power**; *e.g.*
>
> 4 is a power of 2 because $4 = 2 \times 2$; 27 is a power of 3 because $27 = 3 \times 3 \times 3$; 625 is a power of 5 because $625 = 5 \times 5 \times 5 \times 5$.
>
> *The product of two equal factors* is a **square**; *e.g.*
>
> 4 is the square of 2; 9 is the square of 3; 25 is the square of 5.

The area of a square surface is the product of its length and breadth. Since these are equal, the area of a square is the *square* of either dimension. For example, the area of a square whose side is 7 ft. is 49 sq. ft. 49 is the *square* of 7. Any number that is the product of two equal factors is called a square because it may be supposed to represent a square whose side is represented by one of the two equal factors.

> *The product of three equal factors* is a **cube**; *e.g.*
>
> 8 is the cube of 2; 27 is the cube of 3; 125 is the cube of 5.

The contents of a cubical solid are equal to the *cube* of one of its dimensions. For example, 125 cu. in. are the contents of a cube whose edge is 5 in.

> *An* **exponent** *is a figure placed above and at the right of a number to show which power of the number is to be taken; e.g.*
>
> In the expressions 11^2 and 5^3, the 2 shows that the square of 11 is to be taken, and the 3 shows that the cube of 5 is to be taken.

Find the powers indicated:

1. 15^2	**4.** 87^2	**7.** 108^3	**10.** $.835^2$	**13.** $(15\frac{1}{8})^2$
2. 33^2	**5.** 18^3	**8.** 25.3^2	**11.** 4.05^3	**14.** $(.08)^3$
3. 98^2	**6.** 24^2	**9.** 4.06^2	**12.** $(\frac{116}{231})^2$	**15.** $(1.07)^2$

Finding the Square of a Number Expressed by Two Figures

$$
\begin{array}{lllll}
37 = & 30 + 7 & = & t + u \\
\underline{37 =} & \underline{30 + 7} & = & \underline{t + u} \\
259 = & 30 \times 7 + 7^2 & = & t \times u + u^2 \\
\underline{111 =} & \underline{30^2 + 30 \times 7} & & \underline{t^2 + t \times u} \\
1369 = & 30^2 + (2 \times 30 \times 7) + 7^2 & = & t^2 + (2 \times t \times u) + u^2
\end{array}
$$

From the above illustration we may observe that the square of a number expressed by two figures may be found by adding the *square of the tens*, *twice the product of the tens and units*, and *the square of the units;* thus,

$$
\begin{array}{l}
43 = 40 + 3 \\
43^2 = 40^2 + (2 \times 40 \times 3) + 3^2 \\
\quad 1600 + \quad\quad 240 \quad\quad + 9 = 1849
\end{array}
$$

Oral

Find the value of:

1.	21^2	**5.**	31^2	**9.**	45^2	**13.**	25^2	**17.**	65^2
2.	22^2	**6.**	46^2	**10.**	52^2	**14.**	34^2	**18.**	55^2
3.	41^2	**7.**	38^2	**11.**	91^2	**15.**	73^2	**19.**	42^2
4.	44^2	**8.**	92^2	**12.**	82^2	**16.**	61^2	**20.**	43^2

Squares of Numbers to 25

The squares in this table should be committed to memory.

$1^2 = 1$	$6^2 = 36$	$11^2 = 121$	$16^2 = 256$	$21^2 = 441$
$2^2 = 4$	$7^2 = 49$	$12^2 = 144$	$17^2 = 289$	$22^2 = 484$
$3^2 = 9$	$8^2 = 64$	$13^2 = 169$	$18^2 = 324$	$23^2 = 529$
$4^2 = 16$	$9^2 = 81$	$14^2 = 196$	$19^2 = 361$	$24^2 = 576$
$5^2 = 25$	$10^2 = 100$	$15^2 = 225$	$20^2 = 400$	$25^2 = 625$

Roots of Numbers

One of the equal factors that produce a number is **a root** *of that number;* *e.g.* 2 is a root of 4, of 8, and of 16; 5 is a root of 125 and of 625.

One of the two equal factors that produce a number is the **square root** *of that number;* *e.g.* 2 is the square root of 4; 3 is the square root of 9; 5 is the square root of 25.

One of the three equal factors that produce a number is the **cube root** *of that number;* *e.g.* 2 is the cube root of 8; 3 is the cube root of 27; 5 is the cube root of 125.

The **radical sign** ($\sqrt{}$) *placed over a number indicates that a root of the number is to be taken. A small figure placed within the radical sign to indicate which root is to be taken* is called the **radical index**. When the square root is to be taken, the index is omitted, *e.g.* $\sqrt{625}$ indicates that the square root of 625 is to be taken.

A number whose square root can be exactly obtained is a **perfect square**; *e.g.* 25, 144, 100.

A number whose cube root can be exactly obtained is a **perfect cube**; *e.g.* 8, 64, .027, 1728.

Read the following expressions and state the value of each:

1. $\sqrt{4}$	**5.** $\sqrt[4]{16}$	**9.** $\sqrt[5]{32}$	**13.** $\sqrt{100}$
2. $\sqrt{49}$	**6.** $\sqrt[4]{81}$	**10.** $\sqrt[3]{1728}$	**14.** $\sqrt{121}$
3. $\sqrt[3]{27}$	**7.** $\sqrt{144}$	**11.** $\sqrt{1600}$	**15.** $\sqrt{36}$
4. $\sqrt[3]{125}$	**8.** $\sqrt[3]{1000}$	**12.** $\sqrt{81}$	**16.** $\sqrt{1}$

17. The area of a square field is 100 square rods. How long is it?

18. What is the width of a square page whose area is 81 square inches?

Finding the Square Root

Complete the following table, filling in the results:

$1^2 =$	$10^2 =$	$100^2 =$	$1000^2 =$
$2^2 =$	$20^2 =$	$200^2 =$	$2000^2 =$
$9^2 =$	$90^2 =$	$900^2 =$	$9000^2 =$
	$99^2 =$	$999^2 =$	$9999^2 =$

From the results found, we may generalize as follows:

The *square* of a number contains twice as many places, or twice as many less one, as the number itself contains, and

The square root of a number contains as many places as the square contains periods of two figures each, counting from the right, the left-hand period sometimes containing but one figure.

$\sqrt{5329}$, then, contains how many places?

$$53 \cdot 29)\overline{70 + 3} = 73 \ Ans.$$

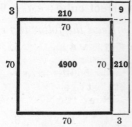

$70^2 \qquad\quad = 4900$	
$70 \times 2 = 140\ \overline{)429}$	
$429 \div 140 = 3\ |429$	
$140 + 3 = 143\ |\overline{000}$	
$143 \times 3 = 429$	

By trial, we find that the greatest number of tens whose square is not greater than 5329 is 7 tens, or 70.

Let 70 be the side of a square. Its area is 70×70, or **4900**. We may call this **4900** sq. ft., sq. in., or any other kind of square units.

Subtracting **4900** from 5329, we find that there are **429** square units remaining. If we make additions to two sides of the square, we must make additions whose combined length is 70 × 2, or 140 units. If **429** square units are added, the width of the addition must be as many units as **429** ÷ 140, or 3 units, with a small remainder. In order to make a complete square, we must again add a small square 3 units long and wide. The entire length of the three additions is 2 × 70 + 3, or 143 units, and the width is 3 units. Their combined area is 143 × 3, or **429** square units, the exact number necessary to complete a square containing **5329** square units. The entire length of one side of this square is 70 + 3, or 73 units.

The following form shows the usual convenient arrangement of the work and the steps required :

53·29)73 square root   Find the greatest square (of tens) not
49   greater than 53 (hundred). It is 49
143|429   (hundred). Its square root is 7 (tens).
   |429   Write 7 (tens) in the root, and subtract 49 (hundred) from 53 (hundred). Bring down 29.

Multiply 7 (tens) by 2, and write the product, 14, at the left of 429 for a *trial divisor*. (This is 14 tens, or 140, but we omit the cipher because we shall have another figure to take its place.) 429 ÷ 140 = 3, with a small remainder.

Write 3 in the root, annex 3 to 14, making 143. Multiply 143 by 3, the new figure in the root, and write the product, 429, under 429, the trial dividend. If we subtract, there is no remainder, which shows that 73 is the exact square root of 5329.

If after the new root figure has been annexed to the trial divisor and the result multiplied by the new root figure, a product is obtained that is greater than the *trial dividend*, we must retrace our work and take the next lower figure in place of the new root figure, both in the root and in the divisor.

When the given number contains only three figures, we first find the greatest square not greater than the *left-hand figure*. For example,

7·29)27
4
47|329
  |329

To find the number of figures in the root, point off the given square into periods of two figures, beginning at the right.

For example, let it be required to find $\sqrt{399424}$.

SOLUTION

$$39 \cdot 94 \cdot 24 \;\big|\; 632 \text{ square root}$$
$$36$$

$$60 \times 2 + 3 = \quad 123 \;\big|\; 394$$
$$369$$

$$630 \times 2 + 2 = \quad 1262 \;\big|\; 2524$$
$$2524$$

Summary

To find the square root of an integer:

1. *Point off the integer into* **periods** *of two figures each, beginning at the right.*

2. *Find the* **greatest perfect square** *that is not greater than the left-hand period. Subtract it from the left-hand period and write its square root at the right of the given integer for the first figure of the root.*

3. *Bring down the next period.*

4. *Multiply the part of the root already found (assuming that a cipher is annexed),* **by 2,** *and write the product at the left of the remainder for a* **trial divisor.**

5. *Divide the remainder (with period annexed) by the trial divisor. Write the quotient in the root, and also annex it to the trial divisor, making the divisor complete.*

6. *Multiply the complete divisor by the new figure in the root. Subtract the product from the last remainder (with period annexed) and proceed as before until all the periods of the square have been used.*

7. *When the remainder (with period annexed) will not contain the trial divisor, place a cipher in the root, bring down another period, and annex a cipher to the trial divisor for a new trial divisor.*

Find the square root:

1. 8836	**6.** 60,025	**11.** 235,225
2. 585,225	**7.** 41,616	**12.** 16,184,529
3. 137,641	**8.** 822,649	**13.** 5,322,249
4. 80,089	**9.** 164,836	**14.** 826,281
5. 101,761	**10.** 95,481	**15.** 788,544

The Square Root of a Decimal

To find the square root of a decimal:

1. *Beginning at the decimal point, point off the decimal, both to the left (in a mixed decimal) and to the right, into periods of two figures each.*

2. *Find the square root as with integers.*

3. *Point off one decimal place in the root for every two decimal places in the square.*

If the given decimal contains an odd number of decimal places, a cipher must be annexed to complete the right-hand period.

The square root of a decimal or an integer that is not a perfect square may be found correct to any desired number of decimal places by annexing decimal periods of ciphers and continuing the work of extracting the square root.

Find the square root of:

16. .0625	**19.** .0256	**22.** .00005625	**25.** 24.3049
17. .1225	**20.** .007921	**23.** 158.76	**26.** 6130.89
18. .8836	**21.** .092416	**24.** 29.0521	**27.** .000121

Find, correct to two decimal places, the square root of:

28. 17	**31.** 62.5	**34.** 3	**37.** 4.096
29. 8	**32.** 45	**35.** 67.3	**38.** 31.3
30. 120	**33.** .75	**36.** 172.341	**39.** .016

Finding the Square Root by Factoring

Let us study the relation between the factors of a number and the factors of the square of that number.

$42 = 2 \times 3 \times 7$; therefore $42^2 = (2 \times 3 \times 7)^2 =$
$$2 \times 3 \times 7 \times 2 \times 3 \times 7, \text{ or } 1764.$$

We observe that every factor of 42 occurs twice in the square of 42. Likewise, every factor of any number occurs twice in the square of that number, three times in its cube, four times in its fourth power, and so on.

Conversely, $\sqrt{1764} = \sqrt{2 \times 2 \times 3 \times 3 \times 7 \times 7} = 2 \times 3 \times 7$, or 42.

Likewise $\sqrt{225} = \sqrt{3 \times 3 \times 5 \times 5} = 3 \times 5$, or 15.

Summary

1. *The square root of a perfect square may be found by factoring the square and multiplying together one out of every pair of equal prime factors found in it.*

Written

Find, by factoring, the values of the following :

1. $\sqrt{3600}$	9. $\sqrt{1089}$	17. $\sqrt{126 \times 14}$
2. $\sqrt{100}$	10. $\sqrt{784}$	18. $\sqrt{98 \times 8}$
3. $\sqrt{441}$	11. $\sqrt{.1296}$	19. $\sqrt{32 \times 18}$
4. $\sqrt{1225}$	12. $\sqrt{20.25}$	20. $\sqrt{40 \times 10}$
5. $\sqrt{484}$	13. $\sqrt{.2401}$	21. $\sqrt{45 \times 125}$
6. $\sqrt{625}$	14. $\sqrt{2304}$	22. $\sqrt{5184}$
7. $\sqrt{2401}$	15. $\sqrt{3969}$	23. $\sqrt{1936}$
8. $\sqrt{6561}$	16. $\sqrt{1225}$	24. $\sqrt{784}$

Squares and Right Triangles

1. A farmer gave to the school district a playground of $2\frac{1}{2}$ acres to be taken, in the form of a square, from the corner of a meadow. How long was the playground and how wide was it?

$2\frac{1}{2}$ A =
400 sq. rd.

$$\sqrt{400} = 20$$
20 rd. *Ans.*

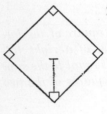

2. The area of a baseball "diamond" is 8100 sq. ft. It is in the form of a square. How long is each side?

3. Find the side of a square whose area is 625 square feet.

A triangle that contains a right angle is a **right triangle.**

The side opposite the right angle in a right triangle is the **hypotenuse** *of the right triangle.*

The two sides that form the right angle of a right triangle are the **legs** *of the right triangle.*

RIGHT TRIANGLE

When a right triangle rests upon one of its legs, the leg upon which it rests is called the **base** *and the other leg* is called the **perpendicular** *of the right triangle.*

In triangle *ABC*, which lines are the legs? In triangle *DEF*? In triangle *KLM*?

In triangle *DEF*, which line is the hypotenuse? In triangle *KLM*?

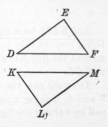

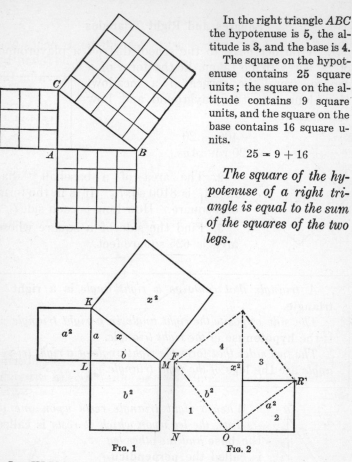

In the right triangle ABC the hypotenuse is **5**, the altitude is **3**, and the base is **4**.

The square on the hypotenuse contains **25** square units; the square on the altitude contains **9** square units, and the square on the base contains **16** square units.

$$25 = 9 + 16$$

The square of the hypotenuse of a right triangle is equal to the sum of the squares of the two legs.

Fig. 1   Fig. 2

Let KLM be a right triangle of any shape and b^2 and a^2 of Fig. 2 equal respectively to b^2 and a^2 of Fig. 1. Take the point O, in Fig. 2, so that the line NO will be equal to the line KL, in Fig. 1, and draw OF and OR.

In every case the triangles 1 and 2 may be placed in the position of 3 and 4, making a square equal to x^2 of Fig. 1. Verify this for yourself by cutting the figures from paper, using various lengths for a and b.

Problems

1. In the right triangle *ABC*, let *AB* be 4 inches and *BC* be 3 inches. Then *AC* may be found by adding the squares of 3 and 4 and taking the square root of their sum; thus,

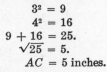

$$3^2 = 9$$
$$4^2 = 16$$
$$9 + 16 = 25.$$
$$\sqrt{25} = 5.$$

Therefore, $AC = 5$ inches.

2. In the right triangle *LNR*, let *LR* = 10′ and *NR* = 6′.

Then $LN = \sqrt{10^2 - 6^2} = \sqrt{100 - 36} = \sqrt{64} = 8$. Therefore, *LN* = 8 feet.

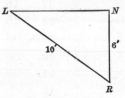

Find the missing sides of these triangles, remembering that the hypotenuse is always the side opposite the right angle.

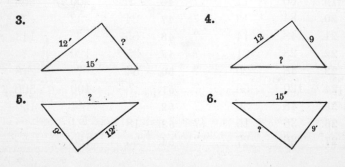

3.

4.

5.

6.

Right Triangles

Draw a diagram of the figure described in the exercise before solving.

	BASE	ALT.	HYP.		BASE	ALT.	HYP.
1.	12	9	?	28.	4	3	?
2.	12	5	?	29.	96	40	?
3.	72	30	?	30.	20	15	?
4.	72	21	?	31.	8	?	10
5.	120	27	?	32.	24	?	26
6.	120	22	?	33.	24	?	25
7.	200	45	?	34.	40	?	41
8.	112	15	?	35.	60	?	61
9.	40	30	?	36.	84	?	85
10.	40	9	?	37.	16	?	20
11.	24	10	?	38.	45	?	117
12.	24	7	?	39.	96	?	100
13.	240	44	?	40.	80	?	82
14.	80	18	?	41.	36	160	?
15.	96	28	?	42.	?	120	122
16.	84	35	?	43.	?	252	255
17.	44	33	?	44.	?	144	145
18.	60	25	?	45.	?	168	170
19.	60	11	?	46.	?	300	305
20.	84	13	?	47.	24	32	?
21.	48	14	?	48.	55	?	143
22.	28	21	?	49.	35	120	?
23.	48	20	?	50.	54	?	246
24.	120	50	?	51.	?	400	500
25.	48	36	?	52.	?	144	150
26.	36	15	?	53.	18	24	?
27.	36	27	?	54.	33	180	?

1. Find the value of the side marked x in figures A, B, C, D, E, F, and G. Approximate roots should be carried to two decimal places.

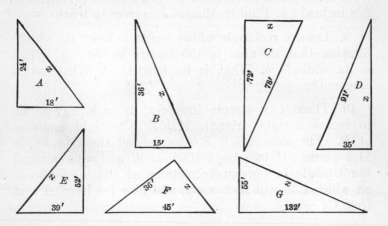

2. A rectangular park is 32 rods by 24 rods. A walk extends diagonally across the park, connecting opposite corners. How long is the walk? (Make a drawing.)

3. One side of a rectangular field is 68 rods. The diagonal distance between opposite corners is 85 rods. Find the other three sides.

4. One side of a rectangle is 69 feet. The diagonal is 115 feet. Find the perimeter of the rectangle.

5. The area of a square is 169 square inches. *a.* What is the length of one side? *b.* What is the length of its diagonal? *c.* Draw the square, exact size, on the blackboard, and verify your work by measuring the diagonal.

6. Find the perimeter of a square whose area is 4489 sq. ft.

7. Find the diagonal of a square whose area is 324 square inches. Verify your work by drawing the square, exact size, and measuring the diagonal.

8. *a.* What is the area of a square whose perimeter is 228 inches? *b.* Find its diagonal, correct to tenths.

9. Draw a rectangle whose length is twice its width. Suppose that its area is 450 square inches. *a.* What is its width? *b.* What is its length? *c.* What is its diagonal?

10. Three city streets intersect in such a way as to inclose a right triangle *ABC*. The right angle is at *B*. The side *AB* is 8.4 yards and the side *BC* is 11.2 yards. If two boys start at *B* and walk around the triangle in opposite directions at the same speed, on which side will they meet, and how far from *A* and from *C*?

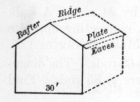

11. This cut represents the gable end of a barn. The ridge of the roof is 11 feet 3 inches higher than the plates on which the rafters rest. The rafters extend 18 inches beyond the plates. How long must the rafters be made?

12. How long a ladder is needed to reach a window 24 feet from the ground, when the foot of the ladder is 10 feet from the side of the building?

13. This cut represents the end of Fred's chicken house. The roof extends 6 inches over each side. Find the slant height of the roof, correct to the nearest hundredth of a foot.

The Circle

Put a mark on the tire of a small wheel. *Call it A.* Place the wheel on the floor or the blackboard so that this mark meets a similar  mark on the board. Roll the wheel in a straight line until the mark again touches the board, and make a second mark on the board, as *B*. The distance between the two marks is equal to the circumference of the wheel.

Measure the diameter of the wheel. See how many times this is contained in the circumference. It will be found to be more than 3, and less than 3¼. It is approximately 3⅐.

The circumference of a circle is about **3.1416** *times its diameter.* 3.1416 *is commonly indicated by the Greek letter* π. NOTE. — Diameter = 2 × Radius.

Give answers in terms of π :

1. Diameter 6.   Circumference ?

Circumference = π × 6 or 6 π

2. D. 10; C.?
3. D. 8; C.?
4. D. 12; C.?
5. D. 14 ft.; C.?
6. D. 20 in.; C.?

7. R. 9; C.?
8. R. 12; C.?
9. R. 8 in.; C.?
10. R. 10 ft.; C.?
11. R. 7 yd.; C.?

Use 3.1416 for π

12. D. 10 ft.; C.?
13. D.? C. 3.1416 in.
14. D. 3 yd.; C.?
15. D. 15″; C.?

16. D. 4′; C.?
17. D. 2′ 6″; C.?
18. C. 40″; D.?
19. C. 82″; R.?

It is proved by geometry that the area of a circle is equal to one half of the product of its circumference by its radius. The circumference of a circle is equal to π 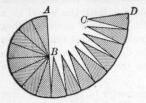 times the diameter or π times $2R$. Therefore the area of a circle is equal to $\frac{1}{2}$ the circumference times the radius, or R. Hence the area of a circle is $\frac{1}{2} \times 2\pi R \times R = \pi \overline{R}^2$.

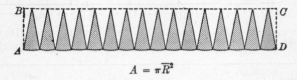

$$A = \pi \overline{R}^2$$

The area of a circle is equal to π (or 3.1416) times the square of its radius.

Give answers in terms of π.

1. Radius 7; Area ?

Area $= \pi R^2$ or $\pi 7^2$ or 49π.

2. Radius $= 3$; Area ?

3. Radius $= 11$; Area ?

4. Radius $= 15$; Area ?

5. Diameter $= 10$ in.; Area ?

6. Radius $= 13$ ft.; Area ?

7. Radius $= 4$ ft.; C. $= ?$; A. $= ?$

8. Radius $= 6.5$ in.; C. $= ?$

9. Radius $= 9$ in.; A. $= ?$

10. Diameter $= 11.5$ ft.; C. $= ?$

11. Radius $= 2.5$ ft.; A. $= ?$

$C = D \times \pi$

$D = C \div \pi$

$a = a^2 \times \pi$

12. Diameter = 24 in.; C. = ?; A. = ?

13. Circumference = 16 π; R. = ?; A. = ?

14. Circumference = 28 π; A. = ?

15. Area = 400 π sq. in.; C. = ?

16. Area = 81 π sq. ft.; C. = ?

Use $\frac{22}{7}$ for π.

17. R. = 14; A. = ?; C. = ?; D. = ?

18. R. = 21; C. = ?; D. = ?; A. = ?

19. C. = 88; D. = ?; R. = ?; A. = ?

$C = \pi D$; $88 = \frac{22}{7} \times D$; $D = \frac{\overset{4}{88}}{1} \times \frac{7}{\underset{22}{\cancel{22}}} = 28$. The diameter

equals $C \div \pi$.

20. C. = 44 in.; D. = ?; R. = ?; A. = ?

21. A. = 154 sq. in.; R. = ?

22. D. = 42 in.; C. = ?; A. = ?

Use 3.1416 for π.

23. R. = 10; A. = ?

24. D. = 40; A. = ?

25. R. = 5 ft.; A. = ?

26. D. = 12 in.; A. = ?

27. D. = 3.5 ft.; A. = ?

28. R. = 2.1 ft.; A. = ?

29. C. = 12.5664 in.; R. = ?; A. = ?

30. C. = 18.8496 ft.; R. = ?; A. = ?

31. C. = 8 π; A. = ?

32. C. = 94.248; D. = ?; R. = ?; A. = ?

33. A. = 314.16; R. = ?; C. = ?

34. R. = 17 in.; A. = ?

In problems 1–9 use $\frac{22}{7}$ for π.

1. Find the diameter of a circle whose circumference is 13 times $\frac{22}{7}$.

2. The diameter of a circular city park is 350 feet. Find its circumference and area.

3. A circular cistern is 70 inches in diameter. What is the area of the bottom?

4. The area of a circular window is $50\frac{2}{7}$ square feet. What is its diameter?

5. A cow is tied with a rope 21 feet long. Over how many square feet of area can she graze?

6. A water pipe is 6 inches in diameter. Find the area of its cross section.

The cross section of this pipe is a circle 6″ in diameter.

7. The circumference of a cylindrical marble column is $56\frac{4}{7}$ inches. What is the area of its cross section?

8. If $R^2 = 841$, what is D? What is C?

9. If $R^2 = 225$, what is C? What is D?

In problems 10–14 use 3.1416 for π.

10. What is the diameter of a circle whose area is 63.6174 square feet?

11. Find the circumference of a circle whose area is 12.5664 square rods.

12. Find in rods the radius of a circle whose area is 38.4846 square rods.

13. What is the steam pressure on a cylinder-head one foot in diameter, when the gauge registers 80 pounds per square inch?

14. Find the semi-circumference of a circle whose radius is 5 feet.

Prisms

We have learned that the volume of a rectangular prism is equal to the product of its three dimensions.

In the figure the sides B_1 and B_2 are called the *bases* of the prism. B_1 is the *lower base* and B_2 is the *upper base*. The bases of a prism are equal.

Since the area of the base is the product of *two* of the dimensions of the prism, the volume of the prism is equal to the *area of the base times the altitude*.

Prisms are named *rectangular, triangular, hexagonal*, etc., according to their bases.

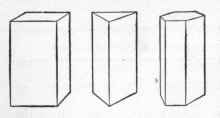

1. Find the volume of a rectangular prism whose base is 3′ by 4′ and whose altitude is 5 ft. 6 in.

2. Find the volume of a square prism 8 ft. long whose base is 12″ on each edge.

3. What is the altitude of a square prism whose volume is 368 cu. in. and whose base is 8″ on each edge?

4. The base of a triangular prism is a right triangle whose legs are 3 in. and 4 in. respectively. The altitude of the prism is 9 in. What is its volume?

5. A school room may be regarded as a prism, the floor and ceiling being the bases. Allowing 200 cubic feet of space to each person, how many may occupy a room 30′ by 40′ and 12′ high?

The Cylinder

A cylinder is a solid having two equal parallel circular bases and a convex surface, all points of which are equally distant from a straight line joining the centers of the bases.

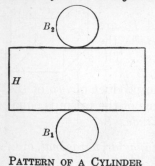

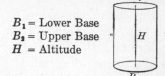

B_1 = Lower Base
B_2 = Upper Base
H = Altitude

Bring a cylindrical tin box to school. Cut a paper that will exactly fit the convex or lateral surface of the box. What figure is the paper? Its length is what of the cylinder? Its width? Its area?

PATTERN OF A CYLINDER

Summary

The lateral area of a cylinder is the product of its altitude and circumference.   Lateral Area = Cir. × Alt.

Find the lateral areas of cylinders having :

In examples 1 to 4 use 3.1416 for π.   In examples 5 to 8 use $\frac{22}{7}$ for π.

1. C. 47 in.; Alt. 2 ft.
2. D. 12 in.; Alt. 10 ft.
3. R. 1 ft.; Alt. 20 ft.
4. R. 20 ft.; Alt. 4 ft.

5. C. 7π in.; Alt. 21 in.
6. R. 14 in.; Alt. 27 in.
7. R. $3\frac{1}{2}$ ft.; Alt. 1 ft.
8. D. 21 ft.; Alt. 3 ft.

The total area of a cylinder is equal to the lateral area plus the sum of the areas of the two bases.

$$Total\ Area = Lateral\ Area + B_1 + B_2$$

Find in terms of π, the total areas of cylinders having :

9. R. = 5; Alt. = 10.

Area of base = $\pi R^2 = 25\pi$.   Area of 2 bases = 50π.
Lateral area = $10 \times 2\pi R$ (circumference) = 100π.
$100\pi + 50\pi = 150\pi$. *Ans.*

10. R. 8; Alt. 14.   **13.** C. 26 π in.; Alt. 30 in.

11. D. 18; Alt. 20.   **14.** R. 2 ft.; Alt. 35 ft.

12. D. 24; Alt. 24.   **15.** C. 16 π in.; Alt. 5 ft.

We have learned that the volume of a prism is equal to the product of the area of its base by its altitude. It is proven by geometry that the same is true of the cylinder.

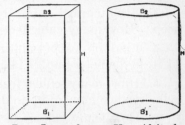

The volume of a cylinder is equal to the product of the area of its base by its altitude. $V = B \times Alt.$

B_1 = Lower base H = Altitude
B_2 = Upper base

Find, in terms of π, the volumes of cylinders having:

16. R. 43; Alt. 5.   **20.** C. 12 π; Alt. 16.

17. D. 12; Alt. 10.   **21.** C. 18 π; Alt. 21.

18. D. 8; Alt. 8.   **22.** D. 30 in.; Alt. 30 in.

19. R. 5; Alt. 7.   **23.** R. 17 in.; Alt. 40 in.

Find the volumes of the cylinders having the following dimensions:

In exercises 24 to 29 use $\frac{22}{7}$ for π; in exercises 30 to 35 use 3.1416 for π.

24. D. 14 in.; Alt. 22 in.   **30.** Alt. 8 in., D. 5 in.

25. R. 21 in.; Alt. 38 in.   **31.** Alt. 3 ft., D. 2 ft.

26. D. 28 in.; Alt. 40 in.   **32.** Alt. 1 ft., R. 4 ft.

27. D. 35 in.; Alt. 70 in.   **33.** Alt. 7 ft., D. 10 in.

28. C. $\frac{44}{7}$ in.; Alt. 35 in.   **34.** Alt. 30 ft., D. 20 in.

29. C. 12$\frac{4}{7}$ ft.; Alt. 5 ft.   **35.** Alt. 25 in., C. 37.6992 in.

In problems 1 to 6 use $\frac{22}{7}$ for π.

1. How many square feet of tin are required to make a heat-pipe 21 inches in diameter and 10 feet long?

2. A cylindrical tank is 42 in. in diameter and 2 ft. long. Find the total area.

3. A cylindrical vat is 14 ft. in diameter and 18 ft. deep. How many cubic feet of water will it contain?

4. Find the cost of painting the lateral surface of a silo 14 ft. in diameter and 27 ft. high at $.20 per square yard.

5. How many cubic feet of marble are there in a cylindrical column 28 in. in diameter and 24 ft. high?

6. How many gallons of oil can be stored in a cylindrical tank 42 inches in diameter and 120 inches long?

In problems 7 to 12 use 3.1416 for π.

7. Find the capacity in barrels of a circular water tank 14 feet in diameter and 24 feet high.

4.21 cu. ft. = 1 bbl.

8. Find the cost of painting the top and sides of the tank in example 7 at $12\frac{1}{2}$¢ per square yard.

9. The foundation for the tank in example 7 is made of concrete. Its radius is 8 ft. and its depth 4 ft. How much will it cost at 50¢ per cubic foot?

10. A circular grain elevator is 24 feet in diameter and 60 feet high. How many bushels of wheat will it contain?

Use 1.25 cu. ft. = 1 bu.

11. What is the volume of the cylinder of an engine, if its diameter is 5 in. and its length 8 in.?

12. The diameter of the cross section of a full water main is 8 in. If the water moves through this main at the rate of 120 ft. per minute, how many gallons will the pipe deliver per minute?

Review

These problems are from Regents' papers. In an examination 15 minutes are allowed for the solving of ten oral problems.

1. Tom received \$3.25 from the sale of *The Saturday Evening Post* at 5 cents a copy; how many copies did he sell?

2. How many days older is a girl on the 27th of April than she was on the 12th of March?

3. How many square inches are there in ⅔ of a square foot?

4. If a glass of lemonade holding a half pint is sold for 5 cents, what is a can holding 4 quarts worth?

5. At \$14 a ton what will 1000 pounds of coal cost?

6. Jack deposited \$60 in the bank at one time and \$15 at another. He drew out \$12 at one time and \$28 at another. How much had he left in the bank?

7. If a grocer charges 20 cents for 4 quarts of potatoes, what is the price per bushel?

8. What is the cost of 6 days' board at \$2¾ per day?

9. Fred has 12 hens that laid 960 eggs in one season. What was the average number of eggs per hen?

10. If candy costs 80 cents a pound, how many ounces can be bought for 20 cents?

11. A train that was due at 3 : 30 P.M. was 45 minutes late; when did it arrive?

12. Of 44 pupils that took examinations 75% passed. How many failed?

13. A man borrowed \$500. How much interest did he pay on the loan in 4 years at 5%?

14. Find the interest on \$600 for 9 months at 6%.

15. The freight on a bicycle costing \$30 was \$2; at what price must the bicycle be sold to gain 37½%?

16. What will be received for 27 eggs at 44 cents a dozen?

17. How much will 1200 pounds of coal cost at $15 a ton?

18. If a reduction of $12\frac{1}{2}\%$ of a man's monthly salary amounts to $25, what is his monthly salary?

19. There are 57 persons present at a meeting; if a vote of more than one half of the persons present is required to elect a chairman, what is the smallest number of votes that Mr. A must receive to be elected chairman?

20. Find the cost of 200 feet of lumber at $50 per M.

21. If a can of beans that cost 12 cents was sold for 18 cents, what was the per cent of profit?

22. A book that cost $2.40 was sold at a gain of 25%; what was the selling price?

23. A landlord raises the rent of a house from $48 a month to $60 a month; what is the per cent of increase?

24. If a player makes 6 hits in 24 times at bat, what is his per cent of hits?

25. If the street car fare is 7 cents, how much change should a man receive from a 25-cent piece after paying two fares?

26. A gas meter shows a consumption of 2500 feet of gas in one month; find the cost at $1.50 per thousand feet.

27. Kate buys 18 oranges at 50 cents a dozen; how much change should she receive from a $2 bill?

28. Add $\frac{1}{3}$ and $\frac{1}{4}$.

29. Find the total area of the faces of a cube the dimensions of which are 4 inches.

30. George misses 8 words from a list of 40 words; what per cent credit does he receive?

Written

Copy and add the following:

31.	379.685	**32.**	213.37
	4268.5		1650.25
	57.692		.0875
	4.37		3276.5
	946.869		7984.
	5507.098		62843.08
	7685.95		205.205
	8.7		37567.375
	99.7769		29.87
	9875.889		436.29

33. Subtract .255 from 1000.

34. Divide 651.021 by .3207.

35. Divide 297.0875 by .625.

36. Copy and add the following:

27.8; 384.52; 927.3; 6.285; 303.25; 87; 832.04; .0375; 94.666; 436.9.

37. What is the product of 345 and $6\frac{2}{3}$?

38. Divide 12.39 by 2.9, carrying the result to *three* decimal places.

39. From $38\frac{1}{4}$ subtract $10\frac{2}{3}$; to the difference add $59\frac{3}{8}$.

40. Find (a) the sum of $2\frac{1}{3}$ and $3\frac{1}{4}$, (b) the difference between $4\frac{1}{4}$ and $2\frac{3}{4}$, (c) the product of the two results.

41. Divide 11.357 by 67.3, carrying the quotient to *four* decimal places.

42. From the product of $\frac{7}{8}$ and $\frac{4}{5}$ subtract the quotient of $\frac{1}{5}$ divided by $\frac{3}{10}$.

43. Find the product of 8.7096 and $80.65\frac{7}{8}$.

44. Divide 529 by 67 to *four* decimal places.

45. Add $\frac{7}{8}$ and $\frac{2}{3}$. Divide the sum by $\frac{5}{8}$ and from the quotient thus obtained subtract $\frac{4}{5}$. $1\frac{1}{20}$

46. From the sum of $3\frac{1}{2}$, $2\frac{3}{4}$, and $7\frac{5}{8}$ subtract 3.875.

47. Multiply the sum of $2\frac{3}{4}$ and $5\frac{3}{8}$ by the difference between $7\frac{1}{4}$ and $3\frac{1}{2}$.

48. At Lincoln School the average daily attendance for February was 123.37; for March 109.68; for April 135.6; for May 136.08; for June 129.45. What was the average attendance for the entire five-month term?

49. How do you check your work in multiplication? Illustrate by the following example: 467 multiplied by 48.

50. How many pieces $1\frac{3}{16}$ inches long can be cut from a rod $14\frac{1}{2}$ inches long?

51. Answer both a and b:

$a.$ Change to common fractions:
$87\frac{1}{2}\%$, 5%, $16\frac{2}{3}\%$, $33\frac{1}{3}\%$, 20%

$b.$ Change to per cents: $\frac{3}{8}$, $\frac{1}{2}$, $\frac{5}{6}$, $\frac{5}{4}$, $\frac{2}{3}$

52. On seven successive days at noon the thermometer registered 80 degrees, 76 degrees, 82 degrees, 79 degrees, 85 degrees, 90 degrees, and 88 degrees; what was the average temperature for the week?

53. A fruit dealer bought 500 bushels of apples at $1.50 per bushel. After repacking them, he sold them for $6 per barrel. Each barrel holds $2\frac{1}{2}$ bushels. How much was his profit?

54. The pump of a city pumping station can pump 3,600,000 gallons of water in 24 hours. The pump is operated on an average 14 hours a day. The population of the city is 15,000. Determine the average number of gallons of water pumped every day for each resident of the city.

55. If pencils are bought at the rate of 3 for 2 cents and sold at the rate of 2 for 3 cents, how much will the profit be on 72 pencils?

56. A man raises 4000 barrels of apples; he makes $\frac{1}{8}$ of them into cider, sells $\frac{1}{4}$ of them locally, and ships the remainder. At $3.79 per barrel, what does he receive for the shipment?

57. State with reference to the following problem (a) what you are required to find, (b) what facts are given you to work with, (c) what you must first find with the facts given, (d) how you will use what you first find to obtain your answer:

Mr. Gregg buys for a vacation trip an automobile for $335, a spare tire for $18, and a camp kit for $85; when he returns from his trip, he sells the whole outfit for $290. What has the use of the outfit cost him?

58. Six loads of coal weighed 1900 pounds, 2100 pounds, 2600 pounds, 2340 pounds, 2560 pounds, and 2290 pounds respectively; how much did the six loads cost at $13.25 per ton?

59. A dealer bought 4 loads of hay at $22.75 a ton. The loads including the wagon weighed respectively 4156 pounds, 4720 pounds, 4384 pounds, and 4460 pounds; the wagon weighed 1180 pounds. What was the cost of the hay?

60. At $22.25 a thousand, how much will 15,875 bricks cost?

61. Find the cost of 3 loads of coal weighing respectively 2610 lb., 1965 lb., and 2425 lb., if the coal costs $14.25 per ton and 50 cents extra per ton is charged for carrying it to the second floor.

62. What will be the cost of laying a cement walk 12 rods long and 4 feet wide, at $17\frac{1}{2}$ cents a square foot?

63. Find the cost of painting a tin roof 80½ feet long by 62 feet wide at 20¢ per square yard.

64. A schoolroom is 30 feet long, 24 feet wide, and 12½ feet high; in it are seated 35 pupils. How many cubic feet of air space are there for each pupil?

65. A rug 5 yards long and 3½ yards wide leaves an uncovered space 2½ feet wide around a room; what is the floor area of the room in square feet?

66. If it costs $44.40 to lay a cement walk 48 feet long and 5 feet wide, what is the cost per square foot?

67. A swimming tank is 60 feet long and 20 feet wide and has an average depth of 6 feet; how many gallons of water does it contain? (One gallon contains 231 cubic inches.)

68. How many tons of hard coal may be stored in a bin 12 feet wide, 14 feet long, and 4 feet high? (Allow 35 cubic feet for 1 ton of hard coal.)

69. What will be the total cost of building a cement road 16 feet wide and 5 miles long at $2.50 a square yard?

70. A roof on each side of the ridge is 64 feet long and 18 feet 9 inches wide; at $3.25 a gallon, what will be the cost of the paint required to cover the roof, if a gallon of paint will cover 400 square feet of surface?

71. The cost of building a cold storage plant 100 feet long, 60 feet wide, and 30 feet high, inside measurement, was $49,500; what was the cost per cubic foot?

72. On a certain map of Asia, Bombay and Manila are 7½ inches apart; the scale of the map is 100 miles to every quarter of an inch. How many miles apart are the two places?

73. A cubic foot of copper weighs 552 pounds; how many ounces does 1 cubic inch of copper weigh?

74. A steer weighing 1200 pounds alive, after having been killed and dressed, was sold at 19¾¢ a pound; if the weight of a dressed steer is 65% of its live weight, how much was received for the steer?

75. A real estate dealer sold a house for $6050 and thereby gained 10% on the transaction; what did he pay for the house?

76. A huckster buys sweet corn at $2 per hundred ears and sells it at 30 cents a dozen; what per cent profit does he make?

77. On January 1, 1920, the weekly pay roll of a certain corporation was $45,000; on May 1 all wages were advanced 20%; on December 1 the increased wages were cut 16⅔%. Find the amount of the final pay roll.

78. A dairyman sold in one month 12,500 pounds of milk which contained 3.5% of butter fat; at 38 cents a pound for the butter fat, how much did the dairyman receive?

79. If goods sell at $715 at a profit of 30%, what did they cost? What would be the selling at a 35% profit?

80. A real estate dealer buys a house and lot for $4400; he pays $125 for painting, $175 for plumbing, and $100 for grading and walks. At what price must he sell the property to make a profit of 12½%?

81. A clerk was paid $5 a day for his services. He was to receive in addition 2% on all daily sales above $50. If on Wednesday his sales amounted to $97.86, how much did he receive for that day's work?

82. How much more does a table cost marked $16.50 with a discount of 20% than one marked $11.75 without discount?

83. A man lost 20% of his money and then lost 10% of the remainder; if he had $3600 left, how much did he have at first?

84. An automobile costing $1125 was sold for $1350; what was the per cent of profit?

85. Mrs. John Smith bought of William Jones the following goods: 5 yards dress goods at $2 a yard; 1 skirt at $16; 2 pairs gloves at $2.75 a pair; 4 yards ribbon at 20 cents a yard. If Mr. Jones gives a 5% discount on every cash purchase above $5, what must Mrs. Smith pay?

86. Twenty-five books listed at $1.40 each with a 20% discount were ordered for a class; if the parcel post charges amounted to 50¢, how much did each pupil have to pay for his book?

87. An article is listed in a catalogue at $50; this price is subject to a 25% discount and a further discount of 10% for cash. What is the cash sale price of the article?

88. A coat costing $104 was marked $195; at a special sale it was sold at a reduction of $33\frac{1}{3}\%$ from the marked price. What per cent did the merchant gain or lose?

89. A merchant bought goods listed at $1472 and was allowed successive discounts of $12\frac{1}{2}\%$ and 5%; how much did he pay for the goods?

90. A commission merchant sold a consignment of 400 dozen eggs at 70¢ a dozen; if his commission was 5% and the charges for freight and cartage amounted to $1\frac{1}{2}$¢ a dozen, what amount should he remit to the shipper?

91. A commission merchant sells 6240 pounds of cheese at $19\frac{3}{4}$ cents a pound; what sum should he remit to his principal if his commission is $2\frac{1}{2}\%$?

92. A commission merchant charged a farmer 8% commission for selling his produce; if he remitted to the farmer $3910 for a sale, what was the selling price of the produce?

93. A man buys a house for $4200 and spends $800 on repairs; he then sells it for $5500. What is his gain per cent?

94. A house worth $3600 was insured for $\frac{2}{3}$ of its value and the contents, worth $2800, were insured for $\frac{1}{2}$ of their value; the rate of insurance was 65 cents on $100. The house and contents were entirely destroyed by fire.

a. What did the owner pay for his insurance each year?

b. What should the owner receive from the company for his loss?

95. A merchant carries a stock of goods insured for $84,000. The insurance rate is $12 per thousand annually. The merchant is informed by the agent that if a sprinkler system is installed the rate will be reduced to $4.50 per thousand. What will be the saving in premiums each year to the merchant if the sprinkler system is installed?

96. A man owns a house valued at $6500 and insures it for 80% of its value; find the premium if the rate of insurance is $1\frac{2}{4}$%.

97. A school district has a valuation of $125,000; the district wishes to buy $100 worth of books of which the state will pay half the cost. How much will a man having a farm valued at $4000 pay toward these books?

98. The assessed valuation of the property of a certain town is $300,000; the tax to be raised is $600. What is the rate of taxation? What tax must be paid by a man who owns property worth $7500 in this town?

99. A man paid $8000 for a house. He rents it for $90 per month. Taxes average $160 per year and other expenses $120 per year. What per cent of his investment is his net income?

100. The assessed valuation of a school district is $25,-000,000; the total tax is $168,750. If Mr. Brown's property is valued at $8000, what is his tax?

101. Make out a receipted bill for the following articles bought from E. C. Gray who is doing business in your home town: 4 pounds sugar @ 20¢ a pound; 1½ pounds rice @ 16¢ a pound; 2¾ pounds butter @ 72¢ a pound; 1¼ dozen eggs @ 76¢ a dozen.

102. Make out a bill for the following transaction:

M. F. Kennedy buys today, June 17, 1924, of King and Connor, Lowville, N. Y., 22 pounds white lead at 16 cents a pound, 2 gallons linseed oil at 75 cents a gallon, 3 quarts turpentine at 40 cents a quart, 1 brush at $1.35, 12 rolls paper at 45 cents a roll, 1 pint varnish at 65 cents, 3 pounds paste at 15 cents a pound, 6 pounds kalsomine at 12 cents a pound.

103. Make a receipted bill for the following: On June 14, 1921, Robert Morris sold to James Dow 2 sacks flour @ $1.35 a sack; 15 pounds sugar @ 9¢ a pound; 5 gallons kerosene @ 22¢ a gallon; 3 pounds coffee @ 38¢ a pound; 1 pound tea @ 60¢ a pound. Paid in full June 16, 1921.

104. On October 20, 1919, James Price bought of George Kent, Chicago, Ill., the following goods: 5½ yards of elastic at 16¢ a yard; 3¾ yards of gingham at 96¢ a yard; 7 yards of silk braid at 17¢ a yard; 4 sheets at $2.40 each; 8 pillow cases at 95¢ each; 6 towels at $1.35 each. Make out the receipted bill.

105. The Hollister (N. Y.) Free Library buys today of Gordon Bros., Buffalo, N. Y., the following goods:

> 2500 catalogue cards at $4.50 per M
> 4500 date slip at $1.40 per M
> 500 book pockets at $7 per M
> 30 pamphlet binders at $1.80 per dozen
> 4 stamp pads at $.35
> 12 magazine binders at $5.20 per dozen

Make out the bill and receipt it.

106. On January 5, 1923, Robert Price bought from Platner and Sneck, Albany, N. Y., the following goods: $5\frac{1}{2}$ yards elastic at 16 cents a yard; $3\frac{3}{4}$ yards gingham at 76 cents a yard; 7 yards braid at 17 cents a yard; 4 sheets at $2.50 each. Make out the bill. What amount must be paid if the bill is discounted at 10%?

107. Today Mrs. William Smith pays for the following goods which she bought of John Brown & Co. on January 13: 25 pounds of sugar @ 16¢ a pound; 1 sack of flour @ $3.90; 3 pounds of butter @ 70¢ a pound; $\frac{1}{2}$ pound of mixed nuts @ 50¢ a pound. Make out the receipted bill.

108. A cylindric tank is 3 feet long and 14 inches in diameter; how many gallons of gasoline will it hold? ($\pi = \frac{22}{7}$; one gallon contains 231 cubic inches.)

109. How many gallons of gasoline will a tank car that is 30 feet long and 10 feet in diameter contain? (One gallon contains 231 cubic inches.)

110. How many cubic feet of silage will a cylindric silo 14 feet in diameter and 30 feet high hold?

111. Find in gallons the capacity of a cylindric cistern 56 inches in diameter and 8 feet deep.

112. If 40 cubic feet of ensilage weigh 1 ton, find the number of tons of ensilage that a cylindric silo will hold if it is 18 feet in diameter and 35 feet high.

113. How many gallons of gasoline will a cylindric tank 2 feet long and 10 inches in diameter contain?

114. Which is the better investment and how much on each $1000 invested, 6% stock selling at 90 *or* 5% stock selling at 70?

115. Find the simple interest on $450 at 5% from July 1, 1920, to March 17, 1921.

116. Which will yield more interest in 6 months and how much more: two $500 bonds, one bearing interest at 6% and the other bearing interest at $4\frac{1}{2}$% annually, *or* a $1000 mortgage bearing interest at 5%?

117. A man owns thirteen $500 United States $4\frac{1}{2}$% Liberty Bonds; how much will he receive annually in interest from these bonds?

118. How would you find the income from a certain number of $100 Victory bonds bearing $4\frac{3}{4}$% interest?

119. If a man owns 29 bonds at $500 each, bearing interest at $3\frac{1}{2}$%, how much does he receive at each semiannual interest period?

120. A man sells a piano for $550, receiving $150 in cash; he takes a 90-day note with interest at 6% for the balance. If the note is discounted immediately at a bank, what is the net amount received for the piano?

121. A merchant accepts a 60-day note for $350 bearing interest at 6%. Two weeks later he takes it to the bank to be discounted. What are the proceeds?

122. William Brown of Jamestown, N. Y., loans to John Jones, January 1, 1923, $500 at 6% for 90 days.

a. Write a promissory note covering this transaction.

b. How much should Mr. Jones pay when the note is due?

123. John Doe borrowed $75 of William Smith and gave his note for 30 days at 6% interest; write the note and compute the interest due Mr. Smith at the end of the 30 days.

124. A note for $150 which does not bear interest is discounted at a bank 30 days before it is due, the rate of discount being 6%. A suit of clothes at $75 and an overcoat at $45 are purchased with the proceeds. How much money remains?

125. A man sells a $1650 automobile, receiving in payment $800 cash and a 30-day note, without interest, for the balance; if he discounts the note immediately at the bank at 6%, what is the net amount received for the automobile?

126. I borrowed $1200 at 6% on June 1, 1922; on Sept. 25, 1923, I paid the note in full with interest. What was the amount of payment made?

127. What is the amount due on a note for $375 which has run 1 year 5 months and 10 days at 5% interest?

128. At 5% simple interest, find the amount due on a note for $1785 for 1 year 9 months and 6 days.

129. Write a 60-day note, with John Doe as payee and Richard Roe as maker, for $180, interest at 5%. Find its value when due.

130. Find the side of a square field that has the same area as a rectangular field 81 rods long and 64 rods wide.

131. A rectangular park is 40 rods long and 30 rods wide; if A walks the length and breadth of the park and B walks from one corner direct to the diagonally opposite corner, how many rods farther does A walk than B?

132. Two roads meet at right angles; 80 rods down one road is the schoolhouse and 60 rods up the other road is a boy's home. How much nearer is it for the boy to go to school along a straight path from his home to the schoolhouse than to go around by the roads?

133. The diameter of a circular park is 350 feet; find the cost of grading at 12 cents a square foot.

134. A rectangular lot is 24 rods long and 15 rods wide; find the length of the diagonal, carrying your answer to *two* decimal places.

135. A boy lives 30 rods south from a certain street corner; the schoolhouse is 40 rods west from the same corner. How much nearer is it for the boy to go diagonally to the schoolhouse than the longer way around the corner?

136. A square has an area of 7921 square inches; what is the perimeter of the square?

137. Extract the square root of 1428.84.

138. If a candidate for office receives 16,353 votes in 237 election districts in a certain city, state how many votes he may be expected to receive in the whole city which has 789 election districts, assuming the vote to be uniform throughout the city. (Solve by proportion.)

139. If a vertical rod 6 feet high casts a shadow 4 feet long, what is the height of a flagpole which at the same time casts a shadow 28 feet long?

140. A boy in a shop finds that he can dress a pine board in 5 minutes if he uses a smoothing plane; if he uses a machine planer, he can dress a board of the same width, but four times as long, in 15 seconds. How many times as many boards can he dress on the machine as he can with the hand plane?

141. If a standard railway rail is 30 feet long and weighs 115 pounds per linear yard, how many tons of steel will be required to manufacture 40 rails? (One ton contains 2000 lb.)

142. Make a receipted bill for the following: L. F. Brown bought of Otis, Strong & Co., Albany, N. Y., 37 bu. oats @ $.40; 50 bu. corn @ $.67½; 76 bu. wheat @ $1.04¼; 16 bu. potatoes @ $.75. (Date the bill today.)

143. A man gave the use of a piece of land to 121 boys for the purpose of raising potatoes; to each boy was assigned a plot 30 feet long and 24 feet wide. If the average yield was 92 bushels to the acre, how many bushels of potatoes were raised? (1 acre contains 43,560 square feet.)

144. If a $500 Liberty Bond bearing 4¼% interest and purchased at par should be held for 10 years, how much interest on the bond would the owner receive during that time?

145. If 14 barrels of flour last 9 weeks, how many weeks will 24 barrels last?

146. A family uses in one month 1¼ tons of coal at $6.80 per ton and 3500 cubic feet of gas at $1 per thousand cubic feet; the father's monthly salary is $120. What fractional part of his monthly salary does he pay for fuel and light?

147. What is the cost per acre of plowing land, if one man with three horses plows 2 acres in 9 hours, at the rate of 20 cents an hour for the man's time and 10 cents an hour for the time of each horse?

148. Make out a receipted bill such as John Smith, a tailor, might send to Mary L. Brooks for the following: 7 yards serge @ $1.50; 4 yards satin @ $1; $1\frac{1}{2}$ yards canvas @ 20¢; $\frac{1}{4}$ yard wadding @ 16¢; $\frac{1}{2}$ dozen buttons @ $1 a dozen; making suit $15.

149. If the ratio of the volume of water to ice is as 23 to 25, what space will be filled by the ice obtained by freezing 4531 cubic inches of water?

150. *a.* Express in decimal form $\frac{1}{2}\%$, $\frac{1}{8}\%$, 50%, $87\frac{3}{4}\%$, 105%.

b. Express as per cents: .98375; 2.50; .0025; 1.00; .625.

151. If $2.25 per gross is paid for school pencils, and each pupil has one pencil, what is the cost of pencils for 48 pupils?

152. Write in figures six hundred forty-three and seven hundredths and multiply this number by nine thousand six.

153. Henry Palmer bought of Edward Richards & Co., Baltimore, Md., the following goods: $6\frac{1}{2}$ yards silk at $4.20 a yard; $3\frac{3}{4}$ yards broadcloth at $3.80 a yard; 8 yards silk ribbon at 65¢ a yard; 16 yards silk braid at $12\frac{1}{2}$¢ a yard. Make out the receipted bill. (Date the bill today.)

154. Find the interest on $480 for 69 days at 5%.

155. At $32 per ton, find the cost of fertilizer for 600 young peach trees, allowing $1\frac{1}{4}$ lb. to a tree.

156. A stationer bought pencils for $3.60 per gross and sold them for 4 cents each; what per cent did he gain? *60 %*

157. A commission merchant sold for a farmer 350 bushels of potatoes at $1.75 a bushel. The rate of commission was 5%. The freight and other charges amounted to $35. How much per bushel did the farmer receive? *156*

158. A sidewalk 138 feet long and 5 feet wide was laid in front of a building lot; the price was 14¢ a square foot. If the city paid 60% of the expense and the owner of the lot paid the remainder, how much did the walk cost the owner?

159. Express in figures:

Six hundred twenty thousand, four and eight ten-thousandths.

Five and five millionths.

Seventeen thousand, two and six hundred twenty-five thousandths.

Ten million.

Seventy thousand, four hundred sixty.

160. Find the amount due on the following laundry bill: 4 shirts @ 12½¢, 6 collars @ 2½¢, 3 pairs of cuffs @ 5¢ a pair, 9 handkerchiefs at the rate of 3 for 10¢, and 3 pairs of socks @ 5¢ a pair.

161. A baseball team won 30 games and lost 50; what per cent of the games played did the team win?

162. Write the following per cents in a column and after each write the equivalent common fraction in its lowest terms: 6¼%; 37½%; 75%; 12½%; 83⅓%; 16⅔%; 66⅔%; 87½%; 33⅓%; 62½%.

163. The record of a herd of 24 cows showed a yield of 3240 pounds of milk per week; how much milk would be produced per week if 10 cows equally good should be added to the herd?

164. It costs a school $20.40 to furnish supplementary readers for a class of 24 pupils; what will it cost to furnish a class of 19 pupils with readers of the same kind? (Solve by proportion.)

165. Find the fourth term in the following proportion:

$$147 : 378 :: 126 : ?$$

166. If 5 tons of coal cost $60, how much will $12\frac{1}{2}$ tons cost at the same rate?

167. Copy and complete *five* of the following so as to make them correct statements:

a. The dividend divided by the divisor equals the —.

b. One of the two equal factors of a number is called —.

c. To change a common fraction to a decimal —.

d. An expression of equality between two ratios is called a —.

e. One difference between a common fraction and a decimal fraction is —.

f. The writing of numbers is called —.

g. The amount paid periodically for insurance against loss is called prem.

168. Tell how to do *two* of the following:

a. Find the cost of one article when the number of articles and the cost of all of them are known.

b. Change a common fraction to a per cent.

c. Find the amount received when the number of articles and the price of one article are known.

169. Copy and complete *five* of the following so as to make them correct statements:

a. When one number is divided by another, the number divided is called the —.

b. The second and third terms of a proportion are called —.

c. A fraction whose numerator is greater than its denominator is called —.

d. When interest due is added to the principal the sum is called —.

e. The distance from the center of a circle to its circumference is called —.

f. An even number is one which can be exactly divided by —.

g. Changing numbers from a higher to a lower denomination is reduction —.

170. Copy *five* of the following incomplete sentences and make them into true statements by filling in the blanks with the correct words:

a. The number that is to be divided by another number is the —.

b. One or more of the equal parts of a unit is called a —.

c. The result obtained by division is the —.

d. The amount that is paid to an agent for doing business for another is the —.

e. Those numbers which multiplied together produce the given number are the — of the number.

f. Money that is paid for the use of money is —.

g. The one who makes a note is the —.

171. Complete *five* of the following statements:

a. When one number is multiplied by another, the result is called the —.

b. To reduce an improper fraction to a mixed number you must —.

c. The face of a note less the discount is called the —.

d. A signature written across the back of a check is called —.

e. A number can be exactly divided by 5 if it ends in either — or —.

f. When a number is divided by something less than 1, the result will be — than the number.

g. The line from one corner of a rectangle to the opposite corner is called the —.

172. Tell how to do *each* of the following:

a. Divide a fraction by a fraction.

b. Raise a number to the third power.

c. Find the number of bushels in a bin if its length, width, and depth in feet are given.

173. Give the correct name for *each* of the following processes:

a. Finding the difference between two numbers is called —.

b. Changing the form of a fraction without changing its value is called —.

c. Finding what number multiplied by itself will produce a given number is called —.

d. Multiplying the length and breadth of a rectangle is called —.

e. Finding the least number that is exactly divisible by each of two or more numbers is called —.

THE METRIC SYSTEM

Optional

The metric system of weights and measures is a decimal system which originated in France a little more than one hundred years ago.   It is the legal system in most of the civilized world except Great Britain and the United States. In our own country, it is used in the sciences and in some branches of the government business.

Being a decimal system, it is much simpler than the English system which we use, for all reductions may be made simply by moving the decimal point.

Linear Measure

The standard unit of linear measure in the metric system is the **meter**.   It is determined by taking one ten-millionth part (very nearly) of the distance from the earth's equator to either of its poles, measured on a meridian.   It is equal to 39.37 inches.

What denomination in the English linear measure is most nearly like the meter?

How the Table is Made

Divide a meter into ten equal parts.   One of these parts is a **decimeter**.   *Dec* is a Latin prefix meaning *tenth*. About how many inches long is a decimeter?

Divide a decimeter into ten equal parts.   One of these parts is a **centimeter**.   *Cent* is a Latin prefix meaning *hundredth*.   What part of an inch is a centimeter?   Show its length.

Divide a centimeter into ten equal parts.   One of these parts is a **millimeter**.   *Mill* is a Latin prefix meaning *thousandth*.

Ten meters make one **dekameter**. *Deka* is a Greek prefix meaning *ten*. How many rods equal a dekameter?

Ten dekameters make one **hektometer**. *Hekto* is a Greek prefix meaning *hundred*.

Ten hektometers make one **kilometer**. *Kilo* is a Greek prefix meaning *thousand*. How many meters equal one kilometer? How many feet? What part of a mile?

Ten kilometers make one **myriameter**.

TABLE OF LINEAR MEASURE

10 millimeters (mm.) = 1 centimeter (cm.)
10 centimeters　　　 = 1 decimeter (dm.)
10 decimeters　　　 = 1 meter (m.)
10 meters　　　　　 = 1 dekameter (Dm.)
10 dekameters　　　 = 1 hektometer (Hm.)
10 hektometers　　　= 1 kilometer (Km.)
10 kilometers　　　 = 1 myriameter (Mm.)

One Decimeter

One Centimeter

Oral

Read the following expressions as meters; thus, seventy *thousand meters*, fifteen *thousand meters*, eighty *meters*:

1. 7 Mm.	9. 34 m.	17. 5 Dm.
2. 15 Km.	10. 7 cm.	18. 61 Km.
3. 6 Hm.	11. 69 Hm.	19. 384 mm.
4. 8 Dm.	12. 46 Dm.	20. 7865 m.
5. 483 m.	13. 931 Km.	21. 35 cm.
6. 8 dm.	14. 26 Hm.	22. 421 mm.
7. 67 cm.	15. 3 dm.	23. 89 Dm.
8. 152 mm.	16. 341 mm.	24. 58 Hm.

Practice reading such expressions as the above in meters, until you can *think* in meters.

Reduction

The following series of numbers read from the top is reduction descending; read from the bottom is reduction ascending. All metric numbers may be reduced in this way.

$$5.689132 \text{ Km.} =$$
$$56.89132 \text{ Hm.} =$$
$$568.9132 \text{ Dm.} =$$
$$5689.132 \text{ m.} \quad=$$
$$56891.32 \text{ dm.} =$$
$$568913.2 \text{ cm.} =$$
$$5689132 \text{ mm.}$$

Each of these numbers may be read thus: 5 6 8 9 1 3 2.

Oral and Written

1. How may a metric number be reduced to higher denominations? To lower denominations?

2. Reduce 12,345,678 mm. to cm.; to dm.; to m.; to Dm.; to Hm.; to Km.

3. Reduce 9.6538714 Km. to Hm.; to Dm.; to m.; to dm.; to cm.; to mm.

4. Reduce 7 Km. to lower denominations.

5. Reduce 7 mm. to higher denominations.

6. Reduce 6307.1 m. to Km.; to cm.

7. Reduce 31 meters to inches.

8. Write as meters 7 Km.; 6 Hm.; 8 Dm.; 5 m.; 3 dm.; 2 cm.; 9 mm. Write them all as one number.

9. Reduce 1 Km. to feet.

10. Write 7 Km. and 6 mm. in one number, as meters. Reduce it to higher denominations; to lower denominations.

11. Reduce .075 Km. to cm.

12. Reduce 8 Dm. and 6 m. to Km.; to mm.

Surface Measure

Draw a square whose side is one meter.   How many square meters does it contain?   It is how many decimeters on a side?   How many square decimeters does it contain?   How many square decimeters make one square meter?

| One |
| sq. cm. |

Draw a square decimeter.

How many centimeters long and wide is a square decimeter?   How many square centimeters in one square decimeter?   Find how many square millimeters in one square centimeter.

TABLE OF SURFACE MEASURE

100 sq. millimeters (sq. mm.) = 1 sq. centimeter (sq. cm.)
100 sq. centimeters   = 1 sq. decimeter (sq. dm.)
100 sq. decimeters   = 1 sq. meter (sq. m.)
100 sq. meters   = 1 sq. dekameter (sq. Dm.)
100 sq. dekameters   = 1 sq. hektometer (sq. Hm.)
100 sq. hektometers   = 1 sq. kilometer (sq. Km.)

Land Measure

The **are** (pronounced *air*) and **hectare** are the principal units of land measure.

The *are* is equal to one *square dekameter*, and the *hectare* is equal to *one hundred ares*.

TABLE OF VOLUME MEASURE

1000 cu. millimeters (cu. mm.) = 1 cu. centimeter (cu. cm.)
1000 cu. centimeters   = 1 cu. decimeter (cu. dm.)
1000 cu. decimeters   = 1 cu. meter (cu. m.)

The unit chiefly used in measuring wood and stone is the *stere* (pronounced *stair*), which is a cube whose edge is one meter.   What denomination in the English volume measure is most nearly like the stere?   How many cubic meters does the stere contain?

Capacity Measure

The metric capacity measure takes the place of both the liquid and the dry measure of the English system.

The standard unit of capacity measure is the **liter** (pronounced *leeter*), which is a cube whose edge is one decimeter.

TABLE OF CAPACITY MEASURE

The table of capacity measure is formed similarly to the other metric tables, and is as follows:

10 milliliters (ml.)	= 1 centiliter (cl.)
10 centiliters	= 1 deciliter (dl.)
10 deciliters	= 1 liter (l.)
10 liters	= 1 dekaliter (Dl.)
10 dekaliters	= 1 hektoliter (Hl.)
10 hektoliters	= 1 kiloliter (Kl.)

Oral and Written

1. What denomination in our liquid measure is most like the liter?

2. How many liters equal one cubic meter?

3. A bin is 2.5 m. wide, 6.4 m. long, and 17 dm. deep. How many liters of oats will it hold?   How many hektoliters?   How many kiloliters?

4. A tank is 3 m. long and 3 m. wide.   How many decimeters deep must it be to hold 180 Hl. of water?

5. A stone whose volume is 1 stere, if dropped into a pond, would displace how many liters of water?

6. How many liters make one kiloliter?

7. A dry quart is $68\frac{4}{5}$ cubic inches.   A liquid quart is $57\frac{3}{4}$ cubic inches.   Can you find the number of cubic inches in one liter?   (A liter is the same as 1 cubic decimeter.)

Measures of Weight

The **gram** is the unit of weight. It is equal to the weight of a cubic centimeter of distilled water at its greatest density. One gram equals 15.432 grains.

TABLE OF WEIGHT

10 milligrams (mg.)	= 1 centigram (cg.)
10 centigrams	= 1 decigram (dg.)
10 decigrams	= 1 gram (g.)
10 grams	= 1 dekagram (Dg.)
10 dekagrams	= 1 hektogram (Hg.)
10 hektograms	= 1 kilogram (Kg.)

Oral and Written

1. Reduce 6,543,215 mg. to higher denominations.

2. Read the number in example **1**, giving each figure the name of the denomination it represents.

3. Recite the table of weight.

4. Spell the name of each denomination.

5. How many grains are there in 1 Kg.?

6. One pound Avoirdupois contains 7000 gr. How many pounds are equivalent to one kilogram?

7. Mr. Smith weighs 100 Kg. How many pounds does he weigh?

8. How many grams does a cubic meter of distilled water weigh?

9. Would a cubic meter of any other substance weigh the same as a cubic meter of distilled water? State your reason.

10. How many kilograms of water will a tank 4 m. × 3 m. × 12 dm. hold?

11. How many things are to be committed to memory in the Metric System?

12. What is 39.37? 15.432? 10? These are the only numbers that need be remembered.

Practical Problems for Girls

Optional

1. How many desk shields 18″ × 27″ can be cut from fifteen yards of cotton cloth, a yard wide?

2. How much will thirty such shields cost, if, besides the cloth at 12¢ a yard, one spool of white thread, 5¢, one spool of red thread, 5¢, and three bolts of tape at 10¢ a bolt are used?

3. A cooking apron is made from cambric 1 yd. wide; 32 inches are required for the skirt, two pieces each 3″ × 18″ for ties, one piece 10½″ × 11″ for bib, one piece 3″ × 24″ for the band, and one piece 5″ × 5″ for a pocket. Ties and band must be cut lengthwise of the piece. What is the cost of material at 20¢ a yard?

4. A girl's skirt is made of long cloth 36 in. wide. It requires two widths 20 in. long; one piece 2½″ × 26″ for a band; one placket facing 2″ × 24″; for ruffling, two pieces 6½ in. wide cut across the piece. Find the cost of the material at 20¢ a yard.

5. How many sewing bags can be cut from 6 yards of gingham 27 in. wide if each bag is made from a piece 13″ by 24″?

Find the cost of the following:

6. Middy blouse: 2⅝ yd. of 44 in. linen at 75¢; 1½ yd. contrasting linen at 75¢; 1 spool cotton, 5¢; 1 middy lace, 10¢; 1 middy silk tie, 35¢.

7. Girl's suit: 4 yd. of 54 in. serge at $1.85; ⅜ yd. sateen at $1.25 per yard; 3 silk frogs, 25¢ each; 2 spools silk at 10¢; ½ yd. crinoline, 25¢.

8. Boy's overcoat: 2 yd. of 54 in. cheviot at $3.95; 3 yd. sateen for lining at 25¢; 1 spool silk, 10¢; 1 spool twist, 5¢; 8 buttons at 35¢ a dozen; 4 small buttons at 20¢ a dozen.

9. Each of fifteen girls is making an apron requiring:

$1\frac{1}{2}$ yd. nainsook at $.20 per yd.
$2\frac{2}{3}$ yd. lace edge at $.05 per yd.
$1\frac{2}{3}$ yd. ribbon   at $.01 per yd.

They buy the material in common and divide it. Find the cost of all the material, and then determine how much each should pay. Estimate the saving on each garment by buying the materials together.

10. A tuck shortens a skirt by twice the width of the tuck. How many quarter-inch tucks will shorten a skirt three inches?

11. If a skirt is to be 38 in. long when finished, how long must each breadth be cut to allow for a 3-inch hem and 3 quarter-inch tucks?

12. A child's petticoat measures $1\frac{1}{2}$ yd. around the bottom and is to be 16 in. long, finished with a 1-in. hem. (*a*) How much material 30 in. wide must be purchased? (*b*) It is trimmed with a ruffle 3 in. wide when finished, having a half-inch hem and three $\frac{1}{16}$-inch tucks. It takes $1\frac{1}{2}$ yards of ruffle to measure a yard when sewed on a garment. How much material is needed for the ruffle? Will any extra material be needed for the band? (*c*) At 35¢ a yard, what will the material for the petticoat cost?

13. A straight ruffle 4 in. wide is made from material that is 20 in. wide, costing $1.15 a yard. The ruffle must be long enough to go about a skirt that measures 33 in. What will the material cost?

14. How many inches of lace are required to go around the edge of a circular lunch-cloth one yard in diameter?

Business men, managers of corporations, officers of cities, states, and counties, and the officers of our government find it necessary to make an estimate in advance, and to arrange the different items of expense so that the total amount will not exceed their income. Such an estimate is called a **budget**. Having agreed upon the budget, if they are good managers, they are careful to keep their expenditures within the budget. In the same way, a careful housewife, knowing the amount of money available for household expenses, arranges a weekly or monthly budget, and keeps her expenditures within it. Below is given such a budget, and the record for one week.

1. BUDGET AND EXPENSES FOR WEEK ENDING —— 19—

ITEMS	TOTAL ALLOW.	TOTAL EXP.	BAL.	DEF.
Groceries	4.80	3.36		
Meat	3.00	2.25		
Milk and Ice . . .	.90	.80		
Fruit and Vegetables .	.60	.66		
Service				
Utensils, etc. . . .	.25	.30		
Laundry	2.20	2.10		
Fuel and Light . . .	2.25	2.70		
Miscellaneous . . .	1.00	.62		
Total				

Copy this budget; fill in the balance or deficit after each item; foot the columns; find the net balance, and see if it "checks" with the totals.

2. Mr. Lockwood has an income of $200 a month. Make a monthly budget of that amount, including items for rent, clothing, food, insurance, savings, church, and miscellaneous. Fill in four columns as above and make them check.

3. Find out your father's income and make a budget for him.

4. Make a budget of your mother's household expenses for one month.

Table of Food Values

This table gives the food value, in calories, of one pound of each material named.

One Pound	Calories Protein	Calories Fat	Calories Carbo-hydrates	Total Calories
Beans (dried navy) . . .	409	73	1081	1563
Beef (round steak). . . .	384	464	0	848
Beef (sirloin)	382	850	0	1232
Bread (stale)	181	59	1035	1275
Butter	16	3472	0	3488
Celery	21	4	60	85
Cheese (American). . . .	523	1465	5	1993
Chocolate (unsweetened). .	240	1984	544	2768
Clams	118	17	76	211
Corn (green, canned) . . .	49	52	352	453
Corn meal	166	77	1370	1613
Cornstarch	0	0	1651	1651
Cottolene	0	4082	0	4082
Eggs (1 dozen)	300	540	0	840
Flour (barley)	152	46	1394	1592
Flour (graham)	240	90	1296	1626
Flour (rye)	122	38	1427	1587
Flour (white)	206	42	1382	1630
Halibut steak	325	208	0	533
Hominy (dry)	151	23	1343	1517
Milk (whole)	60	161	89	310
Milk (skimmed)	60	13	93	166
Mutton (leg)	440	893	0	1333
Nuts (English walnuts) . .	336	2629	235	3200
Oatmeal	311	305	1236	1852
Peanuts	510	1680	480	2670
Peas (canned)	93	11	270	374
Potatoes (sweet)	27	22	396	445
Potatoes (white)	33	3	266	302
Rice	144	14	1433	1591
Salmon (canned)	400	489	0	889
Sugar (brown)	0	0	1724	1724
Sugar (granulated)	0	0	1814	1814
Tapioca	7	5	1563	1575
Tomatoes (canned)	21	9	71	101

Generally speaking, food is valuable to the human body in proportion to its energy-producing power. The energy-producing power of food is measured by **calories**. One calorie represents the amount of heat required to increase the temperature of one gram of water one degree centigrade.

Three classes of food elements are necessary in a well-balanced diet; namely, **protein, fats, and carbohydrates**. In addition to these, various mineral substances, which with cellulose are found chiefly in fruits and green vegetables, play an important part in the maintenance of health and vigor.

Protein is especially important in the food of children because it furnishes all of the nitrogen for building up the tissues of the body.

(In answering these questions, refer to the table, page 342.)

1. What per cent of the food value of round steak is protein? What per cent of fat?

2. What per cent of the food value of white potato is (a) Protein? (b) Fat? (c) Carbohydrate? Why is beefsteak and potato a good combination?

3. What per cent of the food value of tapioca is (a) Protein? (b) Fat? (c) Carbohydrate? Is this an excellent food for growing children? If tapioca is used at any meal, find from the table two other kinds of food material that could properly be used with it.

4. Prove by per cents that bread and butter is a good combination. Why would it not be well to eat bread and butter in equal quantities?

5. Why are eggs and cornstarch a good combination?

6. What per cent of the food value of whole milk is (a) Protein? (b) Fat? (c) Carbohydrate? Why is milk better than other food materials to be used alone? What other article in the table most resembles milk in the proportion of the three food materials which it contains?

Practical Problems for Boys

Roofing materials are bought by the *square*. An area of 100 square feet is called a *square*.

1. How many squares are there in a barn roof if each half of the roof measures 60 ft. by 20 ft.?

2. How many squares of tin will be required for a flat roof 30 ft. by 80 ft.?

3. Four bunches of shingles are required to cover a square. How many bunches will be needed for the barn roof mentioned in example 1?

4. Cedar shingles cost $2.40 per square at Seattle, Washington, the freight is $1.04, and the dealer wishes to make a profit of 25%. What must be his selling price? What per cent of the total selling price is the profit? The first cost? The freight?

5. At this price find the cost of the shingles required for the barn roof mentioned in example 1.

6. Asphalt shingles are 8 inches by $12\frac{3}{4}$ inches. What is the area in square inches of one of these shingles?

7. Asphalt shingles sell for $7 per square. Find the cost of these shingles for the barn mentioned in example 1 with these shingles.

8. Which cost more and how much to roof the barn with cedar or asphalt shingles?

9. Solve examples 5, 7, and 8 when the following measurements are substituted for 60 ft. and 20 ft. in example 1: (*a*) 90 ft. by 30 ft.; (*b*) 120 ft. by 25 ft.; (*c*) 30 ft. by 20 ft.

1. A class was composed of 20 boys.   Each boy made a sled for the toy department of the following parts : runners, 42 in. long and $4\frac{1}{2}$ in. wide; three crosspieces, each $2\frac{1}{2}$ in. by 12 in.; a top, 12 in. by $28\frac{1}{2}$ in.   What was the cost of the lumber at $70 per M, none of it being more than 1 in. thick, and estimating that 20% of all the lumber purchased was wasted in the work?

2. Fourteen small bread pans can be made from one sheet of iron.   Three feet of wire are used to wire the top of each pan.   21 feet of wire weigh a pound.   The iron costs 63¢ a sheet, and the wire costs 5¢ a pound.   What does the material for one bread pan cost?

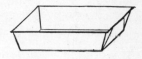

3. Each boy in a class of twenty-one made three bread pans.   What was the cost of all the material?

4. One boy spoiled two pans, and five others each spoiled one pan.   They had to pay for the iron which they wasted.   How much did each have to pay?

5. Ten corn-poppers can be made from one sheet of iron.   Five feet of wire are used in each popper.   What does the material for one popper cost?

6. Nine match boxes can be made from a sheet of tin $20'' \times 28''$.   It is bought by the box of 112 sheets, costing $20.00.   (*a*) How many match boxes can be made from one box of tin?   (*b*) How much does the material for one match box cost?

7. Bring a problem from your manual training class to be solved by this class.

1. Some business men contributed $4000 toward supporting the Boy Scout organization of their city for one year. How much a day could be used and still leave $277 at the end of the year?

2. The chief scout master's salary is $47\frac{1}{2}\%$ of the amount raised. What is his salary?

3. 608 boys enrolled during the year, in 25 troops. The enrollment averaged 76% of full strength. What was the full strength of a troop?

4. One troop of 24 members went on a camping trip. The average weight of the scouts when they left home was 102 lb. 8 oz. When they returned, the combined weight of the troop was $1\frac{1}{4}$ tons. What was the average gain per boy?

5. A camping outfit is listed as follows:

Fry pan, 15¢; 1 qt. stew pan, 10¢; 2 qt. mixing pan, 15¢; 1 pt. tin cup, 5¢; 7″ tin plate, 5¢; universal handle, 20¢; axe, 80¢; pack sack, $1.75; blanket, $2.00; knife, 50¢; combination knife and fork, 50¢; whistle, 25¢; compass, 50¢.

If the entire outfit is purchased for $5.25, the discount is what per cent of the list price?

6. A druggist offers to sell at $62\frac{1}{2}\%$ of the list price a first aid outfit listed as follows:

2℥ iodine, $.25; 2℥ spts. ammonia, $.15; 1 forceps, $.35; pdg. boric acid ointment, $.25; pkg. 1″ cotton bandage, $.10; pkg. 3″ cotton bandage, $.10; pkg. 1″ adhesive plaster, $.10; 1 tourniquet, $.35; 1 pkg. lint, $.10; 1 pkg. surgical pins, $.05; 1 oz. absorbent cotton, $.05; 1 shears, $.20; 1 pkg. zinc oxide ointment, $.25; 1 gauze bandage, $.15; 1 styptic powder, $.15.

What will the outfit cost?

When a dairyman sends milk to a creamery, it is weighed and tested to determine the per cent of butter fat which it contains. The number of pounds of butter fat divided by the entire number of pounds of milk gives the per cent of butter fat. This is generally expressed approximately in decimal per cents, the average being from 3.5% to 5.5%.

1. How many pounds of butter fat are there in 50 lb. of milk, if 3.4% of the milk is butter fat?

2. How much butter fat is there in 342 lb. of milk that tests 5.2 (*i.e.* 5.2% of the milk is butter fat)?

3. Three cows are given the same kind and quantity of food. One cow gives 4450 lb. of milk yearly that tests 5.6; another gives 5120 lb. that tests 3.2; another gives 4875 lb. that tests 4.9. Which of the three cows produces the most butter?

4. 489 lb. of milk were run through a separator and yielded 13.8 lb. of heavy cream. What per cent of the whole milk was cream?

5. It is estimated that when milk is set in deep pans, .2% of the butter fat remains in the milk (does not rise); when shallow pans are used, .8% remains; when a separator is used, .95% remains. Suppose a ton of milk, by exact test, contains 4.9% butter fat. How many pounds would remain in the milk by each of the above methods of separation?

6. Suppose that butter fat is worth 32¢ a pound and skim milk 1¢ a pound, what is the value of the whole milk from a cow which yields 4820 lb. of milk testing 5.3%?

7. It is estimated that in 1850 the average production of milk per cow in the United States was 1436 lb. and that it contained 61 lb. of butter fat. At that rate, what was the average test of the milk?

8. It is estimated that in 1917 the average production of milk per cow was 3732 lb. and that it contained 165 lb. of butter fat. What was the average test of the milk? (What has caused the change since 1850?)

9. A farmer obtains fifty tons of milk annually from his dairy. It tests 4.54%. He can sell the whole milk at $1.80 per cwt. or on the basis of 32¢ a pound for the butter fat and 25¢ per cwt. for the skim milk. Which will bring him the more money?

10. How much milk testing 4.3% contains as many pounds of butter fat as 560 lb. testing 5.1%?

11. The digestible protein of green alfalfa fodder is 2.5% of the weight. How many pounds of digestible protein are there in 3780 lb. of such fodder?

12. A ton of dry alfalfa hay contains 157.2 lb. of true protein. What per cent of the weight is protein?

13. In a ton of potatoes there are 9 lb. of protein. What per cent of the weight of potatoes is protein?

14. How many pounds of potatoes must be fed to a cow to supply her with as much protein as she would get from one pound of dry alfalfa hay?

15. Oat straw contains 1.09%, rye straw .63%, and wheat straw .37% of protein. How many pounds of protein are there in one ton of each of these?

16. When timothy hay (2.06% protein) is $19 a ton, and clover hay (5.5% protein) is $14 a ton, what is the cost of a pound of protein in each of these forms?

1. A 20-acre vineyard contains 540 vines to the acre. All the vines in the vineyard are set in 90 equal rows. How many vines are there in each row?

2. The grapevines are supported by wires fastened to posts. If it requires 609 lb. of wire per acre, costing $52 a ton, what is the cost of the wire for a 15-acre vineyard?

3. The average yield is 1000 baskets of grapes per acre. An empty basket weighs $1\frac{1}{2}$ lb. A filled basket weighs 8 lb. How many pounds of grapes are raised on an acre?

4. How many tons are raised in a 12-acre vineyard?

5. What are they worth at $28 per ton?

6. If it costs $1\frac{1}{2}$ cents per basket to pick and pack the grapes and $\frac{6}{10}$ of a cent per basket for cartage, what must be paid for picking, packing, and carting an acre's yield of grapes?

7. Find how much per acre the grower has left to pay him for his labor and the use of his land.

8. If the grapes are retailed at 25 cents per basket, how much is paid for an acre's crop? (See No. **3**.)

9. One grower pays 4 cents a tray for picking grapes. What are the weekly wages of a picker who picks 50 trays of grapes a day?

10. 64 filled trays weigh a ton, and the yield of an acre is $3\frac{1}{4}$ tons, including the weight of the trays. What is the cost of picking three acres of grapes?

11. The weight of an empty tray is 5 lb. What is the weight of the grapes that fill one tray?

12. How many pounds of grapes will fill 64 trays?

13. At 5 cents apiece, what is the cost of trays for an acre of grapes? (See **10**.)

14. At one cent a pound, what is the value of the grapes from an acre of ground?

15. A grape grower in California has 40 acres of grapes. It costs $12 an acre to train and cultivate his vines and $1.35 per ton for picking. The yield is 6 tons to the acre, and he sells the entire crop for $15 a ton. What is his net profit?

16. Each ton of these grapes will make 300 gallons of grape juice. Allowing 32 gallons for a barrel, how many barrels of grape juice can be made from the entire 40-acre vineyard?

17. How many pounds of grapes are used in making one gallon of grape juice?

The following is a record of receipts and expenses for one year of a 94-acre farm in New York State, owned by Mr. Tallcott, and worked by a tenant who received one half of the net income as his share:

RECEIPTS		EXPENSES	
Wheat, 107 bu., at	80¢ per bu.	Phosphates	$47
Potatoes, 598 bu., at	60¢ per bu.	Seed	$23
Cabbage, 44 tons, at	$14.40 per T.	Miscellaneous	$94
Hay, $17\frac{1}{10}$ tons, at	$11.00 per T.		
Milk	$239.00		
Veal	$22.00		
Young stock, growth	$50.00		
Nine pigs	$106.00		
Poultry	$92.00		

1. How much did the tenant receive for his year's work?

2. The owner's entire investment consisted of $2700 paid for the farm, $500 for improvements, and $800 for stock. Out of his share of the profits, he paid $35 taxes and insurance, $68 for repairs, and $90 for other items. His net income was what per cent of his investment?

3. The next year, the income from produce (cabbages, wheat, potatoes, etc.) diminished $388. The income from milk and live stock increased $407, and the expenses increased $107. Was Mr. Tallcott's per cent of net income increased or diminished, and how much?

4. Neyman Carey enrolled in a Mercer County potato club and won a gold watch as a first prize. He raised 349.4 bu. of potatoes on an acre of ground. Potatoes being high that year, he sold them at $1.50 per bushel. He paid $71 for rent, labor, seed, and fertilizer. Estimating the watch to be worth $50, what was his net return from that acre?

Home Problems

These pages show us one way a boy kept an account of his poultry business. From these pages you can find the average amount of money which he is able to earn each hour. Have you a way of keeping an account of the business in which you have an interest? Do you know the average amount of money which you are earning each hour?

Lyman Matteson kept the following account of his poultry project:

I   CASH OUTLAY

DATE	ARTICLE	AMOUNT
April 25	15½ doz. eggs at 30¢ doz.	
26	8⅓ doz. eggs at 30¢ doz.	
August 18	Paid to enter eggs at Fair	10
	Total	

II   THINGS OBTAINED WITHOUT CASH OUTLAY

DATE	ARTICLE	AMOUNT
March 1 to Sept. 12	Estimate for hen feed	$45 00
May 17 to Sept. 12	Estimate for chicken feed	30 00
	Total	

III   MARKET EGGS

Date	No. of Doz.	Price	Amount	Date	No. of Doz.	Price	Amount
March 1	1	28¢		May 13	$13\frac{1}{2}$	37¢	
14	$7\frac{1}{2}$	28¢		18	18	35¢	
23	7	28¢		30	$27\frac{1}{2}$	34¢	
April 2	$2\frac{1}{2}$	26¢		June 8	$13\frac{1}{4}$	32¢	
4	27	27¢		18	8	32¢	
9	4	30¢		23	$\frac{1}{2}$	34¢	
13	$19\frac{3}{12}$	30¢		30	10	38¢	
18	$17\frac{1}{2}$	37¢		July 22	$7\frac{3}{12}$	42¢	
23	$16\frac{1}{2}$	37¢		August 1	1	42¢	
28	20	37¢		8	$5\frac{1}{2}$	44¢	
May 2	16	37¢		21	11	44¢	
May 7	20	37¢		Sept. 1	$8\frac{1}{2}$	49¢	
							Total

IV   OTHER RETURNS

Date	Article	Amount
July 15	5 hens at $1.00 each	
27	5 hens at $1.10 each	
August 1	2 roosters at $2.00 each	
25	10 hens at $1.05 each	
27	35 hens at $1.07 each	
Sept. 2	15 hens at $1.00 each	
2	Premium on 1 doz. eggs at Fair	90
10	10 pullets at $1.00 each	
12	37 pullets at $ .90 each	
	Total	

V   LABOR   VI MONTHLY EGG PRODUCTION

Hours		Hours		No. of Eggs		No. of Eggs	
March	15	July	10	March	400	July	,115
April	15	Aug.	10	April	1330	Aug.	272
May	10	Sept.	5	May	1019	Sept.	10
June	10	Total		June	367	Total	

VI   INCUBATION AND BROODING RECORD

Number of eggs set 260.   Date, May 2, 1925.
Breed Barred Rocks.   Grade X pinebred
Number of eggs rejected after tests 34.   Chicks hatched 196.
Chickens raised to six months 102.
Number pullets 74.   Cockerels 28.

VII   SUMMARY OF COSTS

Value at start — First inventory (Stock, feed, etc.)	90	00
Feed bought		
Feed not bought	75	00
Use of shelter (Estimate at 25¢ per bird)	15	00
Interest (Six per cent of average of two inventories)	3	79
Miscellaneous expenses	6	94
Total		

VIII   SUMMARY OF RETURNS

Market eggs (From table III)		
Hatching eggs (From table IV)		
Hens sold (From table IV)		
Roosters sold (From table IV)		
Pullets sold (From table IV)		
Value of manure (Estimate 30 cents a bird)	14	00
Other returns (From table IV)		
Value at finish (Final inventory)	36	25
Total returns		
Total costs (From table VII)		
Return to owner for work done		
Average amount earned per hour		

Building a Radio

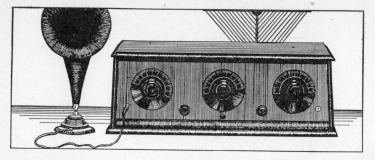

1. Suppose you wish to build a radio. Here is a list of materials for a good two-tube " hook-up."

    1 hard rubber panel $12'' \times 7'' \times \frac{3}{16}''$
    2 40 ohm rheostats with knobs
    1 8 point inductance switch with knob
    2 4'' dials 100°
    1 variable condenser .0005 microfarads capy
    1 .003 grid condenser
    1 2 megohm grid leak
    1 .001 microfarad phone condenser
    1 tapped variocoupler with "tickler" coil
    1 U. V. 199 or C. 299 vacuum tube
    2 U. V. 199 tube sockets
    1 audio frequency transformer
    1 $22\frac{1}{2}$ volt dry "B" battery
    3 standard dry cells ($1\frac{1}{2}$ volts) "A" battery
   15 binding posts
   10' No. 14 tinned bus wire
    5 bd. ft. $\frac{7}{8}''$ clear pine lumber for cabinet
    1 12'' nickel plated piano hinge and screws
    1 doz. No. 10 2'' wood screws
    $\frac{1}{4}$ pint mahogany stain varnish
    1 small brush

Take this list to the store and see how much the materials for the set will cost you.

2. Frank Alden made himself a new radio set last week. It was a one-tube set and had in it the following parts:

1	hard rubber panel 7″ × 9″ @ 1¢ per sq. in.	
1	40 ohm rheostat with knob	$1.40
1	8 point inductance switch	.50
2	4″ dials @ 35¢ ea.	
1	variable condenser .0005 microfarad capy.	.35
1	.003 microfarad grid condenser	.35
1	2 megohm grid leak	.25
1	.001 microfarad phone condenser	.35
1	rapped variocoupler with "tickler"	$2.50
1	U. V. 199 vacuum tube	2.00
1	U. V. 199 tube socket	.50
1	22½ volt dry "B" battery	1.20
3	standard dry cells @ 40¢ ea.	
8	binding posts @ 10¢ ea.	
8 ft.	No. 14 tinned bus wire @ 1¢ per foot	

How much did Frank's set cost?

3. Frank's friend, Johnny Blackmer, wished a radio too, and asked Frank to help him get started by building a crystal set. Here is the crystal set Frank and Johnny made:

1	variometer	$.90
1	.0005 microfarad variable condenser	1.45
1	crystal detector stand	.35
1	crystal, mounted	.25
1	.001 microfarad phone condenser	.25
4	binding posts @ 3¢ ea.	.12
5 ft.	No. 14 bus wire @ 1¢ per foot	.05

How much did the crystal set cost to make?

4. Using the prices Frank Alden paid for his parts in Problem No. 2, see how much it would cost you to build the two-tube set given on page 355. There was no audio transformer in Frank's set. This audio transformer will cost $5.00.

REVIEW OF PRINCIPLES AND PROCESSES

1. How may the area of a parallelogram always be found?

2. How may the area of a triangle be found?

3. If the area and altitude of an oblong be known, how may the base be found?

4. If the area and base of a triangle are known, how may the altitude be found?

5. What must be true of the three dimensions of a prism in order that their product shall be the volume of the prism?

6. When the dimensions of a rectangular field are given in rods, how may its area be found in acres?

7. If you know the number of acres in a field and its width in feet, how can you find its length in rods?

8. How many cubic inches of wood are there in a board foot?

9. How would you find the number of board feet in any piece of lumber?

10. Name three kinds of contracts which you have studied.

11. Why do people pay interest?

12. Interest is the product of what three factors?

13. The interest and any two of its factors being given, how may the other factor be found?

14. What is the difference between ordinary interest and exact interest?

15. In order to obtain an approximate per cent correct to .1 of 1%, to how many places must the division be carried? To get the per cent correct to the nearest .01 of 1%?

PROBLEMS WITH NUMBERS OMITTED

1. A company issued $—— of stock. In one year it paid ——% dividends. How much money did the owners receive in dividends?

2. Mr. Croft bought $—— of bonds, paying a premium of ——%. How much did the bonds cost him?

3. A man bought —— shares of railroad stock at ——% below par and sold it at ——% above par. What was his total profit?

4. What was the cost, including brokerage, of —— shares of United States Steel Company when quoted at ——?

5. The ratio of —— to —— is ——. The second number is ——. What is the first?

6. The extremes of a proportion are —— and ——. One of the means is ——. What is the other mean?

7. Divide —— into parts having the ratio of ——, ——, ——, and ——.

8. The hypotenuse of a right triangle is ——. One leg is ——. Find the other leg.

9. The parallel sides of a trapezoid are —— and ——. The altitude is ——. What is the area?

10. The sides of a trapezoid are —— and ——. The area is ——. What is the altitude?

11. The diameter of a circle is ——. What is its area?

12. The circumference of a circle is ——. What is its radius?

13. The diameter of a cylinder is —— feet. Its altitude is —— inches. What is its volume?

14. The base of a triangle is —— feet. Its altitude is —— feet. What is its area?

Mental Tests

1

1. Find the interest on $3000 for 60 days at 6%.

2. William deposits $100 in the bank and draws out $26 at one time and $24 at another. How much has he left in the bank?

3. What are the prime factors of 30?

4. Find $\frac{3}{5}$ of 50.   **5.** Divide $\frac{3}{5}$ by 3.

6. Twenty per cent of a number is 100. What is the number?

7. What will 12 oranges cost at 3 for 25¢?

8. A horse is bought for $200 and sold for $180. What is the loss per cent?

9. $120 is the interest on $1000 at 4% for a certain time. Find the time.

10. Mr. Wise saves $\frac{1}{4}$ of his wages each week. He spends $30 per week. How much does he earn each week?

2

1. $30 is 5% of what?   **2.** $\frac{1}{2}$ is what per cent of 4?

3. Change 18 pecks to quarts.

4. How many quarts in 50% of two bushels?

5. A merchant gains 20% on an article costing $100. What is the selling price?

6. At what rate must $3000 be at interest to earn $180 in one year?

7. What will $4\frac{3}{4}$ pounds of butter cost at 60¢ per pound?

8. Write five hundred, and five hundredths.

9. Write six hundred six thousandths.

3

1. What is the ratio of $6 to $50?

2. What is the ratio of $60 to $6?

3. One foot is what per cent of one yard?

4. Divide 40 into two parts having the ratio of 3 to 1.

5. A man worked from 8 A.M. to 5 P.M. with one hour out for lunch. How much did he earn at 40¢ per hour?

6. Goods costing $800 were sold at a loss of $12\frac{1}{2}$%. What was the loss?

7. Find the interest on $4000 at 5% for 1 year.

8. Divide 1800 by 300.   **9.** $90 is what per cent of $450?

10. How many cubic feet are there in a block of stone 2 ft. by 3 ft. by 5 ft.?

4

1. Find the cost of 800 lb. of coal at $9 per ton.

2. 5 is 1% of what number?

3. How many times is the square root of 9 contained in the square of 6?

4. What will 10 square yards of tin cost at 10¢ a square foot?

5. Find the interest on $700 from July 6 to September 6 at 6%.

6. What is 5% of $500?

7. Change 82 quarts to gallons.

8. 20 is what per cent of 400?

9. Cost $20, selling price $24. Find the gain per cent.

10. Find the perimeter of a floor 16 ft. by 20 ft.

5

1. What will 9 pictures cost at $8 per dozen?

2. How many bushels of potatoes at $1.20 per bushel can be bought for $12?

3. Square 9, square 12, add, and extract the square root.

4. 8 is 10% of what number?

5. What is the interest at $5\frac{1}{2}$% on $1000 from January 1, 1924, to January 1, 1925?

6. A man sold 20% of his apple crop for $1000. At the same rate, what did he receive for the crop?

7. A load of hay weighing 1600 lb. is sold for $16. What is the price per ton?

8. When 3 lb. of butter are made from 100 lb. of milk, what per cent of the milk is butter fat?

9. One factor is $600, the other 6%. Find the product.

6

1. Cloth costing $2 per yard is sold at a gain of 20%. What will a merchant gain on 10 yards?

2. What is the interest on $5000 for 2 years 6 months at 4%?

3. List price $50, discounts 20% and 5%. What is the cost?

4. How many barrels of apples at $6 a barrel can be bought for $1200?

5. What number multiplied by itself produces 121?

6. What number is $\frac{1}{2}$ of its square?

7. Find the side of a square whose area is 81 square inches.

8. The hypotenuse of a right triangle is 10′, the base is 8′, what is the altitude?

9. How much will be received for a bushel of chestnuts at 10¢ per quart?

10. A chicken weighing 4 pounds and 8 ounces sells for $1.35. What is the price per pound?

7

1. 3 is what per cent of its square?

2. Milk bought at 10¢ per quart is sold for 14¢. What is the gain in per cent?

3. Of 60 pupils who took an examination, 10% failed. How many failed?

4. What is the interest on $800 from March 1, 1916, to May 1, 1917, at 6%?

5. 27 inches is what fractional part of a yard?

6. What will $\frac{7}{8}$ of a pound of cheese cost at 32¢ a pound?

7. The area of a triangle is 30 square inches. Its base is 10 inches. What is its altitude?

8. Find the bank discount of a note for $1000, discounted for 90 da. at 6%.

9. At $33\frac{1}{3}$%, what profit is made on goods costing $60?

10. What is the perimeter of a square 1 ft. 3 in. on a side?

8

1. How many square yards are there in a space 15 feet square?

2. A note due July 1 was discounted May 25. What was the term of discount?

3. The square root of 16 is what % of the square of 6?

4. What number is $33\frac{1}{3}$% of its square?

5. Cost 32¢, gain 8¢. What is the gain per cent?

6. The base of a right triangle is 12, the altitude is 16. Find hypotenuse.

7. The area of a rectangle is 40 square feet and the base is 8 feet. What is the altitude?

8. An agent sold $1000 worth of goods at 5% commission. What did the owner receive?

9. Change 1250 pounds to hundredweight.

10. What is the amount of $600 for 6 months at 6%?

9

1. What is 600 pounds of wheat worth at $2 per bu.?

2. How many square yards of roofing are required for a roof 24 ft. by 30 ft.?

3. Find the area of a parallelogram whose base is 12 ft. and altitude 8 ft.

4. How many board feet are there in a plank 12 ft. long, 6 inches wide and 2 inches thick?

5. What sum of money at interest for two years at 6% will yield $120 interest?   **6.** Find ½% of $1500.

7. The area of floor is 180 square feet. Its width is 9 feet. What is its length?

8. Find the volume of a stone 1 foot by 3 feet by 5 feet.

9. What number is 25% of its square?   **10.** Multiply 36 by 1¼.

10

1. Gain $10; rate of gain 5%. Find cost.

2. What will 2500 feet of lumber cost at $30 per thousand?

3. How many board feet are there in a timber 30 ft. long and 1 foot square?

4. How many acres are there in a field 20 rods by 16 rods?

5. Ten cubic yards equals how many cubic feet?

6. The expense of selling a piece of property was 5% of the selling price. The owner received $950. What was the selling price?

7. Find the area of a trapezoid whose upper base is 20 ft., lower base 30 ft., and altitude 10 ft.

8. What is the area of a circle whose radius is 10, when $\pi = 3.1416$?

9. The area of a circle is 36 π. What is its radius?

10. Find the volume of a rectangular solid 4″ by 9″ by 4″.

11

1. What will it cost to build a wall 10 ft. by 8 ft. by 2 ft. at 50¢ per cubic foot?

2. The area of a parallelogram is 160 square rods and its base is 16 rods. What is its altitude?

3. 30% of a ton equals how many hundredweight?

4. Find the number of board feet in 10 sticks of timber each 12 ft. long, 4 inches wide and 2 inches thick.

5. What will 1500 board feet of flooring cost at $90 per thousand?

6. How many tons of hay at $15 per ton can be bought for $67½?

7. What is the circumference of a circle whose radius is 5?

8. Find the diameter of a circle whose area is 49 π sq. in.

STANDARDIZED TEST — ARITHMETIC PROBLEMS

See suggestions in the introduction for using standardized tests and the directions for scoring a pupil's work upon these problems. A score is given for a correct principle (P) and correct answer (C). Eighth grade pupils should make a score of 17 on correct principle (P) and a score of 9 on correct answer (C).

Solve these problems in the way that you have been taught. Arrange your work so that it can be easily understood in marking your papers. Do not copy the problem. Number the work for each problem. Be sure to put down all of the work. Solve the problems in the order in which they are given. Work rapidly but remember that a problem must be done correctly to count on your score. You will be allowed twenty-five minutes to do as many of these problems as you can.

1. A cow that cost $56 was sold at a gain of $12\frac{1}{2}\%$. What was the gain?

2. A man invested $1750 and lost $192.50. What per cent did he lose?

3. The wages of the men in a certain factory are to be raised 20 per cent from their present scale. How much will a man get after the raise who is getting $2.25 before the raise?

4. A hardware dealer sold a furnace for $180 at a gain of 5 per cent. What did the furnace cost him?

5. If a man saves $18.75 out of his salary of $1250, what per cent does he save?

6. A boat carried 3125 tons of iron ore. This ore will yield 43.8 per cent of iron. How many tons of iron in the cargo?

7. What is the tax on property assessed for $12,480 at $13.50 a thousand?

8. If 33⅓ per cent of the weight of meat is lost in shrinkage when cooked, what ought a ham weighing 12 lb. when raw to weigh when baked?

9. Find the interest at 5% on $640 for 4 years.

10. A salesman sold $75,000 worth of goods one year. His commission was 7½ per cent of his sales. What did he earn?

11. Ellen bought a pocketbook for $.90 just after Christmas. She paid 40 per cent less than was asked for it before Christmas. Find the price before Christmas.

12. A fast train runs from Chicago to a station 356.4 miles distant in exactly 9 hours. What is the average rate of the train?

13. Books that cost $1.50 wholesale were sold at a gain of 10 per cent. What was the selling price?

14. A dealer bought $167.40 worth of clocks and sold them at a profit of 33⅓ per cent. How much did he gain?

15. A clerk had his weekly wages increased $3, or 16⅔ per cent. What were his wages before the increase?

EIGHTH GRADE — SECOND HALF

There are four kinds of angles:

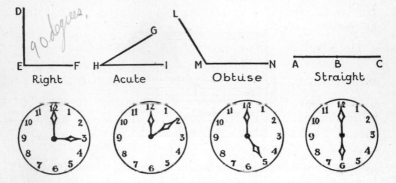

1. What kind of an angle do the hands of a clock make:
(*a*) at 9 o'clock, (*b*) at 10 o'clock, (*c*) at 6 o'clock, (*d*) at
7 o'clock, (*e*) at half past four, (*f*) at twenty minutes of
eleven, (*g*) at five minutes of twelve?

2. The right angle is read: "angle *DEF*." Read
the acute angle, the obtuse angle, the straight angle.

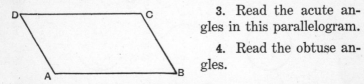

3. Read the acute angles in this parallelogram.

4. Read the obtuse angles.

The protractor is used in measuring angles. The circumference of a circle is divided into 360 parts. Each

365

of these parts is called a degree. A straight angle is an angle of 180 degrees or the angle on one side of a straight line. A right angle equals 90° or $\frac{1}{2}$ a straight angle. An acute angle is less than a right angle. An obtuse angle is greater than a right angle.

The instruments used in making plans and drawings to scale are the drawing board, ruler, ⊤ square, triangle, compass, and protractor.

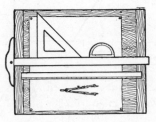

Care should be taken to fasten the paper to the drawing board so that its edge is parallel with the edge of the board. By placing the ⊤ square as shown above, lines may be drawn parallel to the top of the paper. The right triangle may be used to draw lines parallel to the edges of the paper. Rectangles, squares, parallelograms, and triangles may be easily constructed with these instruments.

Lines are straight ——, curved ⌒, and broken – –. The compass is used in constructing circles and arcs;

Angles are read with the vertex letter second, thus angle *ABC* or angle *CBA*.

1. How many degrees are there in the angle *DAE*; angle *DAH*; angle *DAC*; and the angle *BAC*?

2. Find and name a right angle, stating the number of degrees in it. An acute angle of 30 degrees. An obtuse angle of 135 degrees. What kind of an angle is angle *EAC*?

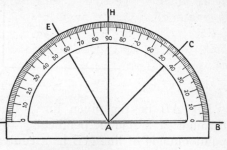

I. *To bisect a straight line.*

Let *AB* be the given line. It is required to bisect *AB*. With *B* as a center and a radius greater than ½ *AB* as *BE* draw an arc *EXN*. With *A* as a center and the same radius draw the arc *OYP*. Call the two intersections of these arcs *C* and *D*. Draw the line *CD*. Then *CD* bisects the line *AB* at the point of intersection *M*.

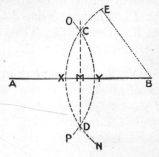

II. *To erect a perpendicular to a given straight line at a given point in the line.*

Let us see how we can draw one line perpendicular to another, through a point on the first line. Draw line *AB*. Take any point *O* on the line. With *O* as center and a radius less than *OA*, draw an arc cutting *AB* at *C* and *D*. With *C* and *D* as centers and a radius greater than *OD*, draw arcs cutting each other at *E*. Draw *OE*. Then *OE* is the line required.

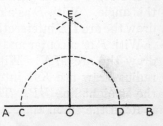

III. *To construct a perpendicular at the end of a line.*

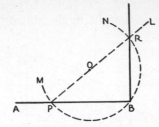

Let *AB* be the given line. It is required to draw
through *B* a line perpendicular to *AB*. With *O*, any
point outside of line *AB* as a center, and with any convenient radius draw arc *MPBN* intersecting the line *AB*
at *P*. Draw the line *POL* intersecting the arc *MPBN*
at *R*. Draw *RB*. Then *RB* is the required perpendicular.
Read the right angle.

IV. *To bisect a given angle.*

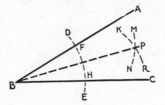

Let *ABC* be the given angle. It is required to bisect
this angle. With *B* as a center and any convenient radius
draw the arc *DE* intersecting line *AB* at *F* and line *BC* at *H*.

With *F* as a center and with a radius greater than $\frac{1}{2}$ *FH*
draw the arc *MN*. With *H* as a center and the same
radius draw arc *KR* intersecting arc *MN* at *P*. Draw
the straight line *BP*. Then *PB* bisects the angle *ABC*.
Read the equal angles.

V. *To construct an angle equal to a given angle.*

Given the angle *ABC*. Required to construct an angle equal to the angle *ABC*.

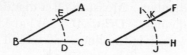

Draw a straight line as *G H*.

With *B* as a center and with a radius equal to *BD* draw the arc *ED*.

With *G* as a center and the same radius draw the arc *IJ*.

With *J* as a center and with a radius equal to *ED* draw an arc intersecting the arc *IJ* at *K*.

Draw the straight line *GF* through points *G* and *K*.

Angle *FGH* is the required angle.

Construct:

(*a*) The bisector of a line 1¾ inches long.

(*b*) The bisector of a right angle.

(*c*) A line perpendicular to the bisector of an angle.

(*d*) Two lines perpendicular to the same line.

(*e*) An angle equal to a given obtuse angle.

(*f*) A line perpendicular to one side of an acute angle.

(*g*) A line two inches long. At each extremity of this line construct a right angle.

(*h*) At one extremity of a line 3 in. long construct a right angle. At the other extremity and on the same side of the line construct an acute angle.

(*i*) At one extremity *B* of a given line *AB* 3 in. long erect a perpendicular. Measure off a distance *BC* of 4 in. on this perpendicular. Draw *AC*. What kind of a figure is *ABC*? How long is the line *AC*? Find the length of *AC* by $\sqrt{\overline{AB}^2 + \overline{BC}^2}$.

(*j*) Construct a triangle containing one right angle. This is called a right triangle.

(*k*) Construct a triangle containing one obtuse angle. This is called an obtuse triangle.

(*l*) Construct a triangle with three acute angles. This is called an acute triangle.

(*m*) Bisect the longest side of a right triangle.

(*n*) Bisect the longest side of an obtuse triangle.

(*o*) Construct the perpendicular bisectors of each side of an acute triangle.

(*p*) If possible, construct a triangle containing two right angles.

(*q*) If possible, construct a triangle containing two acute angles.

(*r*) If possible construct a triangle containing two obtuse angles.

(*s*) Bisect a right angle. How many degrees are there in $\frac{1}{2}$ a right angle?

(*t*) Construct an angle of 45 degrees.

(*u*) Construct an angle of $22\frac{1}{2}$ degrees.

(*v*) Draw a line $4\frac{3}{4}$ inches long. Divide this line into two equal parts. Bisect one half of this.

(*w*) How can you divide a line into four equal parts?

VI. (*a*) *To construct a triangle equal to a given triangle.*

Required to construct a triangle equal to the given triangle *ABC*.

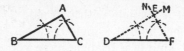

Draw the line *DF* equal to *BC*.

At *D* construct an angle *FDM* equal to angle *CBA*.

At *F* construct an angle *DFN* equal to angle *BCA*.

Then *DEF* is the required triangle.

1. Construct a triangle equal to a given right triangle.

2. Construct a triangle equal to a given obtuse triangle.

3. Construct a triangle equal to a given acute triangle.

VI. (*b*) *Complete the statements in the following:*

To construct a triangle equal to a given triangle *ABC*.

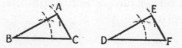

Required to construct a —— equal to given triangle *ABC*. Draw *DF* equal to ——. Construct angle —— equal to angle *CBA*.

Measure on *DE* a distance equal to ——.

Draw ——. Then —— is the triangle required.

1. Construct a triangle with one side 3 inches, the second side 2 inches, and the angle between these two sides equal to $\frac{1}{2}$ a right angle. What kind of a triangle have you constructed?

2. Construct a triangle with one side $2\frac{1}{4}$ inches, a second side $3\frac{1}{2}$ inches, and the angle between these two sides obtuse. What kind of a triangle have you constructed?

3. Construct a right triangle with the two sides adjacent to the right angle each equal to $2\frac{3}{4}$ inches.

VI. (c) *Complete the statements in the following:*

To construct a triangle equal to a given triangle *ABC*.

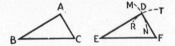

Required to construct —— equivalent to given triangle *ABC*.

Draw —— equal to *BC*.

With *E* as a center and a radius equal to *BA* draw the arc ——.

With *F* as a center and a radius equal to —— draw the arc *RT* intersecting arc *MN* at ——.

Draw ——.

Then triangle *DEF* is the triangle ——.

4. Construct a triangle with sides each equal to three inches. What kind of a triangle is it?

5. Construct a triangle with sides three, four, and five inches. What kind of a triangle is it?

VII. (a) *To enlarge a rectangle.*

Required to enlarge the rectangle *ABCD*.

Draw *EH*, making it twice as long as *DC*.

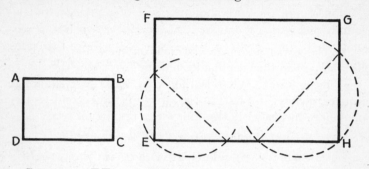

Construct *FE* perpendicular to *EH* and *GH* perpendicular to *EH*.

Make *EF* twice as long as *AD* and *GH* twice as long as *BC*.

Draw *FG*.

Then *FGHE* is the required rectangle.

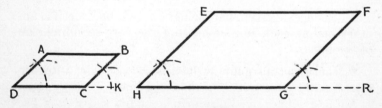

VII. (b) *To enlarge a parallelogram.*

Required to enlarge the parallelogram *ABCD*.

Draw *HG*, making it twice *DC*.

Construct angle *EHG* equal to angle *ADC* and angle *FGR* equal to angle *BCK*.

Make *EH* equal to twice *AD* and *FG* equal to twice *CB*. Draw *EF*.

Then *EFGH* is the required parallelogram.

1. Construct a rectangle each of whose sides shall be three times the corresponding side of a given rectangle.

2. Construct a parallelogram each of whose sides shall be four times the corresponding side of a given parallelogram.

3. Construct a square one inch on each side. Enlarge this square so that each side shall be five times the side of the first square. What is the area of the first square in square inches? What is the area of the second square in square inches? Is the following proportion true?

$$\frac{\text{The area of the first square}}{\text{The area of the second square}} = \frac{(1)^2}{(5)^2}.$$

4. Construct a square four inches on each side. Reduce this square to one having (a) $\frac{1}{2}$ as long a side.

(b) $\frac{1}{4}$ as long a side. (c) $\frac{3}{4}$ as long a side.

5. Reduce a given rectangle by constructing another having each side equal to $\frac{1}{2}$ the corresponding side of the first.

6. Reduce a given parallelogram by constructing another having each side equal to $\frac{1}{4}$ the corresponding side of the first.

7. Construct a square $1\frac{1}{2}$ inches on each side. Reduce this square to one having $\frac{1}{3}$ as long a side. Find the area of the first square in square inches. Find the area of the second square. Is the following statement true?

$$\frac{\text{The area of the first square}}{\text{The area of the second square}} = \frac{(1\frac{1}{2})^2}{(\frac{1}{2})^2}$$

8. If the side of one square is 10 ft. and that of the second is 15 ft., is the area of the first to the area of the second as $(10)^2$ is to $(15)^2$?

Drawing to Scale

In order that drawings may accurately represent the objects indicated they are drawn to scale. Each inch on the drawing represents a certain number of units of length of the object.

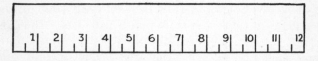

A ruler is twelve inches long. This drawing is three inches long. Each unit on the drawing represents one inch on your ruler.

1. Make a drawing of a ruler two feet long, using the same scale.

2. Make a drawing of a rectangular garden nine rods wide by twelve rods long, using a scale of one half inch to the rod.

In drawing to scale absolute accuracy is essential.

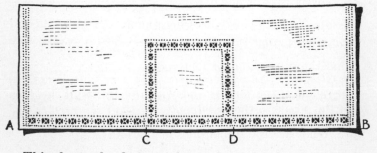

This shows the design to be used as a border for a towel. If the towel is 28″ from A to B, what is the scale used? What is the width of the border? Give the distance on the towel from A to C, from D to B. Give the inside dimensions of the square.

This is the plan of a club house drawn to the scale of $\frac{1}{32}$ inch to the foot. All angles are right angles.

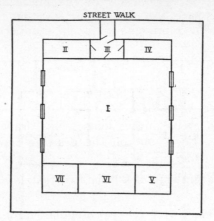

STREET WALK

(*a*) Room I is a gymnasium.

Rooms II and IV are game rooms.

Room III is entrance hall.

Rooms V and VII are dressing rooms.

Room VI is the stage.

Find the dimensions of each room.

(*b*) What is the length and width of the walk leading from the street to the building?

(*c*) What are the dimensions of the lot?

(*d*) First secure the dimensions of a suitable lot for a club house; then make a drawing showing (*a*) the placing of the building on the lot, (*b*) the rooms to be included, and (*c*) the doors and windows. Make the drawing accurate, using $\frac{1}{16}$ inch to the foot.

This is an architect's plan of the first story of a house. The scale is $\frac{1}{32}$ of an inch to the foot. Find the following dimensions: (a) The width of the house from left to right. (b) The depth from front to rear. (c) The dimensions of:

(1) Sleeping porch.

(2) Kitchen.

(3) Bedroom I.

(4) Bedroom II.

(5) Dining room.

(6) Living room.

(7) **Hall.**

(8) Front porch.

Make a drawing of your school room to scale showing exact size of room, location of windows, blackboards and furniture.

From your drawing determine:

(a) The distance from one corner of the room to the other.

(b) The distance from the middle of the east wall to the middle of the south wall.

Exercise Involving the Use of Scale in Reading Maps

By the use of the scale on the maps in your geography determine in miles:

(*a*) The greatest length of Oneida Lake.

(*b*) The distance around Hamilton County.

(*c*) The diagonal of Cortland County.

(*d*) The distance between Toronto and Oswego.

(*e*) The shortest distance between Buffalo and Albany.

(*f*) The shortest distance between Cooperstown and Malone.

(*g*) The greatest length of Seneca Lake.

(*h*) Cape Horn to Rio de Janeiro.

(*i*) Pernambuco to Lima.

(*j*) Tropic of Capricorn to the Equator.

(*k*) Greatest width and greatest length of South America.

(*l*) Chicago to Cleveland.

(*m*) St. Louis to Pittsburgh.

(*n*) Battery Park to Grant's Tomb.

(*o*) White House to the Capitol.

(*p*) The greatest length of U. S. from East to West.

(*q*) The shortest distance from London to Paris.

(*r*) The width of Africa at the equator.

(*s*) The greatest length of Africa.

(*t*) The shortest distance from Rome to Alexandria.

(*u*) Which is greater and how much the distance from Boston to Albany or from Boston to New York City?

(*v*) If you could draw a map of the United States using one inch to the mile, how many feet long and how many feet wide would this map be?

GRAPHS

Comparative amounts are often represented by drawings, called graphs. The simplest, and usually the best, graphs are those composed of lines only. Sometimes a graph is accompanied by the numbers which it represents, the numbers showing exact amounts while the graph shows the comparison.

A slip containing the following graph and figures was inclosed with my tax bill.

WHERE YOUR MONEY GOES

Below is a comparative statement of how the money collected for taxes in —— County is spent:

	PER CENT	AMOUNT
Education	39.30	$1,517,629.33
City of ——	28.57	1,102,951.57
County Expense	10.75	415,209.19
State Highways	7.57	292,074.22
State Government	5.59	215,851.00
Townships	3.82	147,463.24
County Bonds and Interest	1.53	59,100.00
Towns	1.22	47,238.61
Bridges and Roads	1.04	40,000.00
State Military	0.61	23,401.30
Total	100.00	$3,860,918.46
Assessed valuation for —— County		$111,739,515.00
Total taxes to be collected		$3,860,718.46

JOHN H. TILSLEY, *County Treasurer.*

Looking at this graph, estimate the ratio of the line representing education to the line representing county expense. Verify your estimate by dividing the education expense by the county expense.

Make other estimates from the lines, and test your estimates by using the figures given in the table of expenses.

Graphs

Common fractions, decimals, and per cents may be explained by graphs.

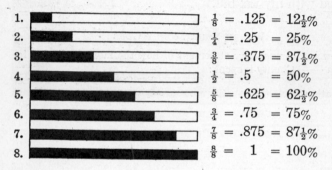

1. $\frac{1}{8} = .125 = 12\frac{1}{2}\%$
2. $\frac{1}{4} = .25 = 25\%$
3. $\frac{3}{8} = .375 = 37\frac{1}{2}\%$
4. $\frac{1}{2} = .5 = 50\%$
5. $\frac{5}{8} = .625 = 62\frac{1}{2}\%$
6. $\frac{3}{4} = .75 = 75\%$
7. $\frac{7}{8} = .875 = 87\frac{1}{2}\%$
8. $\frac{8}{8} = 1 = 100\%$

Make similar graphs for the following:

$\frac{1}{10} = .1 = 10\%$ $\frac{1}{6} = .16\frac{2}{3} = 16\frac{2}{3}\%$

$\frac{1}{5} = .2 = 20\%$ $\frac{1}{3} = .33\frac{1}{3} = 33\frac{1}{3}\%$

$\frac{3}{10} = .3 = 30\%$ $\frac{1}{2} = .5 = 50\%$

$\frac{2}{5} = .4 = 40\%$ $\frac{2}{3} = .66\frac{2}{3} = 66\frac{2}{3}\%$

$\frac{1}{2} = .5 = 50\%$ $\frac{5}{6} = .83\frac{1}{3} = 83\frac{1}{3}\%$

$\frac{3}{5} = .6 = 60\%$ $\frac{6}{6} = 1 = 100\%$

$\frac{7}{10} = .7 = 70\%$ $\frac{7}{20} = .35 = 35\%$

$\frac{4}{5} = .8 = 80\%$ $\frac{1}{12} = .08\frac{1}{3} = 8\frac{1}{3}\%$

$\frac{9}{10} = .9 = 90\%$ $\frac{5}{12} = .41\frac{2}{3} = 41\frac{2}{3}\%$

$\frac{10}{10} = 1 = 100\%$ $\frac{7}{12} = .58\frac{1}{3} = 58\frac{1}{3}\%$

The picture graph is frequently used to show the relation between qualities.

The following **picture graph** shows the interest earned on $100 for one year at various per cents.

Interest on $100 for one year at

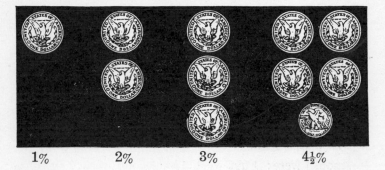

1%   2%   3%   4½%

Make a picture graph showing the interest on $100 for one year at 5%, 5½%, 5¾% and 6%. " Coördinate " or " graph " paper is laid off in squares, and is used in making graphs which show variable facts involving two or more conditions. These are known as **broken line graphs.**

Statistics may be easily represented by broken line graphs. (See pages 388, 390, 392.)

1. John's average for the first five weeks was 92%, second, 89%, third, 85%, fourth, 88%, fifth, 90%, sixth, 94%, seventh, 89%, and eighth, 87%. Plot a graph showing his standings for the year. The standings 80 to 100 are laid off on the vertical line. The eight quarters are indicated on the horizontal line.

Dots are then placed on the vertical line under the proper number and on the horizontal line opposite the right per cent. These dots are then connected in the order of the numbers at the top. This forms a broken line graph.

Represent the following statistics by broken line graphs.

2. Population of United States per sq. mile 1850 was 8; 1860 — 11; 1870 — 13; 1880 — 17; 1890 — 21; 1900 — 26; 1910 — 31; 1920 — 36.

3. Average per cent of year's supply of coal burned Oct. was 7%; Nov. — 11%; Dec. — 17%; Jan. — 18%; Feb. — 17%; Mar. — 14%; Apr. — 10%; May — 6%.

4. Temperature at 6 A.M. was 12°; 7 — 14°; 8 — 18°; 9 — 20°; 10 — 23°; 11 — 27°; 12 — 33°; 1 P.M. — 35°; 2 — 32°; 3 — 30°; 4 — 26°; 5 — 25°.

5. Ola's marks in a test were as follows: Arithmetic 90, Language 60, History 80, Geography 70, Drawing 85. Make a graph of these marks.

6. Roderick's sales of the *Saturday Evening Post* for one month were: First week 150, second week 200, third week 125, fourth week 250. Make a graph showing Roderick's sales for the four weeks.

7. Make other graphs showing facts about the temperature shown by your outdoor thermometer at different hours of the day.

Circular Graph

The circular graph is sometimes an effective means of showing a few simple comparisons. The circular graph given here shows the proportion of races and origin of the inhabitants of a county.

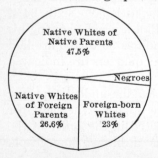

Find the numbers of pupils 12, 13, 14, 15, and 16 years old in your class, and make a circular graph to show the proportions.

The bar graph is also an effective means of showing comparative amounts.

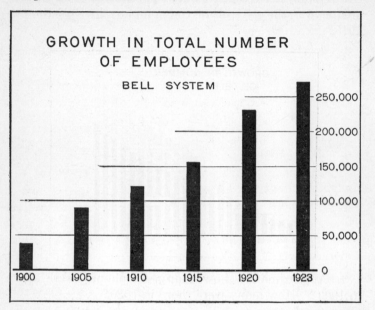

GROWTH IN TOTAL NUMBER
OF EMPLOYEES

BELL SYSTEM

1. Approximately how many employees were working for the Bell Company in 1900? How many were there in 1923?

2. Approximately how many employees were working for this company in 1905? How many were there in 1920?

3. If each employee of the Bell Company averaged $1.85 a day in 1900, what was the approximate daily pay-roll of the company?

4. If each employee of the Bell Company averaged $3.05 a day in 1923, what was the approximate daily pay-roll of the company?

5. Approximately how many more employees were working for the company in 1915 than in 1910?

6. If each employee in 1915 averaged $2.45 and in 1920 each employee averaged $2.80, approximately how much greater was the pay-roll of the company in 1920 than in 1915?

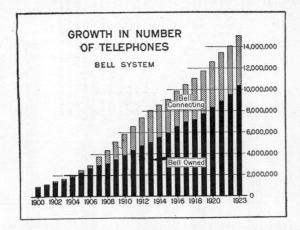

1. Approximately how many telephones were there in 1900? How many were there in 1920?

2. Approximately how many " Bell Owned " telephones were there in 1923? How many " Bell Connecting " telephones were there?

3. If the average monthly rental of a telephone was $3.25 in 1923, find the approximate rental of all the telephones in the Bell System for July of that year.

4. Approximately how many more telephones were there in the Bell System in 1918 than in 1910?

5. Approximately what per cent of all the telephones in the Bell System in 1912 were " Bell Owned "?

6. Approximately how many times as many telephones in 1916 were " Bell Owned " as in 1904?

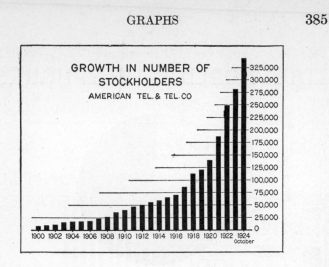

GROWTH IN NUMBER OF
STOCKHOLDERS
AMERICAN TEL. & TEL. CO

1. Approximately how many more stockholders did the Bell Telephone Company have in 1912 than in 1904?

2. Approximately how many more stockholders did this company have in 1922 than in 1916?

3. If the value of the Bell Telephone Company's assets was approximately $2,500,000,000 in 1924, what was the average value of each stockholder's share?

4. Approximately how many times as many telephone stockholders were there in 1924 as in 1900?

5. What was the approximate increase in the number of stockholders in 1918 over the number in 1910?

6. Approximately how many stockholders did the company have in each of the following years, 1902, 1905, 1913, 1920, 1921?

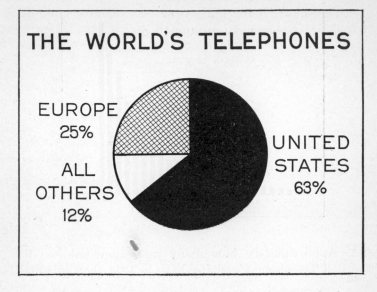

THE WORLD'S TELEPHONES

EUROPE
25%

ALL
OTHERS
12%

UNITED
STATES
63%

1. There are approximately how many more telephones in the United States than in Europe?

2. There are approximately how many more telephones in Europe than in "all other countries"?

3. There are approximately how many more telephones in the United States than in the rest of the world combined?

4. If there are approximately 46,000,000 telephone conversations daily, how many of these occur in the United States?

5. If the value of the Bell Telephone Company's assets is approximately $2,500,000,000, how much of this value is in Europe?

6. If there are approximately about 36,000,000 miles of telephone wire in the world, how many miles are in Europe?   How many are there in the United States?

The calorie is the unit of measure of heat. We know that it takes heat to keep our bodies warm. This heat

TABLE OF CALORIFIC VALUES

1 LB. OF ENTIRE WHEAT FLOUR
" · HOME MADE BREAD
· · RUMP STEAK
· · EGGS
· · CHICKEN
· · POTATOES
· · MILK
· · SPINACH

is produced by the oxidation of the food which we eat. Certain foods contain more fuel than others. In this graph the number of heat units in one pound of spinach is compared with the number of heat units in one pound of entire wheat flour.

1. How many pounds of spinach are required to equal, in heat value, one pound of entire wheat flour?

2. How many pounds of chicken are required to equal, in heat value, one pound of rump steak?

3. If a pint of milk weighs a pound, how many loaves of bread (1 *lb. each*) are required to equal, in heat value, 40 quarts of milk?

4. Which is cheaper, to buy bread at 12¢ a loaf or milk at 12¢ a quart? Why?

5. Assuming that each contain the same percentage of bone, is it better economy to buy chicken at 50¢ a pound or rump steak at 40¢ a pound?

6. Determine the number of pounds of rump steak required to equal, in heat value, one bushel of potatoes.

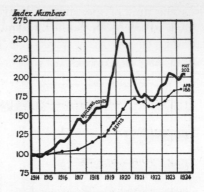

1. Compare rents in 1921 with rents in 1915. A house rented in 1915 for $50. From the graph determine its renting value in 1924.

2. A house was built in 1914 for $7000. Find the cost of duplicating this house in 1920.

3. A man built a double house in 1920 for $16,000. What would he have paid for this house if he had built it at the lowest point in 1922?

SOLUTION: The graph shows the average building costs in 1920 to be about 240, in 1922 about 180 as compared with 100 in 1914.

COST 1920		COST 1922		INDEX 1920		INDEX 1922
$16,000	:	x	: :	240	:	180

$$240\,x = 16,000 \text{ times } 180$$
$$x = ?$$

4. Which increased more rapidly between 1914 and 1920, building costs or rents?

5. Which decreased more rapidly between 1920 and 1922, rents or building costs?

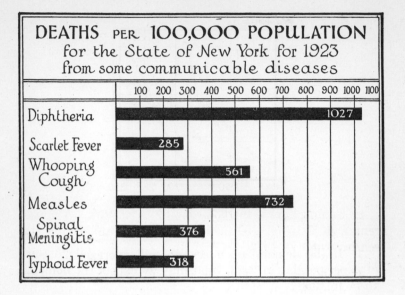

1. If the population of New York City is 7,000,000, how many deaths may we expect were caused by diphtheria; typhoid; scarlet fever; whooping cough?

2. Estimating the population of the city of Syracuse at 200,000, how many may we expect to die in that city of each of the diseases mentioned?

3. Which of these diseases is most dangerous? Which is least dangerous?

4. What is meant by the term "Communicable Disease"?

5. What measures are used to prevent the spread of these diseases?

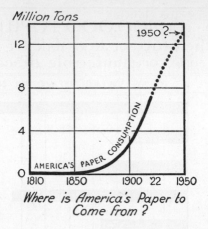

Where is America's Paper to Come from?

1. If the demand on a certain mill averaged 20 tons of paper per day in 1922, what may we expect the demand to be in 1950?

Milk, Cheese

Bread, Cereals, Macaroni, Rice

Vegetables

Meat, Eggs, Nuts

2. Of the foods mentioned, which provide the most nourishment for the money? Which provide the least value?

3. Which will cost more, a lunch of rice or one of vegetables?

1. Make a graph showing:

(*a*) The weight in pounds of boys 11 years old, for the height in inches given in the table below.

(*b*) A similar graph for 11 year old girls.

(*c*) " " " " 10 " " boys.

(*d*) " " " " 10 " " girls.

HEIGHT AND WEIGHT TABLES

Boys									Girls								
Height Inches	Average Weight for Height (Lbs.)	5 Years	6 Years	7 Years	8 Years	9 Years	10 Years	11 Years	Height Inches	Average Weight for Height (Lbs.)	5 Years	6 Years	7 Years	8 Years	9 Years	10 Years	11 Years
38	34	34	34						38	33	33	33					
39	35	35	35						39	34	34	34					
40	36	36	36						40	36	36	36	36				
41	38	38	38	38					41	37	37	37	37				
42	39	39	39	39	39				42	39	39	39					
43	41	41	41	41	41				43	41	41	41	41	41	41		
44	44	44	44	44	44				44	42	42	42	42	42	42		
45	46	46	46	46	46	46			45	45	45	45	45	45	45	45	
46	48	47	48	48	48	48			46	47	47	47	47	48	48	48	
47	50	49	50	50	50	50	50		47	50	49	50	50	50	50	50	
48	53		52	53	53	53	53		48	52		52	52	52	52	53	53
49	55		55	55	55	55	55	55	49	55		54	54	55	55	56	56
50	58		57	58	58	58	58	58	50	58		56	56	57	58	59	61
51	61			61	61	61	61	61	51	61			59	60	61	61	63
52	64			63	64	64	64	64	52	64			63	64	64	64	65
53	68			66	67	67	67	67	53	68			66	67	67	68	68
54	71				70	70	70	70	54	71				69	70	70	71
55	74				72	72	73	73	55	75				72	74	74	74
56	78				75	76	77	77	56	79				76	77	78	
57	82					79	80	81	57	84					80	82	82
58	85					83	84	84	58	89						84	86
59	89						87	88	59	95						87	90
60	94						91	92	60	101						91	95
61	99							95	61	108							99
62	104							100	62	114							104

(*e*) A similar graph for 9 year old girls.

(*f*) " " " " 9 " " boys.

(*g*) " " " " 8 " " girls.

(*h*) " " " " 8 " " boys.

(*i*) " " " " 6 " " girls.

1. What was the temperature, as shown by this graph, at 1 o'clock?   At 4 o'clock?   At 2 o'clock?

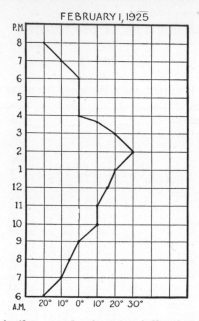

FEBRUARY 1, 1925

2. Make similar graphs for the following temperature readings.

	A.M.						P.M.							
---	6,	7,	8,	9,	10,	11,	12,	1,	2,	3,	4,	5,	6,	7,	8,
(a)	− 10°	− 5°	0°	0°	10°	10°	15°	15°	15°	10°	5°	5°	0°	− 5°	− 10°
(b)	0°	5°	10°	15°	15°	20°	25°	30°	25°	20°	15°	15°	10°	10°	10°
(c)	60°	65°	65°	70°	70°	75°	75°	75°	80°	75°	70°	65°	65°	65°	65°
(d)	90°	95°	95°	95°	98°	98°	98°	98°	95°	95°	90°	85°	85°	85°	85°
(e)	32°	32°	32°	35°	40°	45°	50°	50°	50°	55°	30°	40°	35°	32°	32°
(f)	32°	30°	30°	25°	20°	20°	20°	20°	15°	15°	15°	10°	10°	10°	10°

Tabulation of Accidents to School Children
Detroit, Michigan

Accidents	No.
Fatal	38
Serious	118
Minor	806
To Boys	658
To Girls	304
In Public Schools	733
In Private Schools	229
Total	962

Ages of Children	No. of Children	Ages of Children	No. of Children
5	39	12	91
6	101	13	83
7	128	14	67
8	134	15	42
9	84	16	26
10	86	17	1
11	80	Total	962

Type of Accident	No.
Automobile	792
Street Car	24
Horse-drawn Vehicle	8
Motorcycle	6
Railroad	6

1. Make a circular graph showing the relation between accidents by automobile, street car, horse-drawn vehicle, motorcycle, and railroad.

2. Construct a graph showing the number of accidents to children of ages 5, 6, etc. to 17.

3. On a circle graph show the number of public and private school pupils that meet with accident.

4. On a circle graph show the number of boys and girls injured.

5. On the same kind of graph show the number of persons fatally injured, seriously injured, slightly injured.

6. Make a line graph showing the relative rainfall: (*a*) In 1919 and 1920. (*b*) In 1922 and 1924. (*c*) In 1921 and 1924.

MONTHS

	1,	2,	3,	4,	5,	6,	7,	8,	9,	10,	11,	12.	
1919	1	1	1	2	5	5	6	5	1	0	1	1	inches
1920	0	0	5	5	3	2	1	1	2	5	2	2	
1921	$\frac{1}{2}$	$\frac{3}{4}$	1	2	5	5	3	1	$\frac{1}{2}$	$\frac{3}{4}$	$\frac{1}{4}$	0	
1922	3	5	6	8	12	3	2	1	1	0	0	2	
1923	0	$\frac{3}{4}$	1	$1\frac{1}{2}$	3	5	7	6	2	1	0	$\frac{1}{2}$	
1924	2	1	0	$\frac{1}{2}$	1	$1\frac{1}{2}$	0	5	1	3	4	2	

7. Make a graph showing the average daily attendance in the public schools of a city for the following years: 1916–1650; 1917–1700; 1918–1750; 1919–1800; 1920–1800; 1921–1900; 1922–2000; 1923–2200; 1924–2250; 1925–2400.

8. Make a graph showing the attendance of the pupils in your grade for a week.

9. Of the 42 pupils in a certain 8 A grade, one had repeated 6 grades, one 5 grades, one 4 grades, two 3 grades, five 2 grades, and seven 1 grade. Show by the use of a graph the relative number of pupils who had been in school, eight, nine, ten, etc. years.

10. Make a similar graph for your grade.

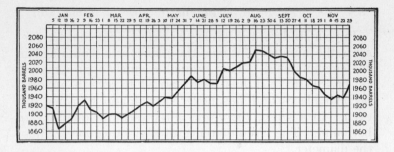

1. Make a bar graph showing the amount of oil produced in the U. S. during the months of January and August. Give one reason for this difference in production.

2. The oil manufactures' reports for Jan., Feb., Mar., and April for the year 1925 are as follows:

Jan. 3, 1960 M barrels   Mar. 7, 1950 M barrels
   "   10, 1910 "   "   "   14, 1900 "   "
   "   17, 2020 "   "   "   21, 1920 "   "
   "   24, 1980 "   "   "   28, 1990 "   "
   "   31, 1940 "   "   Apr. 4, 2020 "   "
Feb. 7, 1960 "   "   "   11, 2030 "   "
   "   14, 2010 "   "   "   18, 2060 "   "
   "   21, 1970 "   "   "   25, 2090 "   "
   "   28, 1990 "   "

Make a graph showing the relation of the oil produced for these months in 1924 and 1925.

3. Of those listed in the 1923 " Who's Who in America," 1814 gave no educational data; 388 were self educated; 1880 received a common school education only; 2756 finished high school; 17,439 attended college, and 14,055 were college graduates. Make a bar graph showing these facts.

4. Name the different kinds of graphs used in this text.

Algebra

In your study of the circle you were taught that π represents the number of times the diameter is contained in the circumference. This symbol π equals approximately $\frac{22}{7}$, or 3.1416+. It has been carried to several hundred decimal places and has never been found to come out even. In a sense, therefore, π represents a quantity to be found. The circumference of a circle equals π times the diameter.

Find the circumferences of the following circles in terms of π:

1. Radius 6 ft.
2. Radius 9 in.
3. Diameter 4 in.
4. Diameter 7 ft.
5. Radius 11 ft.
6. Diameter 15 yd.
7. Radius 14 ft.
8. Diameter 21 rd.
9. Diameter 18 in.
10. Radius 16 in.

The area of a circle is π times the radius squared.
Find the area of each of the above circles.

11. The area of one circle is $144\,\pi$ sq. in. and the area of a second circle is $225\,\pi$ sq. in. Find the area of both circles taken together.

$$144\,\pi \text{ sq. in.} + 225\,\pi \text{ sq. in.} = 369\,\pi \text{ sq. in.}$$

12. The circumference of a circle is $12\,\pi$ ft. The circumference of a second circle is $16\,\pi$ ft. Find the total length of the two circumferences.

13. Find the total length of the circumference and the total area of the circles with the following radii, 8 inches, 7 inches, and 12 inches.

14. The circumference of one circle is $30\,\pi$ feet, that of a second $16\,\pi$ feet. How many π feet larger is the first circumference than the second?

An algebraic expression is a number expressed by literal and arithmetical numbers, connected by mathematical signs which tell what to do with the numbers.

Thus $2x + 3cy$ is an algebraic expression. In the term $2x$, 2 is called the numerical coefficient of x. In the term $3cy$, 3 is called the numerical coefficient of cy.

$$2x = x + x \qquad\qquad 3cy = cy + cy + cy$$

A numerical coefficient is a number written before a quantity to show how many times the given quantity is taken as an addend.

What is 5 in the expression $5abx$?

5 is the numerical coefficient of abx.

What is the meaning of 5 in the expression $5abx$.

$5abx = abx + abx + abx + abx + abx$.

It, therefore, shows how many times abx is taken as an addend.

When the coefficient is 1 it is omitted.

In the following expressions explain the meaning of each coefficient:

1. $2x + 3y$
2. $5a + 2b$
3. $x + y$
4. $mx + ny$
5. $3ab + 7xy$
6. $2x + 3b$
7. $8x + 7y$
8. $5a + 3x$
9. $9y + 6b$
10. $4x + 5y$
11. $3M + 4T$
12. $3z + 8x$
13. $5y + 9z$
14. $3c + 7d$
15. $8a + 11x$
16. $13abcx$
17. $xy + 5z$
18. $3MT + y$
19. $5xy + a$
20. $b + 3cx$
21. $3d + 7xy$

In arithmetic, we add *like* quantities such as dollars and dollars, feet and feet, pounds and pounds. We do not add pounds and dollars.

In algebra we add like quantities by adding the coefficients of those quantities.

Thus $5\pi + 8\pi = 13\pi$ $9y + 15y + y = 25y$

Add the following:

1.	16π	2.	21π	3.	148π	4.	19 ft.
	24π		16π		19π		29 ft.
	$\underline{36\pi}$		$\underline{35\pi}$		$\underline{96\pi}$		146 ft.

5.	11 rd.	6.	45 sq. ft.	7.	13 qt.	8.	95 in.
	6 rd.		19 sq. ft.		79 qt.		18 in.
	17 rd.		89 sq. ft.		43 qt.		67 in.

9.	26 grams	10.	12 lb.	11.	120 bu.	12.	129 mi.
	48 grams		39 lb.		15 bu.		87 mi.
	91 grams		57 lb.		80 bu.		146 mi.

13.	$18x$	14.	$3y$	15.	$75k$	16.	$39x$
	$13x$		$5y$		$14k$		$15x$
	$75x$		$9y$		$35k$		$13x$
	$49x$		$18y$		$18k$		$45x$
	$14x$		$15y$		$21k$		$43x$

17.	$45y$	18.	$38m$	19.	$63a$	20.	$.5x$
	$18y$		$48m$		$14a$		$.3x$
	$14y$		$19m$		$82a$		$.4x$
	$69y$		$85m$		$37a$		$1.2x$
	$23y$		$72m$		$41a$		$2.4x$

21.	$\frac{1}{2}x$	22.	$\frac{1}{5}y$	23.	$\frac{1}{3}B$	24.	$.9c$
	$\frac{1}{4}x$		$\frac{1}{4}y$		$\frac{3}{4}B$		$1.8c$
	$\frac{3}{4}x$		$\frac{3}{10}y$		$\frac{5}{6}B$		$.3c$

1. Find the value of $10\,T + 8\,T + 15\,T + 7\,T + 9\,T$ when T equals 2000 lb.

2. What is the value of $21\,d + 5\,d + 18\,d + 23\,d + 12\,d$ when d equals 10 cents?

3. How many inches is it around a rectangle 9 ft. long and 3 ft. wide?

$$9 \text{ ft.} + 3 \text{ ft.} + 9 \text{ ft.} + 3 \text{ ft.} = 24 \text{ ft.}$$
$$1 \text{ ft.} = 12 \text{ in.}$$
$$\therefore 24 \text{ ft.} = 24 \text{ times } 12 \text{ or } 288 \quad \therefore 288 \text{ in.}$$

4. Find the perimeter in ft. of a rectangle 7 yd. long and 4 yd. wide.

5. Determine the perimeter of a rectangle in feet if it is 11 rods long and 9 rods wide.

6. Find the value of $21\,X + 13\,X + 9\,X + 11\,X + 3\,X$ if X equals $10.

7. What is the value of $7\,M + 19\,M + 24\,M + 13\,M + 63\,M$ when M equals 1000?

8. What is the perimeter in inches of a table $3\frac{1}{2}$ ft. wide by $7\frac{1}{2}$ ft. long?

9. Find in inches the perimeter of a picture that is $3\frac{1}{4}$ ft. long and $2\frac{7}{12}$ ft. wide.

10. A rug is 9 ft. by 12 ft. How many yards of binding tape are required to go around it?

11. Find the value of $3\frac{1}{2}\,Kg + 2\frac{1}{4}\,Kg + 5\frac{1}{3}\,Kg + \frac{3}{4}\,Kg$ when $Kg = 1000$ grams.

12. The areas of three circles are as follows, $49\,\pi$, $121\,\pi$, $145\,\pi$. Find the combined areas of these three circles when $\pi = \frac{22}{7}$.

13. Find the combined area of five circles; $100\,\pi$, $300\,\pi$, $200\,\pi$, $500\,\pi$, and $700\,\pi$ when $\pi = 3.1416$.

14. What is the value of $14\,x + 3\,x + 7\,x + 11\,x + 5\,x$ when x equals 2?

Letters are used to represent numbers in algebra.
$3\ T\ = 3$ tons or $3(2000$ lb$) = 6000$ lb.
5 ft. = 5 feet or 5 (12 inches) = 60 inches.
$9\ M = 9$ thousand or 9 (1000) = 9000.

The sign of multiplication is not used often in algebra since the sign of multiplication is much like the letter x which is frequently used to indicate an unknown quantity.

Thus 9 times x is written $9 \cdot x$ or $9\,x$.

x times y is written $x \cdot y$ or xy.

What is the meaning of 13 xy?

13 xy means 13 times x times y.

What is the value of 13 xy when $x = 2$ and $y = 3$?

13 xy means 13 times 2 times $3 = 78$.

What is the meaning of each of the following? Find the value of each when $x = 2$, $y = 3$, $m = 4$, $a = 5$, $\pi = \frac{22}{7}$.

1. $15\,x$
2. $35\,x$
3. $21\,y$
4. $37\,m$
5. $15\,a$
6. $21\,ax$
7. $35\,mx$
8. $14\,xy$
9. $19\,am$
10. $38\,my$

11. $\frac{1}{2}\,xy$
12. $\frac{1}{3}\,my$
13. $\frac{1}{5}\,am$
14. $.5\,mx$
15. $\frac{1}{2}\,xm$
16. $.2\,am$
17. $\frac{3}{4}\,m$
18. $.75\,m$
19. $.4\,my$
20. $49\,x$

21. $7\,my$
22. $9\,xy$
23. $15\,mx$
24. $14\,am$
25. $4.2\,a$
26. $7.5\,x$
27. $2\frac{1}{3}\,y$
28. $4\frac{1}{4}\,m$
29. $6\frac{1}{2}\,x$
30. $7\frac{1}{3}\,a$

31. $2\,mxy$
32. $\frac{1}{5}\,axy$
33. $.2\,axy$
34. $\frac{1}{3}\,axy$
35. $\frac{4}{5}\,amx$
36. $.6\,amx$
37. $2\,amxy$
38. $5\,axmy$
39. $7\,\pi x$
40. $14\,\pi y$

What is the meaning of $7x + 8y$?

> $7x + 8y$ means 7 times x plus 8 times y.

What is the value of $7x + 8y$ when $x = 1$ and $y = 2$?

> $7x + 8y$ equals 7 times 1 plus 8 times 2.
> $7 \cdot 1 + 8 \cdot 2 = 7 + 16$.
> $7 + 16 = 23$.

Find the value of the following when $x = 1$, $y = 2$, $z = 3$, $a = 4$, $b = 5$, $c = 6$, $\pi = \frac{22}{7}$, $M = 1000$, and $T = 2000$.

1. $3x + 5y$
2. $4x + 2z$
3. $9x + 4a$
4. $2x + 3b$
5. $8x + 7\pi$
6. $5a + 3x$
7. $9y + 15b$
8. $8c + 11x$
9. $3M + 4T$
10. $4x + 5x$

11. $9a + 11a$
12. $3z + 8x$
13. $5z + 9z$
14. $13y + 4y$
15. $5T + 11T$
16. $12c + 5c$
17. $17x + 9y$
18. $21\pi + 35\pi$
19. $\frac{1}{3}c + \frac{1}{2}c$
20. $\frac{2}{5}b + \frac{3}{5}b$

21. $\frac{1}{5}M + \frac{1}{2}M$
22. $15az$
23. $7M\pi$
24. $3y + 2y$
25. $9x + 8x$
26. $49\pi + 77\pi$
27. $18M + 21M$
28. $14c + .5c$
29. $9T + 15T$
30. $11b + 13b$

31. $.5x + .3y$
32. $.9c + .4y$
33. $.3M + .6M$
34. $.1T + .7T$
35. $1.2M + 2.3M$
36. $.4ax + .5ay$
37. $1.5c + 2.5T$
38. $.8zy + 3.2zM$

39. $4abx + 7bcy$
40. $11axy + 13byz$
41. $2MTx + 2MTy$
42. $5abc + 3aby$
43. $8xyz + 7abc$
44. $7\pi MT$
45. $14\pi cb$
46. $\frac{1}{5}bcM$

Add
$$5x + 7y + \quad z$$
$$3x + \quad y + 9z$$
$$\overline{8x + 8y + 10z}$$

Test by using 1 for x, 2 for y, 3 for z.
$5 \cdot 1 + 7 \cdot 2 + 1 \cdot 3 = 5 + 14 + 3$
or 22
$\quad 3 \cdot 1 + 1 \cdot 2 + 9 \cdot 3 = 3 + 2 + 27$
or 32
$\quad 22 + 32 = 54$
$\quad 8x + 8y + 10z = 8 \cdot 1 + 8 \cdot 2$
$+ 10 \cdot 3$ or 54
$\quad 54 = 54 \quad \therefore$ the addition is correct.

Add and test by using 1 *for* x, 2 *for* y, 3 *for* z, 4 *for* a, 5 *for* b, *and* 6 *for* c.

1. $3x + 6y + 7z$
$\quad 8x + 3y + \quad z$

2. $\quad a + 2b + \quad c$
$\quad 2a + 5b + 3c$

3. $4a + 9b + 2c$
$\quad 2a + 3b + \quad c$

4. $5x + \quad a + 3c$
$\quad 2x + 3a + 2c$

5. $9x + 2b + 5c$
$\quad 2x + 3b + 2c$

6. $4a + 7b + 3c$
$\quad a + \quad b + 4c$

7. $8a + \quad b + 2c$
$\quad 2a + 5b + 5c$

8. $9a + 5b + 3c$
$\quad 5a + 3b + 9c$

9. $4x + 8y + 2z$
$\quad x + \quad y + 5z$

10. $2x + 4y + 3z$
$\quad x + 3y + 2z$

11. $\quad 5a + 7x + 8z$
$\quad 11a + 4x + \quad z$

12. $3ab + 5x + 1$
$\quad 4ab + \quad x + 5$

13. $2bc + 2x + 9$
$\quad 3bc + 3x + 2$

14. $\quad bx + 5x + 7$
$\quad 2bx + 3x + 5$

15.
$3\,by + 8\,x + 11$
$2\,by + 2\,x + 5$

16.
$5\,az + 9\,z + 3$
$az + 3\,z + 5$

17.
$6\,bz + 4\,b + 12$
$bz + 3\,b + 5$

18.
$3\,cx + 9\,x + 4$
$7\,cx + 4\,x + 5$

19.
$2\,cy + 11\,c + 16$
$cy + 9\,c + 15$

20.
$8\,cz + 21\,z + 19$
$3\,cz + z + 5$

21.
$3\,ab + 4\,xy + 9$
$ab + 2\,xy + 4$

22.
$4\,bc + 5\,xy + 12$
$6\,bc + 2\,xy + 5$

23.
$11\,ac + 3\,xy + 15$
$2\,ac + 9\,xy + 22$

24.
$4\,ax + 4\,xz + 6$
$2\,ax + 3\,xz + 7$

25.
$9\,cx + 3\,cy + z$
$2\,cx + cy + z$

26.
$ax + by + cz$
$2\,ax + 2\,by + 2\,cz$

27.
$4\,ay + 3\,az + 4\,z$
$3\,ay + 5\,az + z$

28.
$9\,ac + 7\,bc + 4\,cx$
$3\,ac + 9\,bc + cx$

29.
$4\,bx + 3\,cy + 2\,az$
$3\,bx + 5\,cy + az$

30.
$30\,x + 28\,y + 5\,z$
$15\,x + 12\,y + 2\,z$

31.
$21\,abc + 16\,xyz$
$14\,abc + 19\,xyz$

32.
$13\,abx + 12\,cxy$
$21\,abx + 25\,cxy$

33.
$28\,acy + 9\,bxz$
$14\,acy + 11\,bxz$

34.
$54\,bcz + 13\,axy$
$19\,bcz + 18\,axy$

35.
$35\,cxy + 39\,abz$
$63\,cxy + 21\,abz$

36.
$49\,\pi + 35\,a + 15\,b$
$64\,\pi + 25\,a + 19\,b$

37.
$7\,\pi a + 14\,\pi b + 21\,\pi c$
$7\,\pi a + 7\,\pi b + 7\,\pi c$

38.
$3\,\pi x + 2\,\pi y + 11\,\pi z$
$4\,\pi x + 5\,\pi y + 3\,\pi z$

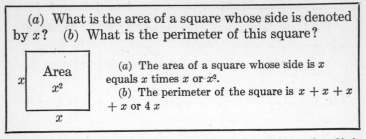

(*a*) What is the area of a square whose side is denoted by x?   (*b*) What is the perimeter of this square?

x **Area** x^2 x	(*a*) The area of a square whose side is x equals x times x or x^2. (*b*) The perimeter of the square is $x + x + x + x$ or $4\,x$

The small figure or letter placed to the right and a little above a quantity to show how many times the quantity is taken as a factor is called an exponent.

Find the areas and perimeters of the following squares:

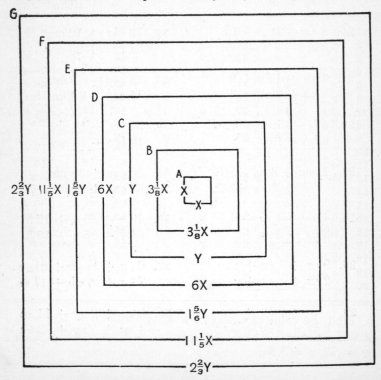

Find the area and the perimeter of a rectangle whose length is denoted by $2x$ and width by x.

x | $2x$

The area of a rectangle is equal to the product of the base by the altitude.

The area is, therefore, x times $2x$ or $2x^2$.

The perimeter is equal to $x + 2x + x + 2x$ or $6x$.

Determine the area and the perimeter of each of the following rectangles and squares:

	Width	Length		Width	Length		Width	Length
1.	a	$2a$	21.	d	$4d$	41.	$4m$	$4m$
2.	a	$3a$	22.	$2S$	$9S$	42.	15	25
3.	a	$5a$	23.	$3R$	$8R$	43.	$19x$	$21x$
4.	x	$3x$	24.	z	$7z$	44.	$17y$	$34y$
5.	x	$4x$	25.	5	8	45.	z	$10z$
6.	x	$6x$	26.	3	7	46.	$14R$	$19R$
7.	$2x$	$3x$	27.	$9y$	$11y$	47.	$11y$	$11y$
8.	$2a$	$3a$	28.	$10x$	$13x$	48.	25	25
9.	b	$3b$	29.	x	y	49.	2	4
10.	2	x	30.	$3x$	$5y$	50.	6	12
11.	3	b	31.	$11m$	$13m$	51.	18	36
12.	5	c	32.	5	7	52.	x	$2y$
13.	c	$2c$	33.	y	$16y$	53.	$2x$	$5y$
14.	3	$3c$	34.	$3x$	15	54.	a	$35a$
15.	5	$5x$	35.	$7y$	21	55.	b	$33b$
16.	$6y$	$7y$	36.	$5z$	$18z$	56.	c	$2m$
17.	m	$5m$	37.	$8x$	$8x$	57.	a	$5b$
18.	$2k$	$4k$	38.	$3y$	$3y$	58.	$5a$	$5b$
19.	$3m$	$7m$	39.	$2x$	$2x$	59.	$7c$	$7x$
20.	2	$2k$	40.	$5z$	$5z$	60.	$6a$	$14a$

Find the value of each of the above when $a = 1$, $b = 2$, $c = 3$, $d = 4$, $k = 5$, $m = 6$, $R = 7$, $s = 8$, $x = .5$, $y = .75$, $z = 5.25$.

Find the volume of a cube whose edge is x.

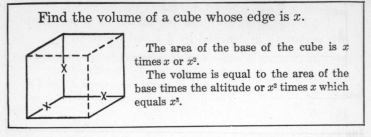

The area of the base of the cube is x times x or x^2.

The volume is equal to the area of the base times the altitude or x^2 times x which equals x^3.

The surface of the cube consists of six equal faces or $6 x^2$.

Find the volume and total surface of the cubes whose edges are as follows:

1. y	6. $2 x$	11. $6 m$	16. K
2. z	7. $2 y$	12. $9 z$	17. $2 R$
3. a	8. $3 a$	13. $4 y$	18. $5 d$
4. b	9. $4 b$	14. $5 x$	19. $7 c$
5. c	10. $5 c$	15. $8 a$	20. $4 n$

21. What exponent is always used in indicating the area of a square when the side is designated by a letter like x, y, or a?

22. What coefficient is used to indicate the perimeter of such a square?

23. What exponent is always used in indicating the volume of a cube when the edge is designated by a letter like x, y, or a?

24. Write an expression using 5 as a coefficient and 3 as an exponent.

Like terms are terms which have the same literal factors. Thus $3 x^2 y$ and $9 x^2 y$.

Unlike terms are terms which do not have the same literal factors. Thus $5 x^2 y$ and $5 x y^2$.

Underline the like terms in each of the following:

    (a) $3\,x^2y$; $4\,xy^2$; $5\,x^2y$; $8\,x^2y$.

    (b) $2\,ab$; $5\,a^2b^2$; $4\,ab$; $4\,xy$.

    (c) $4\,mn$; $4\,nm$; $5\,n^2m^2$; $3\,m^3n$.

    (d) x^2y^2; $3\,x^2y^2$; $9\,x^2y^2$; $6\,xy^2$.

    (e) $6\,cd^2$; $4\,c^2d$; $7\,c^2d$; $5\,c^2d$.

    (f) $4\,c^2x^3$; $3\,c^3x^2$; $8\,c^2x^3$; $3\,c^2x^3$.

Add

$$3\,x^2 + 5\,xy + 9\,y^2$$
$$2\,x^2 + 7\,xy + y^2$$
$$\overline{5\,x^2 + 12\,xy + 10\,y^2}$$

Say " $3\,x^2$ and $2\,x^2$ are $5\,x^2$ "
plus
$5\,xy$ and $7\,xy$ are $12\,xy$
plus
$9\,y^2$ and y^2 are $10\,y^2$

Like terms are added by adding the coefficients of those terms.
Unlike terms cannot be added.

Add:

1. $x^2 + 2\,xy + y^2$
   $5\,x^2 + xy + 4\,y^2$

6. $26\,y^3 + 5\,y + 10$
   $y^3 + 8\,y + 11$

2. $x^3 + 3\,x^2 + 5\,x$
   $4\,x^3 + 7\,x^2 + 9\,x$

7. $15\,c^2 + 13\,cd + d^2$
   $11\,c^2 + 9\,cd + 3\,d^2$

3. $8\,m^3 + 9\,m + 5$
   $4\,m^3 + 7\,m + 3$

8. $5\,K^3 + 6\,K^2 + 8$
   $3\,K^3 + 6\,K^2 + 7$

4. $6\,n^2 + 3\,n + 7$
   $9\,n^2 + 12\,n + 8$

9. $11\,c^3 + 3\,cx + 5\,x$
   $9\,c^3 + 8\,cx + 9\,x$

5. $M^2 + 5\,M + 9$
   $3\,M^2 + 8\,M + 11$

10. $x^3 + x^2 + x + 9$
   $3\,x^3 + 5\,x^2 + 9\,x + 7$

11. $5\,y^3 + 8\,y^2 + 3\,y + 8$
$\underline{7\,y^3 + 9\,y^2 + 11\,y + 10}$

21. $9\,x^3 + 7\,y^3$
$\underline{4\,x^3 + 8\,y^3}$

12. $16\,z^3 + 7\,z^2 + 8\,z + 6$
$\underline{14\,z^3 + 8\,z^2 + 6\,z + 9}$

22. $a^3 + 37\,b^3$
$\underline{16\,a^2 + 15\,b^3}$

13. $a^3 + 8\,a^2 + 6$
$\underline{3\,a^3 + 7\,a^2 + a + 7}$

23. $39\,m^3 + y^2$
$\underline{m^3 + 8\,y^2}$

14. $4\,b^3 + 6\,b^2 + 8\,b + 7$
$\underline{3\,b^3 + 4\,b + 5}$

24. $m^2 + n^2$
$\underline{5\,m^2 + 4\,n^2}$

15. $6\,d^3 + 8\,dc + 7$
$\underline{4\,d^3 + 5\,dc + 3}$

25. $16 + 13\,m + m^2$
$\underline{4 + 2\,m^2}$

16. $5\,T^2 + 8\,T + 12$
$\underline{6\,T^2 + 5\,T + 4}$

26. $15 + 4\,n + 7\,n^2$
$\underline{6 + n + n^2}$

17. $7\,b + 8\,c + 9\,d$
$\underline{6\,b + 4\,c + 8\,d}$

27. $36 + 8\,y + 6\,y^2$
$\underline{5 + 4\,y + 8\,y^2}$

18. $7\,x + 18\,y + 92$
$\underline{6\,x + 7\,y + 52}$

28. $T^2 + M^2$
$\underline{3\,T^2 + 4\,M^2}$

19. $2\,a^2 + b^2$
$\underline{a^2 + 3\,b^2}$

29. $19\,K^2 + 6\,K + 7$
$\underline{4\,K^2 + 3\,K + 11}$

20. $2\,x^2 + 3\,y^2$
$\underline{5\,x^2 + 7\,y^2}$

30. $26\,R^2 + 8\,R + 4$
$\underline{3\,R^2 + 7\,R + 3}$

Add:

31. $3\,x + 4\,y + 3$; $2\,x + 5\,y + 7$.

32. $5\,a + 7\,b + 6$; $6\,a + 3\,b + 7$.

33. $10\,x^2 + 3\,x + 8\,y + z$; $7\,x^2 + 4\,x + 3\,y + 6\,z$.

Add: $3x^3 + 5x^2 + 7x + 6$; $4x^2 + 9x^3 + 5 + 3x$;
$\quad 7x^3 + 4 + 6x^2$

$$\begin{array}{r} 3x^3 + 5x^2 + 7x + 6 \\ 9x^3 + 4x^2 + 3x + 5 \\ 7x^3 + 6x^2 + 4 \\ \hline 19x^3 + 15x^2 + 10x + 15 \end{array}$$

First — Place the like terms in columns.

Second — Add the coefficients of these like terms.

Arrange like terms in columns and add:

1. $x^3 + 8x^2 + 7x + 5$; $3x^3 + 7x^2 + 9x + 7$; $15x^3 + 8x^2 + 15x + 7$.

2. $7y^3 + 8y^2 + 11y + 6$; $14y^3 + 6y^2 + 4y + 5$; $6y^3 + 9y^2 + 8y + 3$.

3. $a^2b + a^2c + a + 6$; $a^2c + 3a^2b + 7a + 5$; $4a^2b + 6a^2c + 8a + 9$.

4. $x^4 + 6x^3 + 8x^2 + 6x + 7$; $4 + 9x^2 + 3x^3$; $9x^4 + 4x^2 + 11x + 5$.

5. $y^2 + 5y + 9$; $y^2 + 6y^2 + 4y + 13$; $9y^2 + 4 + 7y + 13k^2$.

6. $3ab + 4cd + 2ac$; $ab + 3cd + 3ac$; $3cd + 2ab$; $4cd + 7by$.

7. $7ax + 13by + 6$; $9ax + 8by + 4$; $3by + 12ax$; $4ax + 7by + 9$.

8. $m^4 + 4m^3n + 6m^2n^2 + 4mn^3 + n^4$; $4m^4 + 16m^3n + 24m^2n^2 + 16mn^3 + 4n^3$.

9. $9 + y^2$; $16 + 5y + 7y^2$; $5y^2 + 6$; $15y + 4y^2 + 7$; $y^2 + 8$.

10. $z^3 + 8z^2 + 7z + 3$; $6z^3 + 4z^2 + 9 + 3z$; $5z^2 + 8z^3 + 6z + 7$.

11. $25 + 36\,k + k^2$; $13\,k^2 + 4 + 9\,k$; $6\,k + 5$; $11\,k^2 + 6 + 15\,k$.

12. $m^2 + 8\,mn + 16\,n$; $25\,m^2 + 10\,mn + n^2$; $49\,m^2 + 6\,n^2$.

13. $14\,b^3 + 8 + 3\,b^2 + 7\,b$; $\quad 16\,b^2 + 9\,b^3 + 7 + 8\,b$; $14\,b^3 + 16\,b^2 + 3\,b + 9$.

14. $cy + c^2y^2 + 3\,c^3y^3 + 8$; $3\,cy + 5\,c^2y^2 + 3\,c^3y^3 + 8$; $2\,cy + 8\,c^2y^2 + 9$.

15. $x^3 + 3\,x^3y + 6\,x^2y^2 + 3\,xy^3 + y^4$; $\quad 4\,x^3 + 7\,x^3y + 8\,x^2y^2 + 7\,xy^3 + 4\,y^4$.

16. $2\,m + 3\,n$; $3\,n + 2\,m$; $5\,m + 7\,n$; $8\,n + 4\,m$; $15\,m + 6\,n$.

17. $3\,a^2 + 6\,ab + 3\,b^2$; $5\,a^2 + 10\,ab + 5\,b^2$; $7\,a^2 + 14\,ab + 7\,b^2$.

18. $6\,T^3 + 8\,T^2 + 7\,T + 6$; $R^2 + R + 6\,T^3 + 7\,T^2$; $5\,R^2 + 6\,R + T$.

19. $4\,ab + 7\,cd + 8\,xy + 6\,mn$; $3\,ab + 4\,cd + 6\,mn + 3\,xy$.

20. $6\,a + 4\,b + 7\,c + dx + cy + fz$; $\quad 4\,a + 7\,b + 3\,c + 9\,dx + 10\,cy + 11\,fz$.

21. $a^3 + 3\,a^2b + 3\,ab^2 + b^3$; $5\,a^3 + 15\,a^2b + 15\,ab^2 + 5\,b^3$.

22. $m^4 + 4\,m^3n + 6\,m^2n^2 + 4\,mn^3 + n^4$; $3\,m^4 + 12\,m^3n + 18\,m^2n^2 + 12\,mn^3 + 3\,n^4$.

23. $9\,a^2 + 7\,b^2$; $2\,a^2 + 3\,b^2$; $6\,a^2 + 4\,b^2$; $8\,a^2 + b^2$.

24. $25\,x^2 + 3\,y$; $19\,x^2 + 4\,y$; $6\,x^2 + 6\,y$; $4\,x^2 + 11\,y$; $3\,x^2 + 6\,y$.

The plus (+) sign may be used to indicate money saved, the minus (−) sign may be used to designate the indebtedness.

I. Mr. Jones has $200 in the bank, he owes $90 for groceries. How much will he have left after this debt is paid?

Show the amount in the bank thus	+ $200
Show the amount of indebtedness thus	− $90
Then the amount left would be shown thus	+ $110

II. Mr. Jones has $400 in one bank and $375 in a second bank. How much has he in both banks?

+ $400
+ $375
+ $775 the amount in both banks

III. Mr. Jones owes $380 to one man and $495 to another. How much does he owe both men?

− $380
− $495
− $875 the amount owed both men

Make and solve problems using the following quantities:

1. + $800; + $750
2. + $350; − $150
3. − $650; − $375
4. + $1100; − $630
5. + $560; + $380
6. − $265; + $978
7. − $185; − $317
8. + $238; + $567
9. + $3.00; − $.75
10. + $¾; − $½
11. + $⅞; − $¾
12. + $½; + $1½

13. − $⅗; − $⅘
14. + $675; + $340
15. + $485; − $265
16. − $18.50; − $.75
17. − $20; − $.20
18. + $30; − $.60
19. + $16; + $.30
20. + $5; + $13
21. − $7; + $15
22. − $21; − $37.50
23. − $240; + $540
24. + $160; + $375

I. *Add:* + \$9 − \$7 + \$3 − \$8 + \$21 − \$3 − \$2.

+ \$ 9	− \$ 7	+ \$33
+ \$ 3	− \$ 8	− \$20
+ \$21	− \$ 3	+ \$13
+ \$33	− \$ 2	
	− \$20	

II. *Add:* + 11 xy − 8 xy + 5 xy − 7 xy − 9 xy + 12 xy − 3 xy.

+ 11 xy	− 8 xy	+ 28 xy
+ 5 xy	− 7 xy	− 27 xy
+ 12 xy	− 9 xy	+ xy
+ 28 xy	− 3 xy	
	− 27 xy	

1. $7\,T + 4\,T + 9\,T - 3\,T - 5\,T - 8\,T - T.$

2. $4\,\pi - 3\,\pi - 7\,\pi + 9\,\pi + 15\,\pi - 11\,\pi + 8\,\pi.$

3. $7\,d - 2\,d + 5\,d - 3\,d + 8\,d - 7\,d + 4\,d + 9\,d.$

4. $11\,a - 3\,a + 5\,a - 7\,a + 9\,a - 2\,a + 6\,a.$

5. $24\,x - 11\,x - 8\,x + 12\,x - 4\,x - 6\,x - x.$

6. $3\,y^2 - 21\,y^2 + 35\,y^2 - 14\,y^2 + 81\,y^2 - 11\,y^2 - 15\,y^2.$

7. $9\,xy - 16\,xy - 3\,xy + 21\,xy + 8\,xy.$

8. $15\,a^2 + 23\,a^2 - 7\,a^2 - 9\,a^2 + 15\,a^2 - 4\,a^2 - 11\,a^2.$

9. $-9\,x^2 - 11\,x^2 - 17\,x^2 + 35\,x^2 + 5\,x^2 + 21\,x^2 + 8\,x^2.$

10. $-12\,y^3 + 8\,y^3 + 5\,y^3 - 13\,y^3 - 7\,y^3 - 13\,y^3 + 18\,y^3.$

11. $+4\,ab + 7\,ab - 3\,ab - 12\,ab + 5\,ab + 8\,ab - 19\,ab.$

12. $7\,\pi R + 11\,\pi R + 9\,\pi R + 3\,\pi R + 49\,\pi R - 64\,\pi R.$

Add:

1. $-\ 5\,x$	**2.** $+\ 17\,y^2$	**3.** $+\ 9\,xy$	**4.** $+\quad mx$
$+\ 12\,x$	$-\ 3\,y^2$	$-\ 10\,xy$	$-\ 4\,mx$
$+\ 9\,x$	$+\ 8\,y^2$	$-\ 13\,xy$	$+\ 6\,mx$
$-\ 4\,x$	$-\ 12\,y^2$	$+\ 7\,xy$	$-\ 13\,mx$
$-\ 6\,x$	$+\ 5\,y^2$	$+\ 5\,xy$	$+\ 5\,mx$

5. $+\ 7\,c$	**6.** $-\ 15\,t^2x$	**7.** $+\ 30\,xy$	**8.** $+\ 4\,b$
$-\ 9\,c$	$-\ 6\,t^2x$	$-\ 5\,xy$	$-\ 7\,b$
$-\ 8\,c$	$+\ 3\,t^2x$	$+\ 6\,xy$	$+\ 9\,b$
$+\ 14\,c$	$+\ 20\,t^2x$	$-\ 14\,xy$	$-\ 14\,b$
$+\ 7\,c$	$-\quad t^2x$	$-\ 3\,xy$	$+\ 8\,b$

9. $+\ 3.5\,b$	**10.** $+\ \frac{1}{2}\,x$	**11.** $-\ 4.1\,y$	**12.** $+\ 6.2\,z$
$+\ 7.2\,b$	$+\ \frac{1}{4}\,x$	$-\ 6.3\,y$	$-\ .5\,z$
$+\ 8.1\,b$	$+\ \frac{3}{4}\,x$	$-\quad y$	$+\ 7.8\,z$
$+\ 4.3\,b$	$+\quad x$	$-\ 9.5\,y$	$-\ 6.5\,z$
$+\ 9\quad b$	$+\ 3\,x$	$-\ 8.3\,y$	$+\ .9\,z$

13. $-\ \frac{1}{8}\,k$	**14.** $+\ 7\,a^2b$	**15.** $-\ 6\,x^2y$	**16.** $+\quad x^2y^2$
$-\ \frac{1}{4}\,k$	$+\ 3\,a^2b$	$+\ 4\,x^2y$	$-\ 7\,x^2y^2$
$-\ \frac{3}{4}\,k$	$-\ 8\,a^2b$	$-\ 8\,x^2y$	$-\ 13\,x^2y^2$
$-\ \frac{1}{2}\,k$	$-\ 5\,a^2b$	$+\ 11\,x^2y$	$+\ 19\,x^2y^2$
$+\ 8\,k$	$+\ 9\,a^2b$	$-\quad x^2y$	$+\ 4\,x^2y^2$

17. $+\quad abc$	**18.** $+\ 21\,x^2yz$	**19.** $+\ \frac{7}{8}\,y$	**20.** $+\ .5\,x$
$+\ 17\,abc$	$+\ 36\,x^2yz$	$+\ \frac{1}{4}\,y$	$+\ .3\,x$
$-\ 14\,abc$	$+\ 15\,x^2yz$	$-\ \frac{1}{2}\,y$	$-\ .7\,x$
$-\ 24\,abc$	$-\ 6\,x^2yz$	$-\ \frac{1}{8}\,y$	$-\ .1\,x$
$+\ 49\,abc$	$-\ 11\,x^2yz$	$+\ 5\,y$	$+\ .9\,x$

21. $9\,x - 8\,x + 3\,x - 12\,x + 5\,x + 11\,x - x + 15\,x.$

22. $13\,y - 5\,y + 3\,y - 15\,y - 8\,y + 17\,y - 9\,y -$
$3\,y + 15\,y - 8\,y - y.$

Add: $3x + 5y - 7$
$\underline{4x - 3y - 4}$
$7x + 2y - 11$

Say "A plus $3x$ and a plus $4x$ are a plus $7x$

A plus $5y$ and a minus $3y$ are a plus $2y$

A minus 7 and a minus 4 are a minus 11."

When the signs of the terms are alike, the sum is given the same sign as that governing the terms.

When the signs of the terms are unlike, the sum is given the sign of the larger coefficient.

Add the following:

1. $x^2 + 7x - 5$
$\underline{x^2 - 3x + 4}$

9. $x^4 + x^2y^2 + y^4$
$\underline{x^4 - x^2y^2 + y^4}$

2. $5a + 7b - 11c$
$\underline{2a + 3b + 5c}$

10. $a^2 + ab$
$\underline{\quad - ab - b^2}$

3. $11x + 13y - 14z$
$\underline{4x + 9y - 16z}$

11. $x^2 + xy$
$\underline{\quad - xy - y^2}$

4. $2t + 7s - 10y$
$\underline{3t - 4s + 2y}$

12. $25x^2 + 35xy$
$\underline{\quad - 35xy - 49y^2}$

5. $12x^2 - 10x - 6$
$\underline{9x^2 - 6x + 5}$

13. $y^2 - 5y$
$\underline{\quad - 7y + 35}$

6. $7y^2 - 8y + 9$
$\underline{3y^2 + 4y - 7}$

14. $z^2 - 10z$
$\underline{\quad - 8z + 80}$

7. $3a^2 - 9a + 4$
$\underline{- a^2 - 4a + 3}$

15. $w^2 - 12w$
$\underline{\quad + 4w - 48}$

8. $4x^2 + 13x - 10$
$\underline{- 3x^2 - \quad x - 5}$

16. $6x^2 + 4z$
$\underline{\quad + 15z + 10}$

Equations

Every true statement which shows that one number, or quantity, or combination of numbers or quantities is equal to another number, quantity, or combination of numbers or quantities is an **equation**: *e.g.*

6 + 7 = 13 is an equation; also 10 + 14 = 12 + 12.

15 ÷ 5 = 7 + 4 is not an equation.   Why not?

x + 5 = 12 is an equation only when x has a certain value.   What is that value?

1. When b − 3 = 4, what is the value of b?

2. When 19 y = 38, what is the value of y?

3. What is the value of y when y + 4 = 13?   When y − 2 = 13?   When y ÷ 9 = 3?

Finding the value of a letter in an equation is called *solving the equation.*

Solve the following equations:

4. $2 x = 4.$

5. $5 b = 10.$

6. $3 c = 15.$

7. $6 a = 24.$

8. $9 a = 18.$

9. $21 y = 3.$

10. $10 x = 5.$

11. $36 y = 9.$

12. $x − 2 = 8$

13. $y − 3 = 7.$

14. $c − 1 = 11.$

15. $d − 7 = 14.$

16. $x − 8 = 20.$

17. $3 x = 30.$

18. $5 y = 25.$

19. $y − 9 = 21.$

20. $2 y − 5 = 7.$

21. $2 x + 9 = 17.$

22. $y + 11 = 20.$

23. $x + 3 = 7.$

24. $5 x − 1 = 9.$

25. $7 x − 1 = 15.$

26. $9 x = 81.$

27. $7 y = 63.$

28. $13 a = 39.$

29. $15 b = 60.$

30. $11 c = 88.$

31. $2 y − 8 = 12.$

32. $8 T = 40.$

33. $7 \pi = 22.$

	(a)	I is an equation.
I	$20 = 20$	II is a true equation because the
II	$20 + 5 = 20 + 5$	sum of the numbers on the left of the
III	$25 = 25$	sign of equality $(=)$ is equal to the

sum of the numbers on the right side
of the sign of equality.

(b)

I	$36 = 36$
II	$36 + 7 = 36 + 7$
III	$43 = 43$

What effect has the adding of the
same number to both sides of the
equation?

Principle I. — *The same number can be added to both sides of an equation without destroying the equality.*

Solve by adding 3 to each side of the following equations:

1. $x - 3 = 12$

SOLUTION: $x - 3 + 3 = 12 + 3$
$x - 3 + 3 = 15$
$\therefore x = 15.$

2. $x - 3 = 21$

SOLUTION: $x - 3 + 3 = 21 + 3$
$x - 3 + 3 = 24$
$\therefore x = 24.$

3. $x - 3 = 7$ **7.** $x - 3 = 8$ **11.** $x - 3 = 9$

4. $x - 3 = 11$ **8.** $x - 3 = 15$ **12.** $x - 3 = 19$

5. $x - 3 = 6$ **9.** $x - 3 = 1$ **13.** $x - 3 = 5$

6. $x - 3 = 12$ **10.** $x - 3 = 0$ **14.** $x - 3 = 22$

Solve by adding 5 to each side of the following equations:

15. $x - 5 = 9$ **19.** $x - 5 = 13$ **23.** $x - 5 = 0$

16. $x - 5 = 11$ **20.** $x - 5 = 28$ **24.** $x - 5 = 14$

17. $x - 5 = 22$ **21.** $x - 5 = 36$ **25.** $x - 5 = 35$

18. $x - 5 = 6$ **22.** $x - 5 = 23$ **26.** $x - 5 = 26$

27. Solve $x - 8 = 13$ by adding 8 to each side of the equation.

$$(a)$$

I $\qquad 18 = 18$

II $\qquad 18 - 9 = 18 - 9$

III $\qquad 9 = 9$

$$(b)$$

I $\qquad x + 8 = 18$

II $\ x + 8 - 8 = 18 - 8$

$\qquad x + 8 - 8 = 10$

III $\qquad x = 10$

I is an equation.

II is a true equation because the algebraic sum of the numbers on the left of the sign of equality (=) is equal to the algebraic sum of the numbers on the right side of the sign of equality.

What effect has the subtracting of the same number from both sides of an equation?

Principle II. — *The same number can be subtracted from both members of an equation without destroying the equality.*

Solve by subtracting 7 from each member of the following equations:

1. $x + 7 = 17$ 5. $x + 7 = 3$ 9. $x + 7 = 14$
2. $x + 7 = 21$ 6. $x + 7 = 15$ 10. $x + 7 = 8$
3. $x + 7 = 35$ 7. $x + 7 = 39$ 11. $x + 7 = 51$
4. $x + 7 = 7$ 8. $x + 7 = 0$ 12. $x + 7 = 4$

13. Solve $x - 9 = 15$ by adding 9 to each side of the equation.

14. Solve $x - 4 = 7$ by adding 4 to each side of the equation.

15. Solve $x - 7 = 0$ by adding 7 to each side of the equation.

16. Solve $x - 11 = 16$ by adding 11 to each side of the equation.

17. Solve $x - 19 = 36$ by adding 19 to each side of the equation.

18. Solve $x - 14 = 35$ by adding 14 to each side of the equation.

Solve by subtracting 12 from each member of the following equations:

1. $x + 12 = 24$ **5.** $x + 12 = 6$ **9.** $x + 12 = 0$

2. $x + 12 = 36$ **6.** $x + 12 = -3$ **10.** $x + 12 = -7$

3. $x + 12 = 30$ **7.** $x + 12 = -5$ **11.** $x + 12 = 12$

4. $x + 12 = 38$ **8.** $x + 12 = -8$ **12.** $x + 12 = 60$

Solve the following equations by either adding or subtracting 15:

13. $x + 15 = 30$ **17.** $x - 15 = 5$ **21.** $x + 15 = 0$

14. $x - 15 = 25$ **18.** $x + 15 = 37$ **22.** $x - 15 = 0$

15. $x - 15 = 10$ **19.** $x + 15 = 45$ **23.** $x + 15 = -7$

16. $x + 15 = 18$ **20.** $x - 15 = 33$ **24.** $x - 15 = -7$

Solve the following equations:

25. $x + 5 = 25$ **29.** $x - 7 = 8$ **33.** $x + 12 = 22$

26. $x - 11 = 33$ **30.** $x + 9 = 12$ **34.** $x - 12 = 36$

27. $x - 6 = -7$ **31.** $x - 16 = 15$ **35.** $x + 13 = -33$

28. $x + 8 = 18$ **32.** $x + 3 = 11$ **36.** $x - 21 = -20$

---

1. $7 = 7$ This is a true equation.

$3(7) = 3(7)$ Multiplying both sides of the equation

$21 = 21$ by the same number.

The equation is still true.

2. $\frac{1}{12} y = 4$ Principle III. — *Both sides of an equation*

$\frac{12}{12} y = 412$ *may be multiplied by the same number with-*

$y = 48$ *out destroying the equality.*

Multiply both sides of the following equations by the numbers indicated:

37. $\frac{1}{4} x = 6$ by 4 **38.** $\frac{1}{8} x = 7$ by 8

39. $\frac{1}{2} y = 3$ by 2 **40.** $.1 y = 10$ by 10

1. $3(5) = 3(5)$ This is a true equation.

$$\frac{3(5)}{3} = \frac{3(5)}{3}$$

Dividing both sides of the equation by the same number the equation is still true.

$$5 = 5$$

2. $3x = 36$ Principle IV. — *Both sides of an equation*

$$\frac{3x}{3} = \frac{36}{3}$$

may be divided by the same number without destroying the equality.

$$x = 12$$

Solve:

1. $5x = 20$
2. $7y = 49$
3. $3a = 15$
4. $4z = 24$
5. $8m = 64$
6. $6x = 30$
7. $11y = 22$
8. $9h = 18$

9. $2y = 18$
10. $7x = 21$
11. $9x = 36$
12. $17y = 34$
13. $25x = 100$
14. $15z = 45$
15. $19x = 57$
16. $21a = 84$

17. $13m = 65$
18. $14x = 112$
19. $11y = 66$
20. $17x = 85$
21. $35z = 105$
22. $60a = 300$
23. $15x = 225$
24. $9x = 81$

$$3x + 7 = 16$$
$$3x + 7 - 7 = 16 - 7$$ Principle II.
$$3x = 9$$ Addition.
$$x = 3.$$ Principle.

PROOF: $3(3) + 7 = 16$ Substituting 3 for x.

$$9 + 7 = 16$$

The value for x is correct since it makes the equation true.

$$16 = 16$$

Solve and prove:

25. $2x + 3 = 13$ **26.** $4x + 9 = 21$ **27.** $2x + 3 = 45$
28. $5x + 2 = 27$ **29.** $5x + 5 = 40$ **30.** $4x + 1 = 45$

$$7x - 5 = 30$$
$$7x - 5 + 5 = 30 + 5 \qquad \text{Principle I.}$$
$$7x = 35 \qquad \text{Addition.}$$
$$x = 5. \qquad \text{Principal IV.}$$

Substitute 5 for x.

Proof: $\qquad 7(5) - 5 = 30 \qquad$ This value of x is
$$35 - 5 = 30 \qquad \text{therefore correct since it}$$
$$30 = 30 \qquad \text{makes the equation true.}$$

Solve:

1. $2x - 3 = 9$ **5.** $9x - 4 = 86$ **9.** $16x + 2 = 50$

2. $5x - 7 = 28$ **6.** $7x + 4 = 88$ **10.** $11x - 5 = 28$

3. $7x - 1 = 20$ **7.** $12x + 4 = 100$ **11.** $3x + 7 = 37$

4. $12x - 8 = 52$ **8.** $12x - 5 = 19$ **12.** $4x - 9 = 35$

13. $5m - 6 = 19$ **22.** $\frac{1}{4}x = 8$

14. $21x - 13 = 50$ **23.** $5y = 9$

15. $19y - 5 = 90$ **24.** $x + 12 = 18$

16. $24x + 6 = 102$ **25.** $5m + 5 = 110$

17. $36y + 20 = 200$ **26.** $3t + 2 = 20$

18. $21x - 10 = 200$ **27.** $11h + 1 = 100$

19. $4m - 5 = 75$ **28.** $16k + 5 = 181$

20. $7z - 6 = 8$ **29.** $8m - 8 = 80$

21. $8y = 64$ **30.** $3x + 9 = 100$

31. $12y = 96$ **32.** $11y + 2 = 90$

33. $7x - 3 = 32$ **34.** $4k + 7 = 37$

35. $3y + 9 = 69$ **36.** $8c + 8 = 48$

37. $16z + 5 = 38$ **38.** $13y + 4 = 30$

39. $5a + 3a = 48$ **40.** $2x + 8x = 60$

41. $6y + 3y = 63$ **42.** $21a + 4a = 100$

43. $4a - 7 = 53$ **44.** $9x - 11 = 70$

45. $3y + 9 = 30$ **46.** $17m + 3 = 20$

$$5x - 5 = 2x + 10$$

Subtract $2x$ from each side then:

$$5x - 5 - 2x = 2x - 2x + 10$$
$$3x - 5 = 10$$
$$3x - 5 + 5 = 10 + 5$$
$$3x = 15$$
$$x = 5$$

The same result may be secured by transposing the $2x$ from the right to the left of the sign of equality. The sign of the $2x$ must be changed when it is transposed. The 5 may be likewise transposed to the right side by changing its sign.

Thus:
$$5x - 5 = 2x + 10$$
$$5x - 2x = 10 + 5$$
$$3x = 15$$
$$x = 5$$

Changing a quantity from one side of the sign of equality (=) is transposition. When a quantity is transposed its sign must be changed.

Solve the following examples by transposition:

1. $15x + 25 = 19x - 7$ 2. $7x + 10 = 6x + 16$

3. $12x + 4 = 14x - 12$ 4. $x - 9 = \frac{1}{2}x - 4$

5. $6x + 2 = 4x + 12$ 6. $5x + 25 = 50$

7. $3x + 25 = 10x - 10$ 8. $9x + 24 = 20x - 53$

9. $2x + 10 = 5x - 17$ 10. $12x - 60 = 10x + 46$

11. $3x + 5 = 6x - 22$ 12. $6x - 2 = 5x + 3$

13. $3x - 7 = 4x - 14$ 14. $5x + 3 = 6x - 2$

15. $5x - 4 = 3x + 10$ 16. $7x + 12 = 8x + 8$

17. $3x + 8 - 2 = 2x + 14$ 18. $3x + 2 = 4x - 2$

19. $2x + 26 = 7x - 14$ 20. $12x - 14 = 22 + 9x$

21. $8x + 11 = 11x - 7$ 22. $5x + 10 = x + 30$

Solve the following equations:

1. $9x - 7 = 6x + 23$
2. $3x + 9 = 2x + 16$
3. $7x + 3 = 3x + 19$
4. $8x + 4 = 9x - 3$
5. $5x - 7 = 2x + 5$
6. $12x + 1 = 10x + 5$
7. $7x - 5 = 2x + 20$
8. $5x - 5 = 4x + 1$
9. $8x - 20 = 6x - 10$
10. $36x = 144$
11. $3x + 8 = 2x + 14$
12. $15x - 15 = 11x + 1$
13. $11x - 2 = 10x$
14. $27x - 10x = 20x - 9$
15. $12y - 30 = 7y$
16. $.5x + 5 = x$
17. $.5x - 10 = 15$
18. $.25x + 4 = 24$
19. $.25x - 5 = 15$
20. $.25x + .5x = 75$
21. $.5x - .25x = 30$
22. $.75x - .5x = 18$
23. $.75x - .25x = 21$
24. $.625x = 40$
25. $.375x = 24$
26. $.875y = 49$
27. $.3x = 18$
28. $.7y = 35$
29. $3x + 35 = 11x + 11$
30. $5y + 20 = 8y + 2$
31. $35y - 18 = 26y$
32. $16y + 2 = 11y + 17$
33. $3a + 8 = 2a + 18$
34. $7a + 11 = 5a + 21$
35. $9b - 7 = 6b + 2$
36. $5b - 16 = 2b + 1$
37. $8c - 2 = 7c + 2$
38. $11c - 16 = 7c + 4$
39. $13d - 81 = 5d - 1$
40. $13m + 1 = 20m - 20$
41. $8x + 3 = 10x$
42. $9x + 2 = 30x$
43. $8x + 2 = 16x$
44. $30x - 2 = 20x$
45. $5x + 7 = 7x + 1$
46. $4x - 5 = 3x$
47. $7x - 2 = 6x + 4$
48. $9x + 7 = 10x$
49. $4x - 7 = 3x + 2$
50. $12x - 16 = 6x + 2$
51. $x + 9 = 49 - x$
52. $3x + 7 = 52 - 2x$

1. The perimeter of a square is 44 ft. What is the side of the square? What is the area of the square?

Let x = the side of the square
Then $4\,x$ = the perimeter
Then $4\,x$ = 44
x = 11 Principle IV
∴ the side of the square is 11 ft.
Area of the square is 11 times 11 or 121 sq. ft.

Find the side and the area of each of the following squares:

1. Perimeter 40 ft.
2. Perimeter 56 ft.
3. Perimeter 32 ft.
4. Perimeter 76 ft.
5. Perimeter 92 ft.
6. Perimeter 100 ft.
7. Perimeter 52 ft.
8. Perimeter 28 ft.
9. Perimeter 16 ft.
10. Perimeter 8 ft.
11. Perimeter 116 ft.
12. Perimeter 72 ft.
13. Perimeter 48 ft.
14. Perimeter 36 ft.
15. Perimeter 24 ft.
16. Perimeter 80 ft.
17. Perimeter 136 ft.
18. Perimeter 140 ft.
19. Perimeter 108 ft.
20. Perimeter 120 ft.

21. The length of a rectangle is 5 times its width. Its perimeter is 60 ft. Find its length, width, and area.

Let x = the width
* Then $5\,x$ = the length
Then $x + 5\,x + x + 5\,x$ = the perimeter
$12\,x$ = 60 ft.
x = 5
$5\,x$ = 25
Area = 5 times 25 = 125 sq ft.

* The length is 5 times the width. If the width is represented by x, then the length may be indicated by $5\,x$.

22. The length of a rectangle is 3 times its width. Its perimeter is 96 ft. Find its width, length, and area.

23. The perimeter of a rectangle is 72 ft. Its width is one half its length. Find its length, width, and area.

Let $2x$ = length, then x will = the width.

24. The width of a rectangle is found to be one third of its length. Its perimeter is 80. Find its width, length, and area.

Find the width, length, and area of each of the following rectangles:

25. Length 2 times the width ; perimeter 12 ft.

26.   "   5   "   "   "   "   60 "

27.   "   7   "   "   "   "   48 "

28.   "   6   "   "   "   "   98 "

29.   "   3   "   "   "   "   48 "

30.   "   9   "   "   "   "   80 "

31.   "   4   "   "   "   "   30 "

32.   " 11   "   "   "   "   192 "

33.   "   8   "   "   "   "   180 "

34.   " 14   "   "   "   "   150 "

35.   " 12   "   "   "   "   182 "

36. Width $\frac{1}{4}$ of the length   "   40 "

37.   " $\frac{1}{5}$ "   "   "   "   120 "

38.   " $\frac{1}{3}$ "   "   "   "   48 "

39.   " $\frac{1}{10}$ "   "   "   "   440 "

40.   " $\frac{1}{8}$ "   "   "   "   288 "

41. The perimeter of a square is 640. Find the side of the square.

Suggestions to be followed in the solution of problems:

I. Read the problem very carefully in order that you may grasp the entire thought.

II. Read the problem to determine what value is to be found first. This value will make it possible for you to find all the other values that are required.

III. Let x represent this value.

IV. Read the problem again to determine how you may represent the other unknown values in terms of x.

V. State the relationship which exists between these values. This statement will take the form of an equation.

VI. Solve the equation.

VII. Check your answers by substituting the values in equation. Read the problem to ascertain whether the answers satisfy all the conditions stated.

Use the above suggestions in the solution of the following problems:

1. The sum of a number and 5 equals 15. Find the number.

$$\text{Let } x = \text{the number}$$
$$\text{Then } x + 5 = 15 \qquad\qquad \textbf{Proof: } 10 + 5 = 15$$
$$x = 15 - 5 \quad \text{Prin. II} \qquad\qquad 15 = 15$$
$$x = 10$$

2. The sum of three times a number and 3 equals 63. Find the number.

$$\text{Let } x = \text{the number}$$
$$\text{Then } 3\,x = \text{three times the number}$$
$$3\,x + 3 = 63 \qquad\qquad \textbf{Proof: } 3(20) + 3 = 63$$
$$3\,x = 63 - 3 \quad \text{Prin. II} \qquad\qquad 60 + 3 = 63$$
$$3\,x = 60$$
$$x = 20 \qquad\qquad \text{Prin. IV} \qquad\qquad 63 = 63$$

3. What number plus 7 equals 37?

4. Eleven plus a certain number equals 16. Find the number.

5. A certain number added to 13 equals 20. Find the number.

6. If 6 is added to a certain number, the sum is 17. Find the number.

7. If a certain number and 5 are added, the sum is 13. Find the number.

8. Three times a certain number plus 4 equals 22. What is the number?

9. The sum of 4 times a number and 7 is 19. What is the number?

10. If 7 times a number and 3 are added, the sum is 38. Find the number.

11. What number added to 7 equals 43?

12. What number added to three times itself equals 20?

13. If 7 is subtracted from 4 times a number, the difference is 9. What is the number?

$$\begin{array}{ll} \text{Let } x = \text{the number} & \text{PROOF: } 4(4) - 7 = 9 \\ \text{Then } 4\,x = 4 \text{ times the number} & 16 - 7 = 9 \\ \text{Then } 4\,x - 7 = 9 & 9 = 9 \\ \qquad 4\,x = 9 + 7 \quad \text{Prin. II} & \\ \qquad 4\,x = 16 \quad\;\; \text{Prin. IV} & \\ \qquad\; x = 4 & \end{array}$$

14. When 3 is subtracted from 3 times a number, the difference is 15. Find the number.

15. If 6 is subtracted from 5 times a certain number, the difference is 29. Find the number.

16. John placed a certain sum of money in the bank. Later he deposited three times that sum. He then had $80 in the bank. What sum did he deposit at first?

17. After spending $8 of his money, Frank had $22 left. How much had he at first?

18. Four equal sums of money are drawn from a bank account of $110. If $10 still remained in the bank, what was the amount of each of the four sums?

19. From a certain city to New York and return is 198 miles. How far is it from that city to New York? How far is it from New York to that city?

20. A man has $2580 in the bank. He first takes $180 for his own use. He then divides the remainder equally among his four children. What is each child's share?

21. At what price must a chair be purchased if six of them cost $72?

22. What was the average speed per hour of an auto which traveled 198 miles in 9 hours?

23. How much must a boy save each month if he saves $9.60 in a year?

24. A certain number is multiplied by 7. The result is 98. What is the number?

25. How many articles at $2.50 each can be purchased for $30?

26. How much must each of 30 persons contribute to make a fund of $150?

27. The width of a rectangle is 10 ft. Its perimeter is 60 ft. What is its length?

28. The perimeter of a rectangle is 40 ft. Its length is 15 ft. What is its width?

29. A house and lot cost $16,000. If the house cost 7 times the cost of the lot, what was the cost of each?

30. A store and a factory were sold for $40,000. If the factory was sold for three times the store, what was the price of each?

1. $\frac{1}{2} + \frac{1}{4} = ?$

L. C. D. is 4

$$\frac{1}{2} = \frac{2}{4}$$
$$\frac{2}{4} + \frac{1}{4} = \frac{3}{4}.$$

2. $\frac{x}{2} + \frac{x}{4} = ?$

L. C. D. is 4

$$\frac{x}{2} = \frac{2x}{4}$$
$$\frac{2x}{4} + \frac{x}{4} = \frac{3x}{4}.$$

3. $\frac{x}{5} + \frac{x}{8} = 13$

L. C. D. is 40

$40 \div 5 = 8 \quad \therefore \frac{x}{5} = \frac{8x}{40}$

$40 \div 8 = 5 \quad \therefore \frac{x}{8} = \frac{5x}{40}$

$40 \div 1 = 40 \quad \therefore \frac{13}{1} = \frac{520}{40}$

$$\frac{8x}{40} + \frac{5x}{40} = \frac{520}{40}$$
$$8x + 5x = 520 \quad \text{Prin. III}$$
$$13x = 520 \quad \text{Prin. IV}$$
$$x = 40$$

Solve:

4. $\frac{x}{3} + \frac{x}{4} = ?$

5. $\frac{x}{2} + \frac{x}{5} = ?$

6. $\frac{x}{4} + \frac{x}{5} = ?$

7. $\frac{2x}{3} + \frac{3x}{5} = ?$

8. $\frac{5x}{6} + \frac{x}{2} = ?$

9. $\frac{3x}{7} + \frac{x}{2} = ?$

10. $\frac{4x}{9} + \frac{x}{3} = ?$

11. $\frac{x}{12} + \frac{x}{4} = ?$

12. $\frac{x}{12} + \frac{x}{3} = ?$

13. $\frac{7x}{9} + \frac{2x}{3} = ?$

14. $\frac{3x}{4} + \frac{2x}{3} = ?$

15. $\frac{7x}{9} + \frac{5x}{6} = ?$

16. $\frac{x}{3} = 5$

17. $\frac{x}{5} = 7$

18. $\frac{x}{2} = 9$

19. $\frac{x}{2} + \frac{x}{3} = 5$

20. $\frac{x}{3} + \frac{x}{4} = 7$

21. $\frac{x}{5} + \frac{x}{2} = 12$

1. One half a certain number equals 9. What is the number?   SUGGESTION: Let x = no.; then $\frac{x}{2} = 9$.

2. If one third of a number is 6, what is the number?

3. When one fifth of a number is 7, what is the number?

4. Two thirds of John's money is $60. How much money has he?

5. The width of a field is $\frac{1}{6}$ of its length. The perimeter of the field is 70 rods. Find the length and width of the field.

6. Three fifths of a field is planted to corn. If there are 15 acres of corn, how many acres are there in the field?

7. One eighth of a log is found to measure $2\frac{1}{2}$ ft. How long is the log?

8. One fourth of the pupils in a certain room are boys. There are 13 boys in the room. How many students are there in the room?

9. A man sold two thirds of his farm for $8000. What was the value of the farm?

10. At one third off a coat cost $20. What was the original cost of the coat?

11. At one fifth off, an auto sold for $800. What was the original price of the auto?

12. After selling one third of a car load of grain the remainder was sold for $600. What was the value of the car load of grain?

13. One third of a number plus one fifth of the number is 8. Find the number.

14. One fifth of a number plus $\frac{1}{4}$ of the number is 9. What is the number?

15. One third of a number plus the number equals 20. What is the number?

You were taught in percentage that the interest is found
by multiplying the principal by the rate by the time.
Let p stand for principal, r for rate, and t for time, I for
interest, then $I = prt$. (A)

1. Find the interest on $6000 for 2 years at 6%.

$I = prt$.   Substituting in the formula.
$I = \$6000 \cdot 2 \cdot \frac{6}{100}$
$I = \$720$

Solve the following examples by the use of this formula:

	p	r	t		p	r	t
2.	$2000	5%	1 yr.	**9.**	6000	2%	9 mo.
3.	$1200	4%	2 yr.	**10.**	9000	6%	6 mo.
4.	$4000	3%	6 mo.	**11.**	1100	5%	2 yr.
5.	$500	6%	6 mo.	**12.**	$12,000	6%	15 da.
6.	$3300	5%	4 mo.	**13.**	$360	6%	6 mo.
7.	$2400	3%	3 mo.	**14.**	$418	6%	1 yr.
8.	$3600	6%	1 mo.	**15.**	$390	5%	2 yr.

I. $prt = I$.

Dividing both sides of this equation by rt, Principle
IV.

$$\frac{prt}{rt} = \frac{I}{rt} \quad \therefore p = \frac{I}{rt} \quad (B)$$

II. $prt = I$.

By what must we divide both sides of this equation
to secure $r = \dfrac{I}{pt}$? (C)

III. $prt = I$.

By what must we divide both sides of this equation
to secure $t = \dfrac{I}{pr}$? (D)

By the use of the formulas (A), (B), (C), and (D) find the missing quantities in the following:

Miscellaneous Problems in Interest

First estimate the answers.

1. On Mar. 15, 1924, Mrs. Edwards loaned Mrs. DeLong $1854. What amount did Mrs. DeLong pay Mrs. Edwards on Jan. 1, 1925, if the money earned 6% interest?

2. The interest on a mortgage from Sept. 15, 1923 to Mar. 15, 1924 at 6% was $116.85. What amount of money would satisfy the mortgage Sept. 15, 1923? What amount would be required to satisfy it on Mar. 15, 1924?

3. When Mr. Hill, on May 10, 1924, pays the interest on $2280 borrowed by him on Dec. 10, 1923, he finds it to be $57. What was the rate of interest?

4. On April 14, 1923, Mr. Wood sold Mr. Smith $894 worth of flour. When Mr. Smith paid the bill with interest at 6% it amounted to $943.17. On what date did he pay it?

5. A business block valued at $64,500 must be rented so as to pay an interest of 6% on the investment and also the taxes, insurance, and repairs amounting to $2130. What rent must be charged per month for the block?

6. On May 21, 1923 Mr. Cooper invested $34,940 in a business. On Dec. 31, 1924 he finds his investment has become $48,217.20. What rate of interest has his money earned?

7. A farm was bought for $10,000 on Mar. 1, 1924. $863 is spent for repairs, $137 for taxes. On Feb. 15, 1925 the farm is sold for $12,150. Find the interest earned on the first cost of the farm.

8. What rate of interest must be charged on a sum of $20,000 in order to yield an income of $50 a month?

9. A sum of money placed at interest on Jan. 1, 1922 amounts to $7700 on Jan. 1, 1924. If the principal was $7000, what was the rate of interest?

10. From Nov. 29, 1923 till Sept. 29, 1924 $2250 has gained $74.50 interest. Find the rate of interest.

11. The interest on a mortgage of $1854 for 6 months was $55.62. What rate of interest was charged?

12. When the interest on $2000 for 1 year is $110, what is the rate?

13. What rate of interest must be charged on $3000 in order that the interest may be the same for 1 year as that earned by $4000 at 3%?

14. When $15,000 earns $150 in 72 days, what is the rate of interest?

15. A man's income on an investment of $24,000 for one year was $3600. At what rate of interest must this sum be at interest in order to earn this amount?

16. After paying the taxes and repairs on a city block costing $90,000, Mr. Brown finds that he has $9450 left of the rental of the block. This was equivalent to what rate of interest?

17. What rental per month must be charged for a store costing $12,000 in order that the owner may realize 6% on his investment after paying out $240 for taxes, insurance, and repairs?

18. At what rate must $8500 be at interest for 60 days to yield $170 interest?

19. The interest on $12,000 for a certain time at 6% was found to be $360. Find the time the money was at interest.

20. A note of $11,500 bears interest at the rate of 6%. If the interest amounts to $230, what is the time of the note?

21. The interest on a mortgage of $1800 for a certain time was $54. If the rate was 6%, find the time.

22. Mr. Kent loaned Mr. Fry $1950 at 4%. After a time Mr. Fry paid the interest which he found to be $273. What was the interest period?

23. The interest on a bill of goods amounting to $2180 at 6% for a certain time was $43.60. What was the time?

24. In what time will $4500 at 6% gain $652.50, simple interest?

25. In what time will $4000 at 6% gain $800?

26. A man borrowed $8000 at 6%. How long may he keep it in order that the interest shall be $720?

27. Mr. Welch borrowed $2300 of the bank Jan. 1, 1924 at $5\frac{1}{2}$% interest. On what day will there be $63.25 interest due?

28. The interest on a note for $6000 at 5% is paid on April 1, 1924. If the interest is $275, find the term of the note.

29. A bill of goods amounting to $7350 was paid on June 15 by a check of $7460.25. The rate of interest being 6%, find the date on which the goods were shipped.

30. How long will it take $7200 to produce $675 at 6%?

31. What principal at interest for two years at 6% will yield $12 interest?

32. The interest on a certain sum of money for 3 years at 6% is $360. Find the sum of money.

33. Jack loaned his money to his father. At the end of a year Jack received $240 interest. If Jack's father gave him 6% for the use of the money, what was the sum of money?

34. The interest on a mortgage at 5% for 2 years is $400. What is the amount of the mortgage?

35. The interest on a note for 6 months at 6% is $105. What is the face of the note?

36. Find the sum of money which, when placed at interest at 5% for a year, will yield an income of $600.

37. Mr. Jones wishes to give his invalid daughter a sum of money such that when it is placed at interest at 4%, will yield her a yearly income of $1200. Find the sum of money.

38. For 5 years no interest has been paid on a mortgage bearing 6% interest. It is found that the interest for that period amounts to $399. What is the amount of the mortgage?

39. On Jan. 1, 1924, a sum of money was borrowed from the bank at 6% interest. It was paid on July 1 of the same year. What was the sum of money if the interest was $33?

40. The interest earned on a certain sum of money from Aug. 1, 1922 to Jan. 1, 1924 was $382.50. Find the sum of money if the rate was 6%.

In commission let s = sales, r = rate of commission, and c = commission. The commission equals the sales multiplied by the rate of commission. Write the formula for this statement using c, s, and r.

Write the following statements as formulas:

1. The sales equal the commission divided by the rate.

2. The rate equals the commission divided by the sales.

By the use of the above formulas solve the following:

In these examples the agent is *selling* for his principal.

	SELLING PRICE	AGENT'S COMMIS- SION IN %	AGENT'S COMMIS- SION IN DOLLARS	NET PROCEEDS TO THE PRINCIPAL
1.	$8,000	3%	?	?
2.	$2,486	$2\frac{1}{2}$%	?	?
3.	$958	$4\frac{3}{4}$%	?	?
4.	$748	$2\frac{1}{4}$%	?	?
5.	$15,000	?	$300	?
6.	$11,200	?	$336	?
7.	$9,760	?	$122	?
8.	$484	?	$2.42	?
9.	$12,000	?	?	$11,880
10.	$1,523	?	?	$1,462.08
11.	$3,748	?	?	$3,644.93
12.	$16,848	?	?	$16,300.44
13.	?	8%	$9.60	?
14.	?	6%	$17.40	?
15.	?	$4\frac{1}{4}$%	$157.25	?
16.	?	$2\frac{1}{3}$%	$210	?
17.	?	$3\frac{1}{3}$%	?	$3,580
18.	?	7%	?	$2,297.10
19.	?	13%	?	$3,915
20.	?	$18\frac{1}{2}$%	?	$244.50
21.	?	?	$300	$2,700

	Selling Price	Agent's Commission in %	Agent's Commission in Dollars	Net Proceeds to the Principal
22.	?	?	$627.60	$15,062.40
23.	?	?	$692.80	$13,163.20
24.	?	?	$27.78	$898.22
25.	?	5%	$65	?
26.	?	4%	?	$46,560
27.	$12,940	$2\frac{1}{2}\%$	?	?

In the following examples the agent is *buying* for his principal.

	Buying Price	Agent's Commission in %	Agent's Commission in Dollars	Net Cost to Principal
28.	?	4%	$140	?
29.	$100	5%	?	?
30.	$600	?	$60	?
31.	$1200	?	?	$1224
32.	?	6%	$30	?
33.	?	5%	?	$630
34.	?	?	$35	$735
35.	$1600	3%	?	?
36.	$1300	?	$13	?
37.	$1500	?	?	$1560
38.	?	3%	$30	?
39.	?	8%	?	$432
40.	$85	2%	?	?
41.	$900	?	$18	?
42.	$30	?	?	$33
43.	?	$4\frac{1}{2}\%$	$45	?
44.	?	2%	?	$2040
45.	?	?	$80	$880
46.	?	?	$2000	$2060
47.	$6400	$12\frac{1}{2}\%$	?	?
48.	$2000	?	$80	?
49.	$2400	?	?	$2700
50.	?	7%	$49	?
51.	?	10%	?	$180
52.	?	?	$8	$208

Letting p = profit, s = selling price, c = cost, and l = loss write the formulas for the following statements:

1. The profit equals the selling price minus the cost.

2. The loss equals the cost minus the selling price.
Solve the following by using these formulas:

	Cost	Gain	Gain %	Loss	Loss %	Selling Price
1.	$840	$25.20	?			?
2.	$1350	$94.50	?			?
3.	$2890	$173.40	?			?
4.	$565	$84.75	?			?
5.	?	$5.00	?			$17.50
6.	$8450	?	7%			?
7.	$3490	?	13%			?
8.	$8.70	?	20%			?
9.	$928	?	17%			?
10.	?	$3.80	?			$98.80
11.	$575			$115	?	?
12.	$11,175			$558.75	?	?
13.	$956			$105.16	?	?
14.	$8.75			$3.50	?	?
15.	?			$16.10	?	$64.40
16.	$990			?	12%	?
17.	$1250			?	8%	?
18.	$16.80			?	$12\frac{1}{3}$%	?
19.	$975			?	18%	?
20.	$4963			?	21%	?
21.	?	$140	10%			?
22.	?	$290	14%			?
23.	?	$20.91	17%			?
24.	?	$19.89	$8\frac{1}{2}$%			?
25.	?	$603.45	$6\frac{3}{4}$%			?
26.			23.5%			$1193.01
27.	?			?	$12\frac{1}{2}$%	$4228
28.	?			?	19.5%	$545.79

Areas

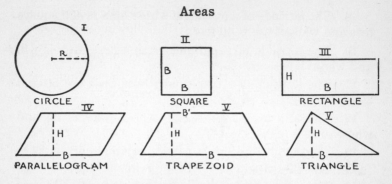

A. Write the formula for the circumference of a circle; perimeter of a square; a rectangle.

B. Write the formula for the area of a circle; square; rectangle; parallelogram; triangle.

C. The formula for the area of a trapezoid is $\frac{1}{2}h(b + b')$.

By using these formulæ find the following:

1. The area and circumference of a circle whose radius is 8.

2. The area and perimeter of a square whose side is 8.

3. The area and perimeter of a rectangle 8 in. by 20 in.

4. The area of a parallelogram with base 14 and altitude 9.

5. The area of a trapezoid whose lower base is 18 in., upper base 12 in., and altitude 10 in.

6. The area of a triangle with base 24 in., altitude 12 in.

Solve the above examples when each dimension is multiplied by 2, by 3, by 4, and by 5.

7. The radius of a circle whose area is $121\,\pi$.

8. The side of a square whose area is 144 square feet.

9. The altitude of a rectangle whose area is 400 square feet and whose base is 40 feet.

10. The altitude of a parallelogram whose area is 640 and whose base is 32.

11. The altitude of a trapezoid whose base are 50 and 30 and whose area is 1200.

12. The altitude of a triangle whose base is 36 and whose area is 360.

13. The radius of a circle whose circumference is 24 π.

14. The side of a square whose perimeter is 80.

15. The base of a rectangle whose altitude is 14 and whose area is 560.

16. The base of a parallelogram whose altitude is 18 and whose area is 540.

17. The base of triangle given the area as 570 and the altitude as 30.

18. Find the total distance an auto travels in 5 hours at the rate of 20 miles per hour.

($D = rt$; where D = distance, r = rate of travel, and t the time traveled.)

19. What was the total distance traveled by a train which maintained a uniform speed of a mile a minute for two hours?

20. How long will it take a man to walk 34 miles at the rate of 4 miles per hour?

21. At what rate must an auto travel to cover 125 miles in five hours?

22. Find the cost of twenty pieces of cloth at $8.50 each.

($C = pn$; where C = cost, p = unit price, and n = number purchased.)

23. Determine the cost of 80 tons of corn at $40 per ton.

24. How many bushels of peaches may be purchased for $60 at $2 per bushel?

25. Find the price per M of brick if 8 M are bought for $320.

26. What is the tax on a piece of property assessed at $4000 if the rate is $17 per thousand?

$T = rv$, where T = tax, r = rate and v = assessed valuation.
$T = \frac{17}{1000} \cdot 4000$. If the rate is $17 per thousand, then it is $\frac{17}{1000}$ per dollar.

Complete solution.

27. Find the tax on a store assessed at $21,000 at $19 per thousand?

28. What is the tax on a farm assessed at $3000 at $1.50 per hundred?

29. If the rate is .016 per dollar, what is the tax on a property assessed at $4600?

30. What must be the assessed valuation of a property if the tax is $64 and the rate is $8 per thousand?

31. What is the rate when a house assessed at $9000 is taxed $252?

32. Find the rate when a vacant lot assessed at $1400 pays a tax of $35.

33. Determine the assessed valuation of a school district if a rate of $21 per thousand is required to pay $42,000 necessary to operate the school.

34. What is the assessed valuation of a factory which pays a tax of $2600 when the rate is $20 per thousand?

35. What is the premium on a policy for $10,000 at $49.14 per thousand?

$P = f \cdot r$; where P = premium, r = rate, and f = face of the policy.
$p = 10,000 \cdot \frac{49.14}{1000}$. If the rate is $49.14 per thousand then it is $\frac{48.14}{1000}$ per dollar.

Complete solution.

36. What is the premium on a life insurance policy for $15,000 at $35 per thousand?

37. Find the premium on a fire insurance policy for $60,000 at $7.50 per thousand.

38. Find the rate when a fire insurance policy for $24,000 requires a premium of $180.

39. What is the rate when a policy for $13,000 requires a premium of $144.00?

40. For what amount may a building be insured if a premium of $700 is paid when the rate is $35 per thousand?

41. A man has yearly $800 to spend in annual life insurance premiums. How much insurance can he carry when the rate is $40 per thousand?

42. A man saved $600 in two years. If he saved twice as much the second year as the first, how much did he save each year?

43. A dealer's sales for two months were $12,000. His sales for the second month were double those of the first. What were the sales each month?

44. A city lot doubled in value after the street in front of it was paved. If it then sold for $1800, what was its value before the street was paved?

What sum of money at interest for one year at 6% will amount to $1060?

$$\text{Amount} = \text{principal} + \text{interest}.$$

$$A = p + prt$$
$$1060 = p + p(\tfrac{6}{100}) \textbf{ (1)} \qquad \text{Multiply both sides of the equation by 100.}$$
$$106000 = 100\,p + 6\,p \qquad \text{Transposition.}$$
$$106\,p = 106000 \qquad \text{Divide both sides by the}$$
$$\therefore p = \$1000. \qquad \text{same number.}$$

Problems in Review

1. What number diminished by 4 equals 20?

2. Find the number which when added to 5 equals thirty.

3. When 9 is subtracted from a certain number the remainder is 11. What is the number?

4. Twice a certain number less 6 equals 24. What is the number?

5. Three times a certain number plus 4 equals four times the number. Find the number.

6. Five times a certain number is greater than 25 by 5. What is the number?

7. The sum of two numbers is 10. The smaller plus 2 equals the larger. Find the numbers.

8. The sum of two numbers is 12. If six is subtracted from the larger, the remainder is equal to the smaller. Find the numbers.

9. The sum of two numbers is 20. If eight is added to the smaller, the sum is equal to the larger.

10. One fifth of a certain number plus one equals six. Find the number.

Solve:

11. $\dfrac{x}{2} + \dfrac{x}{3} + \dfrac{x}{6} = 36$

12. $\dfrac{3x}{5} - \dfrac{x}{4} + 5 = 45$

13. $\dfrac{x}{4} + \dfrac{x}{2} + \dfrac{3x}{4} = 18$

14. $\dfrac{2x}{5} + \dfrac{3x}{4} = x + 15$

15. $\dfrac{x}{3} + \dfrac{x}{5} + \dfrac{1}{2} = 8\frac{1}{2}$

16. $\dfrac{3}{4} \div \dfrac{1}{2} = ?$

17. $\dfrac{x}{5} + \dfrac{x}{7} - \dfrac{1}{2} = 11\frac{1}{2}$

18. $\frac{3}{5}$ times $\frac{1}{3} = ?$

19. $\dfrac{x}{6} + \dfrac{x}{2} - \dfrac{1}{4} = 7\frac{3}{4}$

20. $6 \div \frac{3}{4} = ?$

APPENDIX

SUBTRACTION METHODS

For the convenience of teachers, three methods of subtraction are here illustrated. *Teach but one of them.*

Continental (Austrian) Method

42.96
9.27
―――――
33.69

Say, "7 and **9** are 16
3 and **6** are 9
9 and **3** are 12
1 and **3** are 4"

In this method we consider subtraction the converse of addition, the *language of addition* is employed, and "carrying" is done as in addition.

It is also called the "making change" method and the method of "complementary addition."

Equal Addition Method

42.96
9.27
―――――
33.69

Say, "7 from 16 leaves **9**
3 from 9 leaves **6**
9 from 12 leaves **3**
1 from 4 leaves **3**"

In this method the carrying is explained by saying "having added 10 to 6 to make it 16, we must add 10 (1 ten) to 2 making it 3," etc. The method is based upon the axiom "If the same number be added to each of two numbers, their difference is not changed." It is also called the "borrow and pay back" method.

Disintegration Method

42.96
9.27
―――――
33.69

Say, "7 from 16 leaves **9**
2 from 8 leaves **6**
9 from 12 leaves **3**
0 from 3 leaves **3**"

In this method we "disintegrate" the minuend.

To the Teacher. — The application of the various subtraction methods to operations with mixed numbers is here illustrated.

The pupil should be drilled in but *one* of these. There are advantages in continuing the one already learned.

Continental (Austrian) Method.

4

$2\frac{1}{3}$

$1\frac{2}{3}$ *Difference.*

Say "$\frac{1}{3}$ and $\frac{2}{3}$ (writing $\frac{2}{3}$) = 1 ($\frac{3}{3}$)."

Carry 1 to 2 and call it 3.

Say "3 and 1 (writing 1) = 4."

Equal Addition Method.

$4 + \frac{3}{3} = 4\frac{3}{3}$ Say "$\frac{1}{3}$ from $\frac{3}{3} = \frac{2}{3}$." Write $\frac{2}{3}$.

$2\frac{1}{3} + 1 = 3\frac{1}{3}$ Say "3 from 4 = 1." Write 1.

$\qquad 1\frac{2}{3}$ *Difference.*

Disintegration Method.

$4 = 3\frac{3}{3}$ Say "$\frac{1}{3}$ from $\frac{3}{3} = \frac{2}{3}$." Write $\frac{2}{3}$.

$2\frac{1}{3} = 2\frac{1}{3}$ Say "2 from 3 = 1." Write 1.

$\qquad 1\frac{2}{3}$ *Difference.*

Continental (Austrian) Method.

$4\frac{1}{4} = 4\frac{3}{12}$ Say "$\frac{4}{12}$ and $\frac{11}{12}$ (writing $\frac{11}{12}$) = $\frac{15}{12}$" ($1\frac{3}{12}$).

$2\frac{1}{3} = 2\frac{4}{12}$ Carry 1 to 2, making it 3.

$\qquad 1\frac{11}{12}$ *Difference.* Say "3 and 1 (writing 1) = 4."

Equal Addition Method.

$4\frac{1}{4} = 4\frac{3}{12}$ $4\frac{3}{12} + \frac{12}{12} = 4\frac{15}{12}$

$2\frac{1}{3} = 2\frac{4}{12}$ $2\frac{4}{12} + 1 = 3\frac{4}{12}$

$\qquad\qquad\qquad 1\frac{11}{12}$ *Difference.*

Say "$\frac{4}{12}$ from $\frac{15}{12} = \frac{11}{12}$." Write $\frac{11}{12}$.

Say "3 from 4 = 1." Write 1.

Disintegration Method.

$4\frac{1}{4} = 4\frac{3}{12} = 3\frac{15}{12}$

$2\frac{1}{3} = 2\frac{4}{12} = 2\frac{4}{12}$

$\qquad\qquad 1\frac{11}{12}$ *Difference.*

Say "$\frac{4}{12}$ from $\frac{15}{12} = \frac{11}{12}$." Write $\frac{11}{12}$.

Say "2 from 3 = 1." Write 1.

TABLES OF DENOMINATE NUMBERS

The following tables of linear, square and cubic measure, and of capacity and weight, are commonly known as the *English Tables*. They are used throughout the British Empire and in the United States.

NOTE. — It is not considered correct to use an abbreviation for a denomination unless it immediately follows a numeral — *e. g.* 4 *ft.*, "How many *feet* —" etc.

Linear Measure

$$\begin{array}{ll} \textbf{12 inches (in. or '')} & \textbf{= 1 foot (ft. or ')} \\ \textbf{3 feet} & \textbf{= 1 yard (yd.)} \\ \left.\begin{array}{l} \textbf{5}\tfrac{1}{2}\textbf{ yards} \\ \textbf{16}\tfrac{1}{2}\textbf{ feet} \end{array}\right\} & \textbf{= 1 rod (rd.)} \\ \textbf{320 rods} & \textbf{= 1 mile (mi.)} \end{array}$$

Linear measure is so called because it is used in measuring lines. The word inch is probably derived from a Latin word meaning "one twelfth." The foot was originally the length of the human foot. The yard in England was established by Henry I of England as the distance from the end of his nose to the end of his thumb. The rod was formerly called a "perch" or "pole." The word mile comes from the Latin *mille passuum*, "one thousand paces." The Roman pace was two steps or about five feet. The Roman *mille passuum* was therefore about 5000 ft. The *mile* is also called the *statute mile* to distinguish it from the *nautical* mile.

The *hand* used in measuring the height of horses, is 4 in., or about the width of the human hand.

The *fathom* used in measuring the depth of water is 6 feet.

The *knot* or *nautical mile* is about 1.15 land miles.

The *league*, used in measuring distances at sea, is 3 knots.

By looking up the above terms in an unabridged dictionary much interesting information may be obtained.

The standard yard is obtained by measuring the length of a pendulum vibrating seconds at the latitude of London under certain conditions. This length is divided into 391,393 equal parts and 360,000 of these parts constitute the *standard yard*. The other units of the English Tables are derived from this standard.

Square Measure

144 square inches (sq. in.)	= 1 square foot (sq. ft.)
9 square feet	= 1 square yard (sq. yd.)
30¼ square yards	= 1 square rod (sq. rd.)
160 square rods	= 1 acre (A.)
640 acres	= 1 square mile (sq. **mi.)**

A *rood* is 40 square rods or ¼ A.

A *square mile* is sometimes called a section.

In roofing, flooring, etc., 100 sq. ft. is called a *square*.

The word *acre* is derived from a word meaning field.

Observe that the numbers 144, 9, and 30¼ are the squares of the numbers 12, 3 and 5½ in the table of linear measure.

Cubic Measure

1728 cubic inches (cu. in.)	= 1 cubic foot (cu. ft.)
27 cubic feet	= 1 cubic yard (cu. yd.)

A pile of wood or stone 8′ × 4′ × 4′ is a cord. It contains 128 cu. ft. The word *cord* is applied also to any pile of wood 8′ long and 4′ high. A *cord-foot* is ⅛ of a cord, or 16 cu. ft.

A cubic yard of earth is called a *load*.

A *perch* of stone is a pile 1 rd. long, 1¼ ft. wide and 1 ft. high. It contains 24¾ cu. ft.

Observe that the numbers 1728 and 27 are the cubes of the numbers 12 and 3 in the table of linear measure.

Liquid Measure

4 gills (gi.)	= 1 pint (pt.)
2 pints	= 1 quart (qt.)
4 quarts	= 1 gallon (gal.)

The standard unit of liquid measure is the gallon. It contains *231 cubic inches.* A rectangular box 3″ × 7″ × 11″ contains exactly a gallon. A cylinder 7″ in diameter and 6″ high contains almost exactly a gallon. It is the same as the Old English *wine gallon.* A cubic foot is approximately 7½ gal.

A pint is equal to 16 fluid ounces.

A pint of water weighs about a pound; hence the old couplet:

> "A pint's a pound
> The world around."

A cubic foot of water weighs about 1000 oz. or 62½ lb. avd.

In measuring larger capacities barrels and hogsheads are sometimes used.

$$31\tfrac{1}{2} \text{ gallons} = 1 \text{ barrel (bbl.)}$$
$$2 \text{ barrels} = 1 \text{ hogshead (hhd.)}$$

Dry Measure

$$2 \text{ pints (pt.)} = 1 \text{ quart (qt.)}$$
$$8 \text{ quarts} = 1 \text{ peck (pk.)}$$
$$4 \text{ pecks} = 1 \text{ bushel (bu.)}$$

The standard unit of dry measure is the *bushel* of 2150.42 cubic inches. In England it is known as the *Winchester bushel*. It is the volume of a cylinder 18½ inches in diameter and eight inches high. A bushel equals *approximately* 1¼ cubic ft.

In most states the standard bushel of various commodities is determined by weight.

Standard Weight of a Bushel
New York

Potatoes 60 lb.	Corn (shelled) 56 lb.	Oats 32 lb.
Wheat 60 lb.	Barley 48 lb.	Beans 60 lb.

For a more complete table see page 451.

A barrel of flour weighs 196 lb.

A quarter-barrel sack of flour weighs 49 lb.

Avoirdupois Weight

$$16 \text{ ounces (oz.)} = 1 \text{ pound (lb.)}$$
$$100 \text{ pounds} = 1 \text{ hundredweight (cwt.)}$$
$$20 \text{ hundredweight} = 1 \text{ ton (T.)}$$

The standard unit of avoirdupois weight is the pound. It is the weight of 27.7015 cu. in. of distilled water weighed under certain conditions.

The word avoirdupois is derived from an Old English expression meaning "*goods of weight.*"

The *long ton* or *gross ton* is 2240 pounds.

The long ton is used in weighing coal at the mines.

Apothecaries' Weight

In weighing drugs a table known as *apothecaries' weight* is used.

20 grains (gr.)	= 1 scruple (sc. or ℈)
3 scruples	= 1 dram (dr. or ℨ)
8 drams	= 1 ounce (oz. or ℥)
12 ounces	= 1 pound (lb.)

Troy Weight

In weighing jewels a table known as *Troy weight* is used.

24 grains (gr.)	= 1 pennyweight (pwt.)
20 pennyweights	= 1 ounce (oz.)
12 ounces	= 1 pound (lb.)

The *carat* used in weighing precious stones = $3\frac{1}{5}$ grains.

The troy pound	= 5760 gr.
The apothecaries' pound	= 5760 gr.
The avoirdupois pound	= 7000 gr.

Other Tables

The following tables are in general use throughout the civilized world.

Time

60 seconds (sec.)	= 1 minute (min.)
60 minutes	= 1 hour (hr.)
24 hours	= 1 day (da.)
7 days	= 1 week (wk.)
365 days	= 1 year (yr.)
366 days	= 1 leap year, or bissextile

The year is the time required for the earth to make one complete revolution about the sun. It is 365 da. 5 hr. 48 min. 46 sec. or nearly $365\frac{1}{4}$ da. Hence every fourth year a day is added to the calendar, — Feb. 29 — and that year is called a *bissextile* or *leap year*. The amount thus added is a little too much and creates an error which has to be corrected every 100 years by dropping the added day in one leap year. This in turn creates another error which is corrected by making every fourth centennial year a leap year.

Centennial years whose numbers are divisible by 400, and other years whose numbers are divisible by 4, are leap years. All others are common years.

> "Thirty days hath September,
> April, June and November —
> All the rest have thirty-one
> Save February, which alone
> Hath twenty-eight, and one day more
> We add to it one year in four."

Business men, for convenience in reckoning interest, consider a month as 30 days.

Years are numbered from the birth of Christ. "B.C." following a date means "Before Christ." "A.D." following a date means "In the year of our Lord," from the Latin "*Anno Domini.*"

For the derivation of the names of the months and of days of the week, consult the dictionary.

Arc and Angle Measure

60 seconds (″) = 1 minute (′)
60 minutes   = 1 degree (°)
An arc of 360 = 1 circumference

Counting

12 units or things = 1 dozen (doz.)
12 dozen   = 1 gross (gr.)
12 gross   = 1 great gross
20 units   = 1 score

Stationers' Table

24 sheets = 1 quire
20 quires = 1 ream
2 reams   = 1 bundle
5 bundles = 1 bale

United States Money

10 mills = 1 cent (ct. or ¢)
10 cents = 1 dime
10 dimes = 1 dollar ($)
10 dollars = 1 eagle

English Money

4 farthings (far.) = 1 penny (d.)
12 pence = 1 shilling (s.)
20 shillings = 1 pound or sovereign (£)

Farthings are not coined.
A *crown* is a silver coin worth 5s.
The *guinea* was a gold coin worth 21s.

French Money

100 centimes (c.) = 1 franc (fr.)

Italian Money

100 centimes (c.) = 1 lira (l.)

German Money

100 pfennigs (p.) = 1 mark (M.)

The denominations of Canadian money are like those of the United States.

Foreign Money Equivalents

£1 = $4.8665   1 l. = $.193
1 fr. = $.193   1 M. = $.238

Approximate Equivalents

£1 = $5   1 l. = $.20
1 fr. = $.20   1 M. = $.24

FARMERS' ESTIMATES

To find the number of bushels in a bin,
Divide the number of cubic feet in the bin by 1¼.

To find how large a bin will contain a given number of bushels,
Multiply the number of bushels by 1¼. The result is the number of cubic feet in the required bin.

To find the number of gallons of water in a cistern or tank,
Multiply the number of cubic feet of water by 7½.

To find how large a cistern will hold a given number of gallons,
Divide the number of gallons by 7½. The result will be the number of cubic feet in the required cistern.

To find how many bushels of shelled corn are equal to a given number of bushels of corn in the ear,
Divide the number of bushels of corn in the ear by 2.

The following table shows the number of **pounds in a legal bushel**, of different commodities, in various states:

	CAL.	CONN.	DEL.	ILL.	IND.	IOWA	KY.	LA.	MASS.	MICH.	MINN.	MO.	N.J.	N.Y.	N.C.	OHIO	OREGON	PENN.	VT.	WASH.	WIS.
Wheat	60	56	60	60	60	60	60	60	60	60	60	60	60	60	60	60	60	60	60	60	60
Indian Corn, shelled	52	56	56	52	56	56	56	56	56	56	56	52	56	58	54	56	56	56	56	56	56
Oats	32	28		32	32	32	33½	32	30	32	32	35	30	32		32	34	32	32	36	32
Barley	50			48	48	48	48	32	46	48	48	48	48	48	48	48	46	47	46	45	48
Buckwheat	40	45		40	50	52	52		46	42	42	42	50	48	50		42	48	46	42	42
Rye	54	56		54	56	56	56	32	56	56	56	56	56			56	56	56	56	56	56
Clover Seed				60	60	60	60				60	60	60	64	60	60	60			60	60
Timothy Seed				45	45	45	45					45					45				
Blue Grass Seed				14	14	14	14					14									46

Beans, peas and potatoes usually 60 lb.

Tests of Divisibility

As we have already learned, the solution of a problem is shortened by the use of cancellation. In the process of cancellation, it is of advantage to be able to decide by observation whether or not a number is divisible by another, without going through the actual division. Many times, too, our choice between two or more methods of solving a given problem will depend upon the divisibility of certain numbers used in the problem. Suppose, for example, the solution of a problem is indicated as follows:

$$\frac{714.8 \times 275 \times 71.34}{12 \times 25}$$

Shall we go to the trouble of trying out all of the factors below the line to see if they will divide the numbers above the line? That will be unnecessary if we know certain tests of divisibility; thus: 25 will divide 275 because the number expressed by the last two figures in 275 is divisible by 25. Three, one factor of 12, will divide 71.34 because the sum of the figures in 71.34 can be divided by 3. The remaining factor of 12, or 4, will divide 714.8 because it will divide the number expressed by the last two figures of 714.8. So we know at the outset that all of the factors below the line will cancel out. From this you will see the advantage of learning the following tests of divisibility.

A number is divisible,

1. By 2, if the number expressed by its right-hand figure is even; *e.g.*   34,968; 8 is even.

2. By 4, if the last two figures at the right are ciphers, or if the number expressed by them is divisible by 4; *e.g.*
8300 and 35,772 are divisible by 4.

Which of these numbers are divisible by 4:
8632;   983,700;   6842;   9371;   3,246,716?

3. By 8, if the last three figures are ciphers, or if the number expressed by them is divisible by 8; *e.g.*

783,416, because 416 is divisible by 8.

Which of these numbers are divisible by 8:
47,320;   917,815;   43,512;   24,007;   6,371,000?

4. By 5, if its last figure is 5 or 0; *e.g.*

9765;   23,400;   9230.

5. By 3, if the sum of its figures is divisible by 3; *e.g.*

38,070 is divisible by 3 because 3 + 8 + 7, or 18, is divisible by 3.

Which of these numbers are divisible by 3:
81,023;   21,546;   92,349;   715,625;   2034?

6. By 9, if the sum of its figures is divisible by 9.
Which of these numbers are divisible by 9:
818,181;   27,564;   2,045,871;   913,752?

7. An odd number is never divisible by an even number. Why? Knowing that, we may decide at a glance that 48 will not divide 387,653.

8. Can any even number be divided by an odd number? Give examples.

9. Test the following numbers for divisibility by 2, 5, 3, 9, 4, 8:
24,642;   3,495;   61,340;   86,895;   178,000;   31,432.

Tell by inspection the divisors common to both terms of each of the following fractions:

10. $\dfrac{4624}{39432}$. **11.** $\dfrac{63528}{255936}$. **12.** $\dfrac{36900}{34605}$. **13.** $\dfrac{456372}{714564}$.

14. $\dfrac{675 \times 424 \times 256}{8 \times 4 \times 9}$. **15.** $\dfrac{3860 \times 3885 \times 246}{2 \times 5 \times 3}$.

Short Methods

To multiply when the multiplier is near 10, 100, 1000, etc.

1. $254 \times 97 = ?$

$254 \times 100 = 25400$

$254 \times 3 = 762$

$254 \times 97 = 24638$

The product of 254×100 exceeds the product of 254×97 by 3 times 254 or 762, which must be subtracted from 25,400.

2. $327 \times 102 = ?$

$327 \times 100 = 32700$

$327 \times 2 = 654$

33354

The product of 327×100 is less than the product of 327×102 by 2 times 327 or 654, which must be added to 32,700.

Find the products :

3. 438×99.

4. 274×101.

5. 250×103.

6. 740×98.

7. 356×101.

8. 268×998.

9. 426×1002.

10. 351×1003.

11. $\$28.36 \times 13$.

12. $\$ 5.84 \times 105$.

13. $\$24.16 \times 997$.

14. $\$24.16 \times 1005$.

When the multiplier is near 90, 80, 50, etc.

To multiply by 79, multiply by 80, and subtract the multiplicand from the product.

Multiply 178 by 82.

178

80

14240

356

14596 *Product*

Multiply first by 80, and add twice the multiplicand to the product.

$2 + 178 = 356$.

Find the products :

15. 265×79.

16. 316×81.

17. 212×62.

18. 408×72.

19. 430×48.

20. 215×52.

21. 320×42.

22. 265×69.

23. 2112×83.

24. 1604×78.

25. 2750×49.

26. 1804×62.

A shorter method of multiplying by 11, 22, etc., is as follows:

Multiply 375 by 11.

375   Without performing formal multiplication,
11   Write **5** for the unit figure of the product.
———— $(5 + 7 = 12)$. Write **2** for the tens figure (carrying the 1).
375      $(7 + 3 + 1 = 11)$. Write **1** for the hundreds (carrying the 1).
375        $3 + 1 = 4$ Write **4** for the thousands figure.
————
4125   The product is 4125.

Rule. — *Write the units figure of the multiplicand for the unit figure of the product. Add the units and tens of the multiplicand for the tens of the product (carrying). Add the tens and hundreds of the multiplicand for the hundreds of the product (carrying). Add the hundreds figure of the multiplicand to the carried figure (if any) for the thousands of the product, etc.*

Multiply by 11:

1. 326	**3.** 516	**5.** 228	**7.** 320	**9.** 216
2. 121	**4.** 224	**6.** 114	**8.** 460	**10.** 512

When the multiplier is 22, proceed as above, multiplying the sums by 2, before adding the carried figures.

Multiply 386 by 22.

386   2 times 6 = 12.   Write 2 for units figure (carry 1).
22     $2 \times (6 + 8) + 1 = 29$. Write 9 for tens figure (carry 2).
———— $2 \times (8 + 3) + 2 = 24$. Write 4 for hundreds figure
772   (carry 2).
772     $2 \times 3 + 2 = 8$. Write 8 for thousands figure.
————
8492   The product is 8492.

When the multiplier is 33 multiply by 3 after finding the sums. When it is 44, multiply by 4.

Multiply:

11. 26 by 22.	**14.** 346 by 22.	**17.** 54 by 33.
12. 84 by 22.	**15.** 258 by 22.	**18.** 212 by 33.
13. 275 by 22.	**16.** 450 by 22.	**19.** 309 by 44.

Buying Electric Current

The electric current by which buildings and streets are lighted and power is carried to machines is produced in either of two ways: (*a*) by water power, or (*b*) by steam power.

1. Find out how the electricity that runs your street cars is generated; the electricity that lights your school building at night; that runs the coffee-mill at your grocer's; that runs your dentist's drill.

2. What advantage is there in using electric power rather than in using the water power or steam power directly?

3. What is the price of electric current per kilowatt hour in your town: (*a*) For house lighting? (*b*) For running machinery? (*c*) For cooking? (*d*) For heating an electric iron?

Electric Meter Reading

Commencing at the first right-hand pointer, note that the last figure passed over by the pointer is 4. The next circle to the left shows the figure last passed to be 8, the

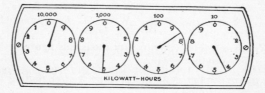

direction of the rotation of this pointer being counter-clockwise. The last figure passed by the next pointer to the left is 5, while that passed by the last pointer to the left is obviously 9. The reading to be set down therefore is 9584.

1. Draw a meter dial registering 6435 kilowatt hours.

2. If that was the reading for January and 9121 was the registration for February, the amount used for the month was 9121 − 6435. Find its cost at 7½¢ per kilowatt hour.

3. Mr. Allenburg's meter shows the following readings for a year:

Jan. 927	May 2095	Sept. 2735
Feb. 1214	June 2240	Oct. 2996
Mar. 1645	July 2485	• Nov. 3214
Apr. 1910	Aug. 2510	Dec. 3545

The rate at first was 8¼¢ per kilowatt. Beginning with the July bill, it was reduced to 6½¢. Find his entire electric light bill for eleven months, beginning with February.

4. A ¼ horse-power motor uses ⅓ of a kilowatt of current per hour. What would be the cost of running such a motor 150 hours at $.046 per kilowatt?

5. The Long Lake power plant can produce electric current at a cost of $.0028 per kilowatt. If the company sells this power at 3½¢ per kilowatt, what is its gross profit on a contract for 1000 kilowatts per day, for 300 days in a year?

Buying Gas

1. From what is illuminating gas made?

2. How is the pressure obtained to force the gas through the pipes?

3. Are the gas works in your city owned by the city, by a private corporation, or by an individual?

4. What price per thousand cubic feet is charged for gas in your city?

5. Does gas for fuel cost the same as for illumination?

Below is a copy of a coupon attached to each gas bill sent out by the gas company in a large city.

Each division on the right-hand circle denotes 100 cubic feet, on the center circle, 1000 feet, and on the left-hand circle, 10,000 feet. To take a statement from the meter, begin at the left and set down the *lowest* figures next to the hand on each circle. In the diagram they are 3, 4, and 6, showing the statement to be 34,600. If at a former observation the hands

were at the *dotted* lines, the statement then was 18,200; and the difference between the two statements is the amount of gas consumed — viz. 16,400 cu. ft.

1. Make a diagram of a meter registering 75,100 cu. ft.

2. Mrs. Jensen's gas meter registered 12,600 cu. ft. March 1 and 14,400 cu. ft. April 1. Find the amount of her gas bill for March, at $1.10 per M.

3. Mr. Brinton's gas meter registered 16,900 and 19,700 at two successive readings. The rate was $1 per M, and 3% was added because the bill was not paid within ten days. How much was needed to settle the bill?

4. Mrs. Newman received a gas bill showing the two successive readings to be 91,000 and 86,400. The rate was $1.15 per M, but Mrs. Newman obtained a reduction of 10% by paying the bill before the 10th of the month. How much did she pay?

5. Read the gas meter at your home or at the school, on two successive Mondays, and compute the cost of the gas used in one week.

Buying Water

Water meters usually show in figures the exact registry to date, like the speedometer of an automobile. Therefore no special directions are needed for reading it.

MORTGAGES

Sometimes, when one borrows money, he gives his note, or bond, promising to pay the debt, and in addition to that, he pledges a specific piece of property, as security for payment. Then if the debt is not paid when due, the creditor may have the property sold and may receive his payment from the proceeds of the sale. The written instrument thus pledging property for the payment of a debt is called a **mortgage.**

The special advantage to the creditor, in having a mortgage in addition to the note or bond, is that if the property is of sufficient value, he is sure of obtaining his pay; for however much the debtor may owe to other creditors, the one holding the mortgage must be paid before any of the mortgaged property can be used in payment of other debts.

Mortgages pledging land are called **real estate mortgages.** Mortgages pledging personal property, like furniture, machines, crops, or animals, are called **chattel mortgages.** Interest on a mortgage debt is computed like that on an ordinary note.

Problems

1. Find the interest due July 1, 1927 on a mortgage of $4000 dated Jan. 1, 1927, interest 6%.

2. Find the amount due Dec. 15, 1927 on a mortgage for $3500 given Dec. 15, 1926, interest at $5\frac{1}{2}\%$, if $500 is to be paid on the principal annually.

3. What will be due on this mortgage Dec. 15, 1928?

INDEX

461